K12 Inc. Staff for this Book

Paul Thomas   *Content Specialist*
Ann Lewis   *Content Specialist*
Robert Lewis   *Content Specialist*
Suzanne Montazer   *Art Director*
Lisa Dimaio Iekel   *Production Manager*
Carol Leigh   *Designer*
Stephanie Shaw   *Designer*
Christopher Yates   *Cover Designer*
Michelle Wulfson Jaeger   *Visual Designer*
Dan Perkins   *Visual Designer*
Annette Scarpitta   *Illustrations Editor*
Henrik de Gyor   *Illustrations Editor*
Bud Knecht   *Text Editor*
Kay McCarthy   *Text Editor*
Lauralyn Vaughn   *Instructional Designer*
Rebecca Woodward-Davis   *Instructional Designer*
Will Ober   *Instructional Designer*
Craig Ruskin   *Project Manager*
Jasmeen Bowmaster   *Project Manager*
Connie Moy   *Quality Control Manager*
Elia Ben-Ari   *Quality Control Specialist*
Lori Burgess   *Quality Control Specialist*

Bror Saxberg   *Chief Learning Officer*
John Holdren   *Senior Vice President for Content and Curriculum*
Maria Szalay   *Senior Vice President for Product Development*
Jennifer Thompson   *Director of Product Delivery*
Tom DiGiovanni   *Senior Director of Instructional Design*
Kim Barcas   *Creative Director*
John G. Agnone   *Director of Publications*
Charles Kogod   *Director of Media and IP Management*
Jeff Burridge   *Managing Editor*
Steve Watson   *Product Manager*

About K12 Inc.

Founded in 1999, K12 Inc. is an elementary and secondary school service combining rich academic content with powerful technology. K12 serves students in a variety of education settings, both public and private, including school classrooms, virtual charter schools, home schools, and tutoring centers. K12 currently provides comprehensive curricular offerings in the following subjects: Language Arts/English, History, Math, Science, Visual Arts, and Music. The K12 curriculum blends high-quality offline materials with innovative online resources, including interactive lessons, teacher guides, and tools for planning and assessment. For more information, call 1-888-YOUR K12 or visit www.K12.com.

978-1-60153-019-6

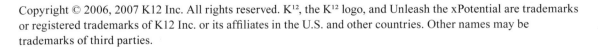

Printed by RR Donnelley, Roanoke, VA, USA, March 2012, Lot 032012

Geometry
A Reference Guide

Geometry
A Reference Guide

Contents

How to Use This Book viii

Navigating a Page ix

UNIT 1   An Introduction   1

Basic Geometric Terms and Concepts 3

Measuring Length 7

Measuring Angles 11

Bisectors and Line Relationships 15

Relationships Between Triangles and Circles 19

Transformations 23

Using Algebra to Describe Geometry 27

UNIT 2   Methods of Proof and Logic   31

Reasoning, Arguments, and Proof 33

Conditional Statements 37

Compound Statements and Indirect Proof 43

Definitions and Biconditionals 47

Algebraic Logic 51

Inductive and Deductive Reasoning 55

UNIT 3   Polygon Basics   59

Polygons and Symmetry 61

Quadrilaterals and Their Properties 65

Parallel Lines and Transversals 69

Converses of Parallel Line Properties 75

The Triangle Sum Theorem 79

Angles in Polygons 85

Midsegments 89

Slope 93

UNIT 4 **Congruent Polygons and Special Quadrilaterals** 99

Congruent Polygons and Their Corresponding Parts 101
Triangle Congruence: SSS, SAS, and ASA 105
Isosceles Triangles and Corresponding Parts 111
Triangle Congruence: AAS and HL 117
Using Triangles to Understand Quadrilaterals 121
Types of Quadrilaterals 127
Constructions with Polygons 131
Transformations and Triangle Inequality 135

UNIT 5 **Perimeter, Area, and Right Triangles** 141

Perimeter and Area 143
Areas of Triangles and Quadrilaterals 147
Circumference and Area of Circles 151
The Pythagorean Theorem 155
Areas of Special Triangles and Regular Polygons 159
Using the Distance Formula 165
Proofs and Coordinate Geometry 169

UNIT 6 **Three-Dimensional Figures and Graphs** 173

Solid Shapes and Three-Dimensional Drawing 175
Lines, Planes, and Polyhedra 179
Prisms 183
Coordinates in Three Dimensions 187
Equations of Lines and Planes in Space 191

UNIT 7   Surface Area and Volume   197

Surface Area and Volume   199
Surface Area and Volume of Prisms   205
Surface Area and Volume of Pyramids   209
Surface Area and Volume of Cylinders   213
Surface Area and Volume of Cones   217
Surface Area and Volume of Spheres   221
Three-Dimensional Symmetry   225

UNIT 8   Similar Shapes   231

Dilations and Scale Factors   233
Similar Polygons   237
Triangle Similarity   243
Side-Splitting Theorem   247
Indirect Measurement and Additional Similarity Theorems   251
Area and Volume Ratios   255

UNIT 9   Circles   259

Chords and Arcs   261
Tangents to Circles   265
Inscribed Angles and Arcs   269
Angles Formed by Secants and Tangents   273
Segments of Tangents, Secants, and Chords   277
Circles in the Coordinate Plane   283

UNIT 10   Trigonometry   287

Tangents   289
Sines and Cosines   293
Special Right Triangles   299
The Laws of Sines and Cosines   303

UNIT 11   Beyond Euclidean Geometry   307

The Golden Rectangle   309
Taxicab Geometry   313
Graph Theory   317
Topology   323
Spherical Geometry   329
Fractal Geometry   333
Projective Geometry   339
Computer Logic   343

Appendices

Postulates and Theorems   A-1
Pronunciation Guide   A-6
Glossary   A-7
Symbols   A-15
Formulary   A-16
Illustrations Credits   A-19
Index   A-20

How to Use This Book

Welcome to *Geometry: A Reference Guide*

This book serves as a reference guide for any student of geometry. It was developed as a companion to the online portion of K12 Inc.'s High School Geometry program.

Each section of this book uses words, pictures, and diagrams to present an overview of a topic area. You can use this book to familiarize yourself with aspects of geometry, or to review materials you're studying in other books or online sources.

How This Book Is Organized

Units of Study

This book is organized in the following units of study:

- An Introduction
- Methods of Proof and Logic
- Polygon Basics
- Congruent Polygons and Special Quadrilaterals
- Perimeter, Area, and Right Triangles
- Three-Dimensional Figures and Graphs

- Surface Area and Volume
- Similar Shapes
- Circles
- Trigonometry
- Beyond Euclidean Geometry

Postulates and Theorems

See pages A-1–A-5 for a complete list of all the postulates and theorems covered in this book.

Pronunciation Guide

See page A-6 for a key to the pronunciations in the Glossary.

Glossary

See pages A-7–A-14 for a Glossary with brief definitions of some key terms.

Symbols

See page A-15 for a list of mathematical symbols.

Formulary

See pages A-16–A-18 for a list of all the formulas with illustrations.

Index

See pages A-20–A-22.

Navigating a Page

Topic Each section explores a topic in geometry.

Keywords What are the new words associated with this topic? The words will be **boldface** when they are explained in the text.

Reconnect to the Big Idea This box contains a connection with one of the Big Ideas in the study of geometry.

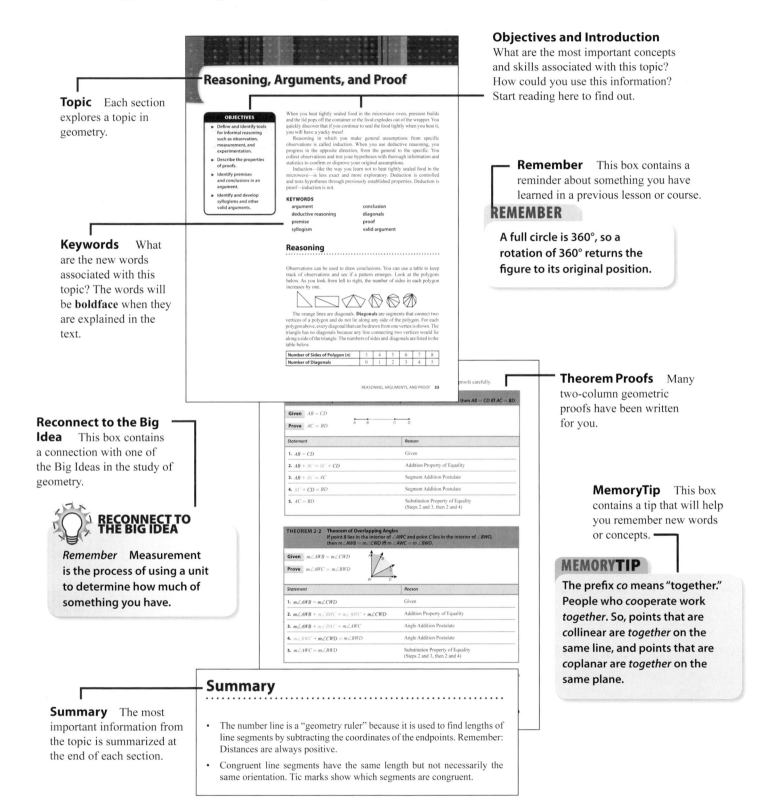

RECONNECT TO THE BIG IDEA

Remember Measurement is the process of using a unit to determine how much of something you have.

Summary The most important information from the topic is summarized at the end of each section.

Objectives and Introduction What are the most important concepts and skills associated with this topic? How could you use this information? Start reading here to find out.

Remember This box contains a reminder about something you have learned in a previous lesson or course.

REMEMBER

A full circle is 360°, so a rotation of 360° returns the figure to its original position.

Theorem Proofs Many two-column geometric proofs have been written for you.

MemoryTip This box contains a tip that will help you remember new words or concepts.

MEMORYTIP

The prefix *co* means "together." People who *cooperate* work *together*. So, points that are collinear are *together* on the same line, and points that are coplanar are *together* on the same plane.

Summary

- The number line is a "geometry ruler" because it is used to find lengths of line segments by subtracting the coordinates of the endpoints. Remember: Distances are always positive.
- Congruent line segments have the same length but not necessarily the same orientation. Tic marks show which segments are congruent.

UNIT 1   An Introduction

Geometry is the part of mathematics concerned with the measurements, properties, and relationships of points, lines, angles, plane figures, and solids. As early as 1800 B.C., the Babylonians discovered many geometric principles while trying to find ways to survey land, construct pyramids, and build canals. Most of their discoveries were a result of trial and error. By about 600 B.C., Greek mathematicians began using a logical method called deductive reasoning to discover new mathematical ideas. This type of geometry is called Euclidean geometry, named after the Greek mathematician Euclid. In his book *Elements,* Euclid outlined a deductive system for geometry that we still use today.

In this course, you will study the geometry of Euclid and use geometry to explore mathematical reasoning. With an understanding of geometry, you will be able to solve many problems.

In this first unit, you will study some basic definitions and properties that are good places to start learning Euclidean geometry.

. . . .

UNIT OBJECTIVES

▶ Describe and name points, lines, and planes.

▶ Understand the difference between a postulate and a theorem and how proofs are used in Euclidean geometry.

▶ Measure segments and angles.

▶ Classify angles by their measures and identify special angle pairs.

▶ Use compass and straightedge or technology to perform constructions.

▶ Identify and construct inscribed and circumscribed circles.

▶ Identify and construct basic transformations.

▶ Use the coordinate plane to graph points and perform transformations.

Basic Geometric Terms and Concepts

OBJECTIVES

▶ Describe basic properties of points, lines, and planes.

▶ Define and describe basic properties of line segments and rays.

▶ Identify collinear and coplanar points.

▶ Identify the intersection of two lines or of two planes.

▶ Describe the difference between postulates and theorems and how they are used in proofs.

▶ Identify the components and purpose of a proof.

How different would your world be without geometry? Think of towns without road plans and maps, rivers without bridges, cities without skyscrapers, and business and living areas without modern transportation. Furthermore, imagine a house built with neither a plan nor high-quality materials. Would the house be strong and keep you comfortable?

So, what is geometry? Geometry is anything with a point, line, angle, shape, or space. It is the study of relationships, characteristics, and measurements of points, lines, angles, surfaces, and solids. It is the exploration of and experience with forms and shapes, and involves skills of the hands and eyes as well as of the mind. In short, geometry is the world!

KEYWORDS

collinear	coplanar
line	line segment
noncollinear	plane
point	postulate
proof	ray
theorem	

Basic Geometric Terms

The terms point, line, and plane are undefined terms that form the basis of other definitions. We have to start somewhere, so starting by agreeing on what these three terms mean will allow us to write good definitions for other terms.

•A

point A

A **point** references a location in space. It has no length, width, or depth. We represent a point with a dot. As shown below, we name a point with a capital letter.

A **line** is a collection of points arranged in a straight path. A line has no thickness, but it does have direction and infinite length. As the picture shows, we use arrows to show that a line continues endlessly in both directions. We name a line by naming any two points on the line in any order. We can also name a line with one lowercase script letter.

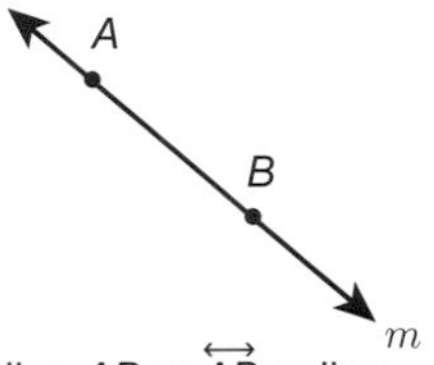

line AB or $\overleftrightarrow{AB}$ or line m

A **plane** is a flat surface. Planes have infinite length and width but no thickness. We name a plane with one capital script letter or any three points on the plane that are not on the same line.

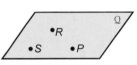

plane *RSP* or plane Ω

More Geometric Terms

A **line segment** is a part of a line. The segment consists of any two points on the line and all the points in between those two points. A line segment has a specific length and can be measured. We name a line segment by naming its endpoints, in either order.

A **ray** is part of a line that extends infinitely in one direction. We name

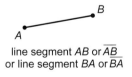

line segment *AB* or $\overline{AB}$
or line segment *BA* or $\overline{BA}$

a ray by naming its endpoint first and then any other point on the ray. The direction of the ray does not affect the naming of the ray.

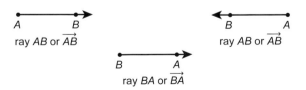

ray *AB* or $\overrightarrow{AB}$ ray *AB* or $\overrightarrow{AB}$

ray *BA* or $\overrightarrow{BA}$

Points that lie on the same line are **collinear**. Points that do not lie on the same line are **noncollinear**. Points that lie on the same plane are **coplanar**. On the pool table below, if the balls represent points, and the table represents a plane, then

- Balls 1, 2, 8, and 10 are collinear.
- Balls 1, 3, and 13 are noncollinear.
- Balls 1, 2, 3, 8, 10, and 13 are coplanar.
- Balls 2, 4, 6, and 13 are not coplanar.

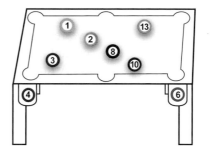

Intersections

In the figure below, line *AB* (another name would be line *BA*) and line *CD* (or line *DC*) share a common point, *X*. That point is where the two lines *intersect*. The figures below show that the intersection of two lines is a point, and the intersection of two planes is a line.

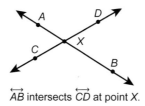

$\overleftrightarrow{AB}$ intersects $\overleftrightarrow{CD}$ at point *X*.

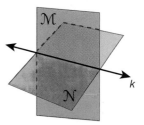

Planes $\mathcal{M}$ and $\mathcal{N}$ intersect in line *k*.

Postulates, Theorems, and Proofs

In mathematics, we accept some statements as true without proof. These statements are called **postulates.** For example:

POSTULATE 1-1 Two points determine a line.

POSTULATE 1-2 Three noncollinear points determine a plane.

Another kind of mathematical statement, called a **theorem,** is not accepted as true but has to be proven to be true. It is proven true by a formal method called a **proof.**

The term *proof* has a specific meaning for mathematicians. In everyday life, proof is evidence that establishes the truth of a claim—for example, in a court of law, a photograph or fingerprints might be used as proof that an accused person committed a crime. In mathematics, however, a proof is a clear, logical structure of reasoning. It begins from accepted ideas, and then proceeds through logic to reach a conclusion.

While proofs can be presented in different ways, all proofs have the same parts and follow the same general order:

- A list of the given information

- A statement of what is to be proven (often with a diagram)

- A sequence of statements that leads logically from one to the next

- The reasons why each statement is true. These reasons can include postulates, previously proven theorems, or accepted definitions.

Summary

- The basic elements of geometry are points, lines, and planes. To understand more complex terms and concepts in geometry, you need to understand those basic terms. For example, to understand what a ray is, you must first understand what a line is.

- A postulate is a mathematical statement assumed to be true. A theorem is a mathematical statement proven true.

- Geometry, like other areas of mathematics, uses logical reasoning to prove mathematical statements through a formal method called a proof.

Measuring Length

► Define and measure line segments on a number line.

► Determine if line segments are congruent.

► Perform basic constructions with a straightedge and compass.

► Identify and use the Segment Addition and Segment Congruence Postulates.

► Identify a point that is between two other points.

How many miles is it from your home to your favorite vacation place? How long will it take you to get there? How much spending money will you need? How many hours will you need to work to earn enough spending money for the trip?

When you measure something, you find its size, amount, capacity, or quantity. It would be difficult to get a desired length of something if you couldn't state a measurement. In everyday life, measurements are often made with rulers and given in inches or centimeters. In geometry, the number line can be considered a ruler as well.

KEYWORDS

between

congruent line segments

coordinate

length of a line segment

number line

RECONNECT TO THE BIG IDEA

Remember Measurement is the process of using a unit to determine how much of something you have.

Rulers and Number Lines

You can build a number line with a straightedge and compass. Draw a straight line, open your compass to a set width, and mark off segments, keeping the compass open at a constant width throughout. This process will ensure you have an equal space between marks.

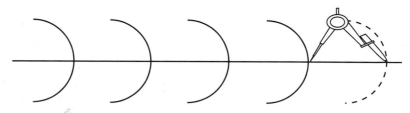

When you make each interval equally spaced and mark each intersection with consecutive numbers you construct a fair ruler. Now this instrument can be used as a measurement tool.

Measuring Line Segments

A **number line** is like a ruler because it has equally spaced intervals that are labeled with numbers. In addition, it contains equal intervals and numbers to the left or below 0, which represent negative numbers. A ruler begins with 0 and contains only positive numbers, those to the right of 0. On a number line, the numbers are called **coordinates.** A coordinate gives the location of a point.

POSTULATE 1-3   Ruler Postulate

The points on a line can be numbered so that positive number differences measure distances.

This means that you can use a number line to measure line segments. The **length of a line segment** is the distance between its endpoints. The length of $\overline{AB}$ is written as AB. When you refer to the length of a segment, you do not include the segment symbol over the two endpoints. When you want to find the length of a line segment by using a number line, subtract the coordinates of the endpoints. If the result is a negative number, make it positive. Distance is always positive.

Look at $\overline{EF}$ on the number line.

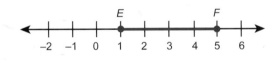

To find EF, subtract the coordinate of point E from the coordinate of point F: $5 - 1 = 4$. Notice that if you subtract the coordinate of point F from the coordinate of point E, the result is negative: $1 - 5 = -4$. Either way, the distance between E and F is 4, so $EF = 4$.

The word *between* was used above without defining it. You intuitively know what the word means, but in geometry, it has a specific definition.

If point B is **between** points A and C, then points A, B, and C are collinear, and the length of $\overline{AB}$ plus the length of $\overline{BC}$ equals the length of $\overline{AC}$.

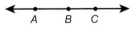

POSTULATE 1-4   Segment Addition Postulate

If B is between A and C, then $AB + BC = AC$. Also, if $AB + BC = AC$ and A, B, and C are collinear, then B is between A and C.

POSTULATE 1-5   Segment Congruence Postulate

If two segments have the same length as measured by a fair ruler, then the segments are congruent ($\cong$). Also, if two segments are congruent, then they have the same length as measured by a fair ruler.

Look at $\overline{EF}$ and $\overline{NM}$ on the number line below.

$EF = 5 - 1 = 4$
$NM = 8 - 4 = 4$
So, $EF = NM$ and $\overline{EF} \cong \overline{NM}$.

Congruent line segments are line segments that have equal length. They do not have to lie on the same line, as pictured above. In the figures below, the tick marks show that $\overline{AB} \cong \overline{BC}$ and $\overline{EF} \cong \overline{GH}$.

Summary

- The number line is a "geometry ruler" because it is used to find lengths of line segments by subtracting the coordinates of the endpoints. Remember: Distances are always positive.

- Congruent line segments have the same length but not necessarily the same orientation. Tick marks show which segments are congruent.

Measuring Angles

► Define and name an angle, the parts of an angle, and angle pairs.

► Measure and classify angles.

► Identify and use the Angle Addition Postulate, the Angle Congruence Postulate, and the Linear Pair Postulate.

Angles are everywhere. They can be found in nature, architecture, and sports. A football player's run on the field may be at an angle to the yard lines. The corners of a picture frame form right angles. Throughout the day, the hands of an analog clock form many different angles. In this lesson, you begin to learn the different types of angles and angle pairs.

KEYWORDS

angle	acute angle
adjacent	complementary angles
exterior of an angle	interior of an angle
linear pair	obtuse angle
right angle	straight angle
supplementary angles	vertex of an angle

Angles

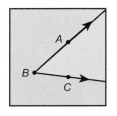

An **angle** is the figure that is formed by two rays, called *sides,* that share the same endpoint. The common endpoint of the angle is called the **vertex.**

For this angle, $\overrightarrow{BA}$ and $\overrightarrow{BC}$ are the sides, and point B is the vertex. A point that does not lie on the sides of an angle lies in either the **interior** (blue region) or **exterior** (pink region) of the angle.

You can name an angle in any of the following ways:

1. with the vertex letter, if there is only one angle having the given vertex;

2. using three points—a point on one side of the angle, the vertex, and a point on the other side of the angle; or

3. using a small letter or number placed between the sides of the angle and near the vertex.

This angle can be named $\angle ABC$, $\angle CBA$, $\angle B$, or $\angle 1$.

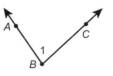

This angle is named $\angle a$.

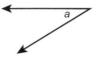

Measuring Angles

The customary measuring unit of an angle is the degree. You can use a protractor to measure angles.

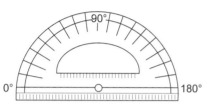

1. Place the center point (the small, open circle) of the protractor on the vertex of the angle.

2. Align either of the rays with the bottom of the protractor so that one of the rays will cross the 0° mark. The figures at left show the protractor may be rotated.

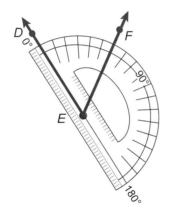

3. Look at the ray that is aligned with the bottom of the protractor. If there are two scales, the 0° mark may be either the inside or outside scale. Whichever scale it is, read that scale where the other ray crosses the protractor's angle marks.

$\angle DEF$ measures 60°. You can write this statement by using m for measure and placing it before the name of the angle: $m\angle DEF = 60°$.

POSTULATE 1-6 Angle Addition Postulate

If point D lies in the interior of $\angle ABC$, then $m\angle ABD + m\angle DBC = m\angle ABC$.

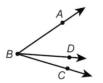

POSTULATE 1-7 Angle Congruence Postulate

If two angles have the same measure as measured by a protractor, then the angles are congruent. Also, if two angles are congruent, then they have the same measure as measured by a protractor.

Classifying Angles

Angles are classified by their measures. **Acute angles** measure less than 90°. **Right angles** measure exactly 90°. **Obtuse angles** measure greater than 90° and less than 180°. **Straight angles** measure exactly 180°. A straight angle is a line.

The "box" symbol shown here indicates that the angle is a right angle.

MEMORYTIP

To remember which pairs of angles sum to 90° and which sum to 180°, remember that C (complementary) comes before S (supplementary) in the alphabet, just as 90 comes before 180 when numbers are ordered from least to greatest.

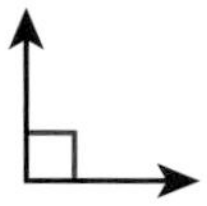

Angle Pairs

Two angles are **adjacent** if they share a common side, have the same vertex, and do not share any interior common points.

Some pairs of angles have special names. Two angles are **complementary** if the sum of their measures is 90°. Two angles are **supplementary** if the sum of their measures is 180°. Complementary and supplementary angles may or may not be adjacent. Complementary and supplementary angles may or may not have a common side.

Pairs of Complementary Angles:

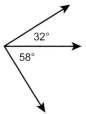

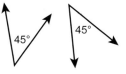

Pairs of Supplementary Angles:

Two angles form a **linear pair** if they have a common side, the same vertex, and their other sides point in opposite directions. In the figures above, the supplementary angles measuring 110° and 70° make up a linear pair. A linear pair is a special kind of supplementary angle pair.

POSTULATE 1-8 **Linear Pair Postulate**

If two angles form a linear pair, then they are supplementary angles.

Summary

- An angle is a figure formed by a pair of rays that have a common endpoint, called the vertex. A point can be on the angle, or in the interior or exterior of the angle.

- Angles are measured in degrees and are classified as acute, right, obtuse, or straight according to their measures.

- Complementary angles are pairs of angles whose measures sum to 90°.

- Supplementary angles are pairs of angles whose measures sum to 180°. If they also have a common side, they are a linear pair.

Bisectors and Line Relationships

Geometry deals with the characteristics, measurements, and relationships of points, lines, surfaces, and solids. Before the age of technology, we used paper, pencil, compass, and straightedge to help us, but the process was often slow and tiresome. With geometry software, we can construct and "see" geometric ideas more easily, allowing us to draw, observe, explore, measure, discover, and make predictions with better insight.

KEYWORDS

angle bisector

midpoint

perpendicular bisector

segment bisector

conjecture

parallel lines

perpendicular lines

Special Lines and Bisectors

Parallel lines are coplanar lines that never intersect. **Perpendicular lines** are lines that meet at right angles. Take a look at the fence. The vertical boards are parallel to each other. Each vertical board is perpendicular to the top and bottom horizontal boards.

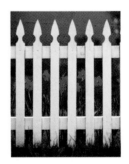

Parallel and perpendicular lines are everywhere—in your home, in sports, at the mall, and in cities, to name just a few examples.

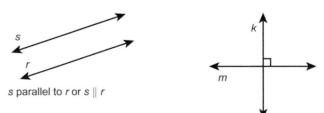

s parallel to r or s ∥ r

k perpendicular to m or k ⊥ m

Bisectors

The **midpoint** of a line segment divides the line segment into two congruent parts. A **segment bisector** is a line, line segment, or ray that passes through the midpoint of a line segment. Although we can draw an infinite number of lines through the midpoint of a segment, we can draw only *one* line that is perpendicular to the line segment as well. We call that line the **perpendicular bisector** of the segment. In the diagram, point M is the midpoint of $\overline{AD}$, line t and line s are segment bisectors of $\overline{AD}$, and line n is the perpendicular bisector of $\overline{AD}$.

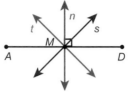

Just as we can bisect lines, we can also bisect angles. An **angle bisector** is a line, line segment, or ray that divides an angle into two congruent angles. In the diagram, $\overrightarrow{EG}$ bisects $\angle DEF$. That means $m\angle DEG = m\angle GEF$.

Using Geometry Software

Because geometry is the study of points, lines, planes, and space, visual sketches help you see and better understand geometric relationships. There are several computer programs you can use to construct geometric figures. This book shows screens that are typical of these programs, along with some general instructions. You can use these general instructions and the instructions that came with your software to construct the figures in the screens.

Constructing Bisectors and Lines

Use your geometry software to construct a line segment. Draw a point above the original segment and then construct a line that passes through the point and is parallel to the original segment.

You can use geometry software to construct a line that passes through a point and is prependicular to a segment.

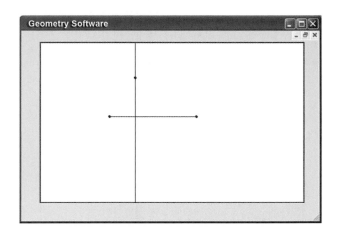

Once you locate the midpoint you can construct the perpendicular bisector for any segment.

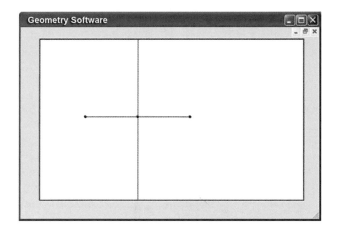

To draw an angle bisector, specify the angle by choosing a point on one side of the angle, the vertex, and a point on the other side. Use geometry software to construct the bisector through the vertex.

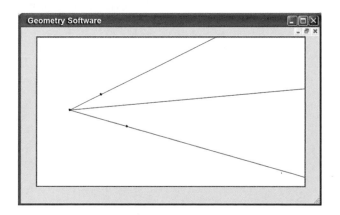

Making Conjectures

A **conjecture** is an educated guess based on observations. For example, in the diagram below we are given that $\overleftrightarrow{AX}$ is the perpendicular bisector of $\overline{CB}$. It certainly looks like $AC = AB$. But that is only a conjecture. It may or may not be true.

Given $\overleftrightarrow{AX}$ is the perpendicular bisector of $\overline{CB}$.
Conjecture $AC = AB$

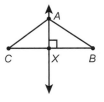

You can use geometry software to investigate the conjecture. Draw the perpendicular bisector of a line segment and a segment from each endpoint to a point on the bisector. Then measure the lengths of the segments. Dragging the point that is point A in this figure up and down the perpendicular bisector, you see that the conjecture appears to be true. You haven't proven anything, but you now have more confidence in your conjecture.

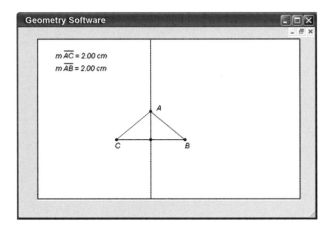

Summary

- Parallel lines are coplanar lines that never intersect, and perpendicular lines intersect at right angles.

- A segment bisector passes through the midpoint of a line segment and divides it into two congruent line segments. If the bisector forms a right angle with the segment, it is the perpendicular bisector.

- An angle bisector divides an angle into two congruent angles.

- A conjecture is an educated guess based on observations.

Relationships Between Triangles and Circles

In your everyday activities, you can see circles overlaying triangles and other figures. We say that these circles are "inscribed in" and "circumscribed about" other geometric shapes. You might see them in windows and art objects. Inscribed and circumscribed circles are often ornamental. However, they can be functional as well. They supply strength while minimizing weight and material in the design of homes, industrial and religious buildings, and bridges.

KEYWORDS

centroid	circumcenter
circumscribed circle	incenter
inscribed circle	median

Points of Intersection in Triangles

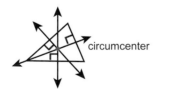
circumcenter

When you draw the perpendicular bisector on each side of a triangle, the bisectors will meet at a point called the **circumcenter.** The circumcenter may lie inside, on, or outside the triangle.

If the triangle is acute, the circumcenter lies inside the triangle, as shown above left. If the triangle is a right triangle, the circumcenter lies on the triangle, and if the triangle is obtuse, the circumcenter lies outside of the triangle.

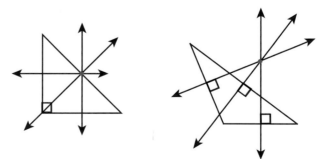

The angle bisectors drawn through each vertex will also intersect. This intersection is called the **incenter** of the triangle and is always on the inside. Just as we can use tick marks to indicate congruent segments, we can use multiple arcs to indicate congruent angles.

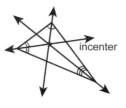

Centroids

When you draw a segment from the vertex of a triangle to the midpoint of its opposite side, you have found a **median** of the triangle. When you draw all three medians, they will intersect at a point called the **centroid.** The centroid is especially interesting because it is also known as the *center of gravity.* You can balance any triangular figure with just your fingertip or pencil tip if you hold it directly under the centroid.

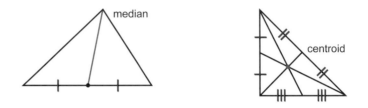

Circumscribed and Inscribed Circles

We say that a circle is **circumscribed** about a triangle if each vertex of the triangle lies on the circle. In the same way, a circle is **inscribed** in a triangle if the circle touches each side of the triangle at a single point.

The circumcenter of a triangle is the center of its circumscribed circle. The incenter is the center of its inscribed circle.

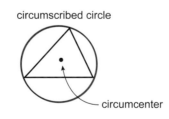

circumscribed circle

circumcenter

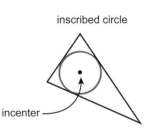

inscribed circle

incenter

Using Geometry Software

The following diagrams were constructed with geometry software.

To construct a circumcenter of a triangle, construct the perpendicular bisectors of each side of a triangle and construct their intersection.

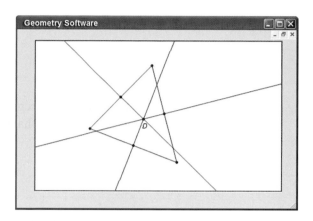

To construct the circumscribed circle, select the circumcenter as the center and one vertex as a point on the circle.

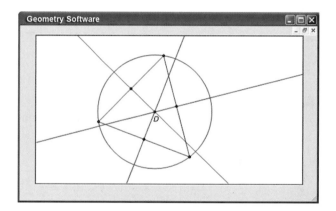

To construct an incenter of a triangle, construct the angle bisectors of each vertex of a triangle and mark their intersection.

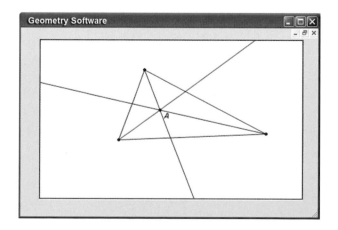

To construct the inscribed circle, first construct a perpendicular line from the incenter to one of the sides. Then construct the circle using the incenter and that intersection. Last, hide the perpendicular line.

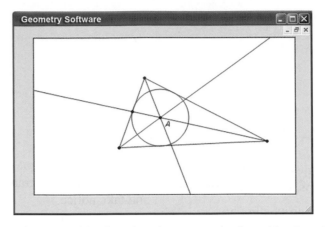

To create the centroid of a triangle, construct the midpoint of each side of the triangle, draw the segment between each midpoint and its opposite vertex, and then mark their intersection.

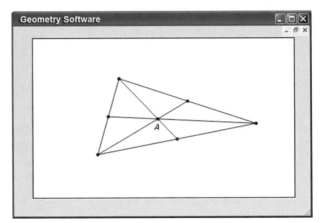

Summary

- Points of intersection in a triangle have special names.
    - The intersection of the three perpendicular bisectors is the circumcenter.
    - The intersection of the three angle bisectors is the incenter.
    - The intersection of the three medians is the centroid.
- The center of a circle circumscribed about a triangle is the circumcenter of the triangle.
- The center of a circle inscribed in a triangle is the incenter of the triangle.

Transformations

OBJECTIVES

▶ Identify and describe properties of reflections, rotations, and translations.

▶ Determine whether a transformation is isometric.

▶ Use compass and straightedge or technology to draw reflections, rotations, and translations.

Think of the logo of a successful company, maybe one that sells food or clothes. Often, the logo began with the drawing of a simple geometric figure. Then this shape or pre-image was "flipped," "turned," or "slid" to create an image that was unique, easily recognized, and evoked emotion. In brief, the designers of logos transform shapes into images that make you remember and take notice.

KEYWORDS

dilation	image	isometry
pre-image	reflection	rotation
transformation	translation	

Types of Transformations

A **transformation** is a change. We can describe sizes, positions, and orientations of shapes under informal transformations such as flips, turns, and slides. In geometry, we describe a transformation as a one-to-one mapping between two sets of points. The original figure is called a **pre-image** and the figure after transformation is called the **image.** Rotations, reflections, and translations preserve the size and shape of the original figure. The image and pre-image are *congruent.*

Any transformation that results in an image that is congruent to the pre-image is called an isometric transformation or an **isometry.** Reflections, translations, and rotations are isometries. **Dilations** are transformations that result in an image that is a different size from the pre-image. Dilations are not isometries.

Reflections

A **reflection** transforms a figure by flipping it across a line (or line segment) creating a mirror image of the figure. When you look at the figures below, you can see the reflection of each image across a line segment or a line. The line segment or line is called the *line of reflection.*

Rotations

A **rotation** turns a figure a certain number of degrees, called the *angle of rotation,* around a central point, called the *center of rotation.* The center of rotation can be on the figure, inside the figure, or outside the figure. The centers of rotation in the figures below are shown in red.

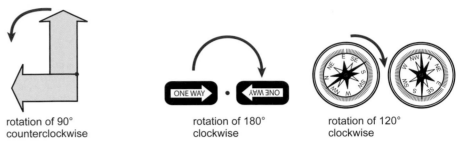

rotation of 90° counterclockwise

rotation of 180° clockwise

rotation of 120° clockwise

Translations

When you **translate** a figure, you slide it in a straight path without rotating or reflecting it. The straight path the figure takes has a distance and a direction. The path of a bowling ball down a lane and a child going down a playground slide are examples of translations.

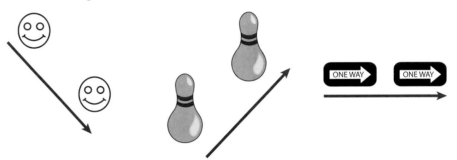

Drawing Transformations with Geometry Software

The following diagrams are examples of transformations constructed with geometry software.

To construct a mirror image of a figure, identify a line, line segment, or ray as the line of reflection (mirror). Select an object and then reflect, or mirror, the object over the line of reflection to create its mirror image. We can further explore these images by changing the shape on either side of the line and watching how the reflection changes.

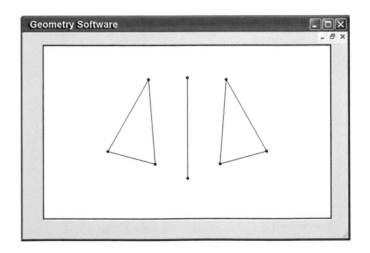

To rotate a figure around a point, you will need to identify a point as the center of rotation. You will also need to enter an angle of rotation, specifying whether you want to rotate the figure in a clockwise direction or in a counterclockwise direction.

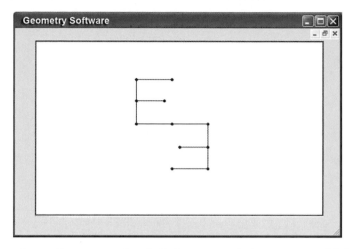

To translate a figure, start by defining a translation vector, which is a line segment that has direction. Once you have your translation vector, you can use it to translate any figure.

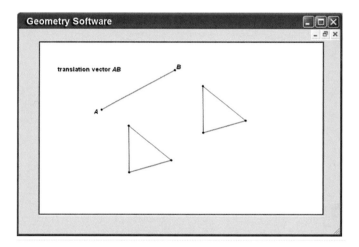

Summary

- Transformations are changes. The original figure is called the pre-image. The figure after transformation is called the image.
- Reflections "flip" a figure across a line of reflection.
- Rotations "turn" a figure some number of degrees about a point called the center of rotation.
- Translations "slide" a figure in a straight path.

Using Algebra to Describe Geometry

In algebra you used the coordinate plane to graph and solve equations. Now you are going to use this impressive tool to help you with geometry. Since the early 1900s, the coordinate plane has become more and more important in solving a variety of mathematics problems. Through the use of a coordinate plane, you can graph a range of geometric figures to help you determine many relationships.

Archaeologists use the coordinate plane as a map to show exactly where objects of art were found and where they were located in relation to one another. Also, coordinate geometry is used in construction, art, clothing design and manufacture, landscaping, and space exploration. You can even use the coordinate plane in organizing your bedroom closet at home!

KEYWORDS

coordinate plane	ordered pair
x-axis	x-coordinate
y-axis	y-coordinate

Transformations in the Coordinate Plane

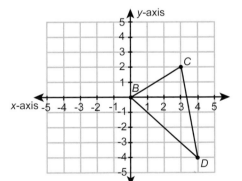

The **coordinate plane** is the intersection of a horizontal number line called the **x-axis** and a vertical number line called the **y-axis.** The intersection of the x- and y-axes is called the origin. To find the location of a point on the coordinate plane, you must look at a pair of numbers, one number from each axis. You identify the point's location as an **ordered pair** where the first number is the **x-coordinate** and the second number is the **y-coordinate.**

On the coordinate plane shown, point B is located at the origin and is named by the ordered pair $(0, 0)$. Point C is named by the ordered pair $(3, 2)$. The x-coordinate of point D is 4. The y-coordinate of point D is –4.

Reflections

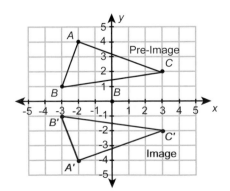

You can reflect a figure in the coordinate plane across either axis, or any line. The triangle in the diagram is reflected across the x-axis. To reflect a figure across the x-axis, you can use the ordered pair rule $(x, y) \rightarrow (x, -y)$. You determine the coordinates of each point in the image by using this rule.

$$A \ (-2, 4) \rightarrow A' \ (-2, -4)$$
$$B \ (-3, 1) \rightarrow B' \ (-3, -1)$$
$$C \ (3, 2) \rightarrow C' \ (3, -2)$$

To reflect a figure across the *y*-axis you use the rule $(x, y) \rightarrow (-x, y)$.

Rotations

You can rotate a figure 180° about the origin by using the rule $(x, y) \rightarrow (-x, -y)$.

$A\ (-4, 4) \rightarrow A'\ (4, -4)$
$B\ (-2, 5) \rightarrow B'\ (2, -5)$
$C\ (-1, 4) \rightarrow C'\ (1, -4)$
$D\ (-2, 2) \rightarrow D'\ (2, -2)$

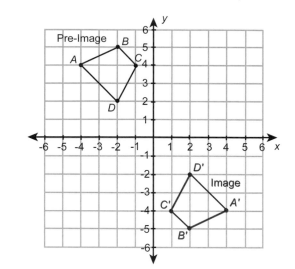

To rotate a figure 90° counterclockwise about the origin, you use the rule $(x, y) \rightarrow (-y, x)$.

Translations

MEMORYTIP

To translate any figure:

direction	operation	coordinate
right	add	*x*
left	subtract	*x*
up	add	*y*
down	subtract	*y*

When you translate a figure, add or subtract to each coordinate a specific amount. To translate the "slow" sign 4 units to the right and 3 units up, we use $(x, y) \rightarrow (x + 4, y + 3)$.

$A\ (-2, 0) \rightarrow A'\ (2, 3)$
$B\ (0, -2) \rightarrow B'\ (4, 1)$
$C\ (-2, -4) \rightarrow C'\ (2, -1)$
$D\ (-4, -2) \rightarrow D'\ (0, 1)$

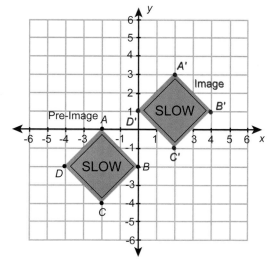

Using Geometry Software

You can mark an axis as a line of reflection (or mirror). In this sketch, the *x*-axis was marked as a line of reflection and a triangle was reflected over it.

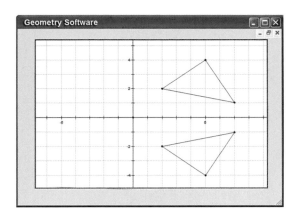

This picture shows a triangle rotated 180° about the origin. Any point, including (0, 0), can be chosen as the center point.

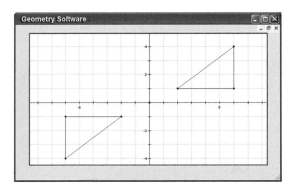

This picture shows a figure being translated two units up and four units right.

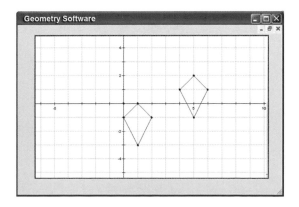

Summary

- Transformations can be performed in the coordinate plane.

- Reflections are made across the x-axis by using the ordered pair rule $(x, y) \rightarrow (x, -y)$ or the y-axis by using $(x, y) \rightarrow (-x, y)$.

- To rotate a figure 90° counterclockwise about the origin, use the ordered pair rule $(x, y) \rightarrow (-y, x)$. To rotate 180° about the origin, use $(x, y) \rightarrow (-x, -y)$.

- Translations are made by adding or subtracting values from the x- and y-coordinates of the pre-image.

UNIT 2

Methods of Proof and Logic

Logic and reasoning will help you in many parts of your life. In talking with friends, listening to political speeches, and learning math, science, and even English literature and composition, you need to be able to understand and create convincing arguments.

Math understanding grows like a tree. It starts with definitions and postulates as its roots and then grows branches (theorems) that extend the tree higher and wider. How do you build or identify solid new branches? You do it through sound mathematical reasoning.

This unit is about mathematical reasoning and proof. With the tools of solid reasoning under your belt, you will be able to write and understand convincing arguments.

. . . .

UNIT OBJECTIVES

▶ Distinguish between formal and informal methods of proof and explain why deductive reasoning is considered proof.

▶ Identify and define a conditional statement and form the inverse, converse, and contrapositive of the statement.

▶ Create truth tables for conditional statements and compound sentences.

▶ Reach conclusions from logical chains.

▶ Determine whether an argument is valid or invalid.

▶ Prove statements indirectly by use of a counterexample.

▶ Determine whether a statement is a definition and create definitions.

▶ Identify and use the algebraic and equivalence properties of equality.

▶ Write proofs in two-column and paragraph formats.

▶ Understand the difference between inductive and deductive reasoning.

Reasoning, Arguments, and Proof

OBJECTIVES

▶ Define and identify tools for informal reasoning such as observation, measurement, and experimentation.

▶ Describe the properties of proofs.

▶ Identify premises and conclusions in an argument.

▶ Identify and develop syllogisms and other valid arguments.

When you heat tightly sealed food in the microwave oven, pressure builds and the lid pops off the container or the food explodes out of the wrapper. You quickly discover that if you continue to seal the food tightly when you heat it, you will have a yucky mess!

Reasoning in which you make general assumptions from specific observations is called induction. When you use deductive reasoning, you progress in the opposite direction, from the general to the specific. You collect observations and test your hypotheses with thorough information and statistics to confirm or disprove your original assumptions.

Induction—like the way you learn not to heat tightly sealed food in the microwave—is less exact and more exploratory. Deduction is controlled and tests hypotheses through previously established properties. Deduction is proof—induction is not.

KEYWORDS

argument	conclusion
deductive reasoning	diagonals
premise	proof
syllogism	valid argument

Reasoning

Observations can be used to draw conclusions. You can use a table to keep track of observations and see if a pattern emerges. Look at the polygons below. As you look from left to right, the number of sides in each polygon increases by one.

The red lines are diagonals. **Diagonals** are segments that connect two vertices of a polygon and do not lie along any side of the polygon. For each polygon above, every diagonal that can be drawn from one vertex is shown. The triangle has no diagonals because any line connecting two vertices would lie along a side of the triangle. The numbers of sides and diagonals are listed in the table below.

Number of Sides of Polygon (*n*)	3	4	5	6	7	8
Number of Diagonals	0	1	2	3	4	5

If you study the table for a bit, you will see that there is a relationship between the number of sides of a polygon and the number of diagonals that can be drawn from one vertex of a polygon. So, from a simple observation, you can conclude that the number of diagonals that can be drawn from a single vertex is three less than the number of sides, or $n - 3$.

The conclusion about the number of diagonals was based on observation and studying of patterns. You can also derive conclusions on the basis of measurement and experimentation. For example, if you measure both diagonals of any rectangle, you will find that their lengths are always equal.

It is important to note that while observation, measurement, and experimentation can lead you to useful assumptions, those tools are not considered proof. Mathematicians rely on **deductive reasoning,** which uses previously proven or accepted properties to reach formal conclusions.

Logic and Proof

An **argument** is a set of statements, called **premises**, which are used to reach a **conclusion**. Both the premises and the conclusion are considered to be part of the argument.

A **syllogism** is a special kind of logical argument. It always contains two premises and a conclusion. Syllogisms have the following form.

Premise: If *a,* then *b.*
Premise: If *b,* then *c.*
Conclusion: Therefore, if *a,* then *c.*

Example:

If Fido is hungry in the morning, then he barks.
If Fido barks, then Jenny wakes up.
Therefore, if Fido is hungry in the morning, then Jenny wakes up.

The validity of an argument is based on the structure of the argument. The syllogism above is a type of valid argument. In a **valid argument,** if the premises are all true, then the conclusion must also be true.

The following is an example of an invalid argument. The structure of the argument is faulty. Notice that both premises can be true and the conclusion can be false.

If you are on a baseball team, then you wear a red hat.
If you are a fireman, then you wear a red hat.
Therefore, if you are on a baseball team, then you are a fireman.

RECONNECT TO THE BIG IDEA

Remember Deductive reasoning enables us to derive true conclusions from statements accepted as true.

Proofs

Earlier in the book, **proof** was defined as a clear, logical structure of reasoning that begins from accepted ideas and proceeds through logic to reach a conclusion. In other words, a proof uses deductive reasoning. In a proof, only valid arguments are used, so the conclusions must be valid. Forms of valid arguments and different types of formal proofs will be shown throughout this unit.

Summary

- Observation, measurement, and experiments are useful, but they are not methods of proof. A formal proof uses deductive reasoning to reach a conclusion.

- An argument is a set of statements that are made up of a set of premises and a conclusion. The premises provide support for the conclusion.

- A syllogism is a special kind of logical argument that contains two premises and one conclusion.

- In a valid argument the premises cannot be true and the conclusion false at the same time.

Conditional Statements

OBJECTIVES

- ▶ Identify and form conditional statements, parts of conditional statements, and forms of conditional statements.

- ▶ Create and interpret truth tables for conditional statements.

- ▶ Create or interpret Euler diagrams that model conditional statements.

- ▶ Use the Law of Contrapositives and the If-Then Transitive Property.

A person who lives in Goodmath must be at least 17 years old to obtain a full driver's license. Nathan, who lives in Goodmath, is over the age of 17. Although the two previous statements are true, can you conclude that Nathan has a driver's license? No, there is not enough evidence. Nathan probably has a driver's license, but you cannot be certain of it. Nathan's sister, Julie, has a driver's license and lives in Goodmath. Can you presume that she is over the age of 17? Yes, this deduction, based on previously known truths, does follow from the given information.

Be aware that although deductive reasoning seems to be an easy concept it's possible for someone to be tricked into faulty reasoning. There is a definite difference between an untrue hypothesis and an argument with flawed logic.

KEYWORDS

conclusion	conditional statement
contrapositive	converse
hypothesis	inverse
logical chain	statement
truth-functionally equivalent	

Conditional Statements

A **statement** is a sentence that is either true or false. A **conditional statement** is a statement that has two parts. The first part begins with the word *if* and the second part begins with the word *then*. The **hypothesis** includes the words following *if* and the **conclusion** includes the words following *then*. In the conditional statement "If it is sunny, then I will mow the grass," the words in blue are the hypothesis and the words in red are the conclusion.

Forms of Conditional Statements

By rearranging and negating the hypothesis and the conclusion, you can form the converse, inverse, and contrapositive of a conditional statement. The **converse** switches the hypothesis and the conclusion. The **inverse** negates, or takes the opposite of both the hypothesis and the conclusion. The **contrapositive** both switches and negates the hypothesis and the conclusion.

MEMORY TIP

The prefix *in-* often means "not." For instance, *insane* means "not sane."

Conditional Statement	*If it is sunny, then I will mow the grass.*
Converse	*If I mow the grass, then it is sunny.*
Inverse	*If it is not sunny, then I will not mow the grass.*
Contrapositive	*If I do not mow the grass, then it is not sunny.*

You can use letters and symbols to represent the forms of these statements. In logic, the letters p and q are usually used. When you use a variable in mathematics, you are using the variable to represent a number. In the same way, the letters p and q represent a group of words.

You can use the symbol $\rightarrow$ to mean "implies" in a conditional statement. When you write $p \rightarrow q$, you are saying that p implies q, which is the same as if p, then q. The symbol $\sim$ is read as "not."

Conditional Statement	If p, then q	$p \rightarrow q$
Converse	If q, then p	$q \rightarrow p$
Inverse	If $\sim p$, then $\sim q$	$\sim p \rightarrow \sim q$
Contrapositive	If $\sim q$, then $\sim p$	$\sim q \rightarrow \sim p$

Both the hypothesis and the conclusion can be either true or false. This is called the truth value of each part. The truth values of those clauses determine whether the entire conditional is either true or false.

Truth Tables

Truth tables are an organized way to look at the possible truth values of an expression. The truth table for a conditional statement lists every possibility of truth values for the hypothesis, conclusion, and statement, where T means true and F means false.

p	q	$p \rightarrow q$
T	T	T
T	F	F
F	T	T
F	F	T

Conditional Statement The truth table for a conditional statement is shown to the left. Notice that the only time $p \rightarrow q$ is false is if the hypothesis is true and the conclusion is false. In the mowing example, this happens when it is sunny and I do not cut the grass. When both the hypothesis and the conclusion are true, the conditional statement is true. In other words, if it is sunny, then I cut the grass. If the hypothesis is false, the conditional statement is true, regardless of the conclusion. You don't know what I will do if it isn't sunny, so the conditional statement is true by default.

p	q	$q \rightarrow p$
T	T	T
T	F	T
F	T	F
F	F	T

Converse When looking at the truth table for the converse, remember that q is now the hypothesis and p is the conclusion. So the converse is only false when q is true and p is false.

Inverse To make the truth table for the inverse, negate each clause first. Notice that the truth values of $\sim p$ and $\sim q$ are opposite those for p and q. The inverse is only false when p is false and q is true.

p	q	$\sim p$	$\sim q$	$\sim p \rightarrow \sim q$
T	T	F	F	T
T	F	F	T	T
F	T	T	F	F
F	F	T	T	T

Contrapositive To make the truth table for the contrapositive, negate p and q and then remember to switch the order so $\sim q$ is the hypothesis. The conclusion is only false when p is true and q is false.

p	q	$\sim p$	$\sim q$	$\sim q \rightarrow \sim p$
T	T	F	F	T
T	F	F	T	F
F	T	T	F	T
F	F	T	T	T

Look at the the far right column in each table. The converse and the inverse columns match. Likewise, the original conditional statement and the contrapositive columns match. Those pairs of statements are **truth-functionally equivalent**—they are either both true or both false.

Most important is that the conditional statement and the contrapositive are equivalent. Because you can write any statement in "if-then" form, this will actually double the number of postulates and theorems you have. It also means that if you prove one of the statements, then you have also proven the other.

Law of Contrapositives If you prove the contrapositive of a conditional statement, then you also prove the conditional statement and vice versa.

Euler Diagrams

Euler diagrams are used to show how the parts of conditional statements are related. The inner circle represents the hypothesis, and the outer circle represents the conclusion. If a point lies in the inner circle, then it also lies in the outer circle. Or, said another way, "If p, then q."

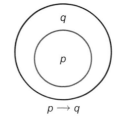

The Euler diagram below represents the conditional statement, which is "If it is sunny, then I will mow the grass." If a point lies in the "it is sunny" circle, then it also lies in the "I will mow the grass" circle. But the converse, "If I mow the grass, then it is sunny," is not necessarily true. There may be days when I cut the grass and it is not sunny, because not every point in the "I will mow the grass" circle is in the "it is sunny" circle.

Think about the contrapositive: "If I do not mow the grass, then it is not sunny." This is true because if you are not in the outer circle, then there is no way you can be in the inner circle. Or, said another way, "If not q, then not p."

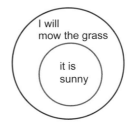

Logical Chains

Euler diagrams are not limited to two circles. There can be several circles, forming a chain of events. The syllogism you saw earlier was a **logical chain**. It is an example of what mathematicians call the *If-Then Transitive Property*. Unlike syllogism, which is limited to two premises, the If-Then Transitive Property can have an unlimited number of premises.

If-Then Transitive Property   If $p \rightarrow q$ and $q \rightarrow r$, then $p \rightarrow r$.

In Euler diagrams, the If-Then Transitive Property looks like this.

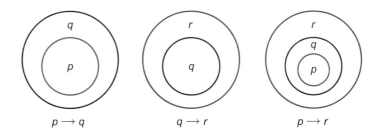

If a point lies in the innermost circle, then it must lie in the middle and outer circles as well. Here are two examples of the If-Then Transitive Property. The first example has two premises; the second example has three premises.

If it is sunny, then I will mow the grass.
If I mow the grass, then I will get paid $20.
Therefore, if it is sunny, then I get paid $20.

RECONNECT TO THE BIG IDEA

Remember Deductive reasoning is based on the premise that if a stated hypothesis is true, then the conclusions logically derived from it must be true.

If it is sunny, then I will mow the grass.
If I mow the grass, then I will get paid $20.
If I get paid $20, then I will buy a new hat.
Therefore, if it is sunny, then I will buy a new hat.

Summary

. . . .

- A conditional statement is a statement in "if-then" form. What follows the word *if* is the hypothesis and what follows the word *then* is the conclusion.

- The converse of a conditional statement switches the hypothesis and the conclusion. The converse of a true conditional may or may not be true.

- The inverse of a conditional statement negates both the hypothesis and the conclusion. The inverse of a true conditional statement may or may not be true.

- The contrapositive switches and negates the hypothesis and the conclusion. The contrapositive of a true conditional statement is always true. Proving the contrapositive of a conditional statement also proves the conditional statement.

- Truth tables can be used to tell you whether a statement is true or false by way of filling in the truth value of each part of the statement.

- Euler diagrams show how the parts of conditional statements are related to each other.

- The If-Then Transitive Property allows you to create logical chains. It says if $p \rightarrow q$ and $q \rightarrow r$, then $p \rightarrow r$.

Compound Statements and Indirect Proof

OBJECTIVES

▶ Identify and create truth tables for conjunctions, disjunctions, and compound statements.

▶ Identify and write compound statements including conjunctions and disjunctions.

▶ Understand the difference between inclusive *or* and exclusive *or*.

▶ Prove statements indirectly.

You are a lawyer representing Zenith Railways in a lawsuit filed by Donald Sleepwell, who claims he was injured in a train accident. Mr. Sleepwell says he received head injuries when the train stopped suddenly, causing his head to hit the wall while he was sleeping in his berth. Mr. Sleepwell has asked the court to order Zenith Railways to pay him $5 million for medical costs and loss of earning power at his job.

The porter and several passengers have testified that the sleeping berths had been set up so people slept with their heads facing the direction the train was going. But they also have testified that the train was traveling in reverse.

You argue that anyone lying in the berths would have been sent feet-first, not head-first, toward the wall when the brakes were slammed on. You win! Because you have shown that Mr. Sleepwell was not telling the truth, the court has ruled in favor of your client, Zenith Railways.

You have proven your case *indirectly*.

KEYWORDS

compound statement	conjunction
contradiction	disjunction
exclusive *or*	inclusive *or*
indirect proof	proof by contradiction

Compound Statements

Recall that a conditional statement contains a hypothesis and a conclusion. In all our examples so far, the hypothesis has been a single statement. A **compound statement** connects two statements with either the word *and* or the word *or*. If they are connected by *and*, then it is a **conjunction.** If they are connected by *or*, then it is a **disjunction**.

Conjunction: It is sunny **and** the temperature is greater than 90°F.
Disjunction: In baseball, a hitter is pitched four balls **or** he is hit by a pitch.

A *compound conditional statement* uses a compound statement as its hypothesis:

If it is sunny **and** the temperature is greater than 90°F, then I will go swimming.

In baseball, if a hitter is pitched four balls **or** he is hit by a pitch, then he can go to first base.

Truth Tables for Compound Statements

You can use truth tables to determine if a compound statement is true or false. The symbol $\wedge$ means *and;* the symbol $\vee$ means *or.*

MEMORYTIP

The symbol $\wedge$ looks like an A without the horizontal piece. *And* begins with A.

And A conjunction is true only when p and q are both true. Otherwise, the compound statement is false.

p	q	$p \wedge q$
T	T	T
T	F	F
F	T	F
F	F	F

MEMORYTIP

A disjunction is false only when *p* and *q* are false.

Or A disjunction is false only when p and q are both false. Otherwise, the compound statement is true.

p	q	$p \vee q$
T	T	T
T	F	T
F	T	T
F	F	F

The disjunction just shown is the **inclusive *or.*** It includes the case where both p and q are true. The **exclusive *or*** excludes the case where both p and q are true. Mathematicians use the inclusive *or,* which is what we will use in this book.

Indirect Proofs

An **indirect proof** is the first type of formal proof we will study. In an indirect proof, we start by assuming the opposite of what we are trying to prove. Then we use deductive reasoning to reach a contradiction. A **contradiction** is a statement that disagrees with another statement. The contradiction will show that the assumption was false and therefore what we wanted to prove must be true. The contradiction can contradict either the given, a definition, a postulate, a theorem, or any known fact. Because an indirect proof uses a contradiction, we can also call this type of proof a **proof by contradiction.**

Given   Triangle ABC

Prove   A triangle cannot have two right angles.

Indirect Proof

Assume triangle ABC has two right angles: $\angle B$ and $\angle C$. Because the measures of the angles of a triangle always sum to 180°, $m\angle A + m\angle B + m\angle C = 180°$. Because a right angle measures 90°, substitute 90° for $m\angle B$ and $m\angle C$. So, $m\angle A + 90° + 90° = 180°$. Simplifying the left side results in $m\angle A + 180° = 180°$. Solving for $m\angle A$ gives $m\angle A = 0°$. But if this is true, then $\overline{AB}$ would lie on top of $\overline{AC}$, and the figure would not be a triangle. This contradicts the given information. The assumption that a triangle has two right angles is false. Therefore, a triangle cannot have two right angles.

Summary

• •

- A compound statement combines two statements with either the word *and* or the word *or.* A conjunction combines two statements with the word *and.* A disjunction combines two statements with the word *or.*

- The inclusive use of *or* allows both statements to be true at the same time. If both statements cannot be true at the same time, the exclusive use of *or* is being used.

- One way to prove a statement is with an indirect proof. An indirect proof assumes the opposite of what you are trying to prove and uses a contradiction to prove the original statement true.

Definitions and Biconditionals

OBJECTIVES

▶ Define and identify adjacent angles and biconditional statements.

▶ Determine if a statement is a definition.

▶ Use Euler diagrams to analyze definitions.

Definitions must be clear and precise. Suppose you define the word *sunflower* as "a flower with yellow petals." Does it then follow that every flower with yellow petals is a sunflower? Roses, marigolds, and tulips also can have yellow petals, so the answer is No. The same problem can happen in mathematics. You need good definitions that will correctly identify or classify objects.

KEYWORDS

adjacent angles   biconditional statement

Definitions

REMEMBER

The converse of "if *p*, then *q*" is "if *q*, then *p*."

If a statement is a definition, then both the original statement and its converse must be true. A statement that is not written as a conditional can be rewritten in the conditional form.

You have learned that a right angle measures 90°. This can be written as: *If an angle is a right angle, then it measures 90°.* In this case the converse is also true: *If an angle measures 90°, then it is a right angle.*

Adjacent angles are two coplanar angles that share a common side and have no interior points in common. As this is a definition, both the statement and its converse must be true.

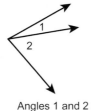

Angles 1 and 2 are adjacent.

Statement   *If two angles are adjacent, then the angles are coplanar, share a common side, and have no interior points in common.*

Converse   *If two angles are coplanar, share a common side, and have no interior points in common, then the angles are adjacent.*

Biconditional Statements

If a statement and its converse are both true, then the statement is **biconditional.** A biconditional statement in mathematics may be written using the phrase *if and only if,* which is abbreviated like this: *iff.* The symbol $\leftrightarrow$ represents a biconditional statement, meaning p implies q and q implies p. The definition of adjacent angles can be rewritten as follows:

Two angles are adjacent if and only if they are coplanar, share a common side, and have no interior points in common.

Euler Diagrams

You can use an Euler diagram to determine if a statement is a definition. Suppose a car was defined as a vehicle with four wheels. Written as a conditional, the statement is: *If it is a car, then it is a vehicle with four wheels.* The Euler diagrams for the statement and its converse are shown.

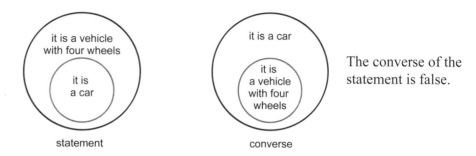

The converse of the statement is false.

statement　　　　　　　converse

Look at the diagram for the converse. Sport utility vehicles, pickups, wheelchairs, and wagons would fall within the center circle, but not within the outer circle. The diagram does not make sense. The converse is not true; the statement is not a definition.

Look at a math definition: A quadrilateral is a polygon with four sides. The conditional and the converse are: *If a figure is a quadrilateral, then it has four sides* and *If a figure has four sides, then it is a quadrilateral.*

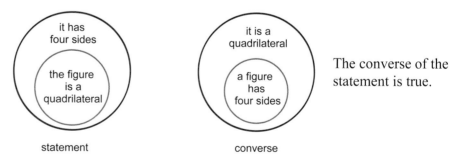

The converse of the statement is true.

statement　　　　　　　converse

The statement and its converse are both true, so you can rewrite the definition of a quadrilateral as: *A figure is a quadrilateral if and only if it is a polygon with four sides.*

Creating Definitions

Creating a definition is not always easy. If you define a square as a rectangle, then its converse is not true. The converse is: *A rectangle is a square.* That statement isn't accurate. Some rectangles aren't squares. A square is a rectangle with consecutive sides congruent. Here are some tips for writing a good definition.

- Be precise. Avoid terms like *sort of.*

- Use only previously defined terms.

- Do not use the word you are defining in the definition.

- Tell what the object is, not what the object is not.

Summary

- A statement is a definition if the statement and its converse are both true. We call them biconditional statements.

- A biconditional statement uses the phrase *if and only if* to show that the statement and its converse are both true.

- A good definition has terms that are clear and that have been defined previously, makes it easy to determine the reasons as to why it is part of a certain classification, and uses as few words as possible.

Algebraic Logic

OBJECTIVES

▶ Identify and use Algebraic Properties of Equality.

▶ Identify and use Equivalence Properties of Equality and Congruence.

▶ Use the two-column format for proofs.

▶ Identify and use the Theorem of Overlapping Segments.

▶ Identify and use the Theorem of Overlapping Angles.

Throughout this unit, you have explored the nature of, and some methods for, proof. The responsibility of supplying convincing evidence in support of your statement or issue rests with you. Just as a competent attorney studies his or her case carefully and thoroughly, you need to investigate your specific assignment completely from every viewpoint. Draw pictures and diagrams to visualize the conditions at hand; build a comprehensive algebraic and geometric "arsenal" of definitions and properties to help you list your options; and be willing to make intelligent, sensible guesses knowing that you may come to a dead end and may have to try another route.

KEYWORDS

conjecture

theorem

direct proof

two-column proof

Properties of Equality

Algebraic Properties of Equality

The Addition Property of Equality	If $a = b$, then $a + c = b + c$.
The Subtraction Property of Equality	If $a = b$, then $a - c = b - c$.
The Multiplication Property of Equality	If $a = b$, then $ac = bc$.
The Division Property of Equality	If $a = b$ and $c \neq 0$, then $\frac{a}{c} = \frac{b}{c}$.
The Substitution Property of Equality	If $a = b$, then b can be substituted for a in any expression.

MEMORYTIP

Reflexive sounds like *reflecting*. A reflection looks exactly the same as the original object.

Equivalence Properties of Equality and Congruence

The Reflexive Property of Equality	$a = a$
The Reflexive Property of Congruence	$a \cong a$
The Symmetric Property of Equality	If $a = b$, then $b = a$.
The Symmetric Property of Congruence	If $a \cong b$, then $b \cong a$.
The Transitive Property of Equality	If $a = b$ and $b = c$, then $a = c$.
The Transitive Property of Congruence	If $a \cong b$ and $b \cong c$, then $a \cong c$.

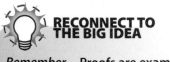

RECONNECT TO THE BIG IDEA

Remember Proofs are examples of deductive reasoning.

REMEMBER

The abbreviation *iff* means the statement is a biconditional statement. Both the conditional and the converse are true. Only one way needs to be proven.

Theorems and Proofs

A **theorem** is a mathematical statement that has been or is to be proven on the basis of established definitions and properties. A major way of proving theorems is the method of **direct proof,** in which the conclusion is drawn directly from previous conclusions, starting with the first statement. Also, geometric proofs can be written in two basic formats: *two-column* or *paragraph*. A paragraph proof is written in sentences and is more difficult than the two-column proof, which is easier to set up and understand.

The statement that is to be proven is called a **conjecture.** A conjecture is a statement you think is true, but still need to prove using deductive reasoning. Once a conjecture is proven, it is called a theorem. You can use inductive reasoning to come up with conjectures, then use deductive reasoning to prove or disprove your conjectures.

A **two-column geometric proof** uses deductive reasoning and consists of a list of statements, each with the formal reason (the given, definition, postulate, theorem already proven, or property) that justifies how you know that the statement is true. The statements are listed in a column on the left, and the reasons for which the statements can be made are listed in a column on the right. Every step of the proof (a subconclusion) is a row in the two-column proof.

Some guidelines for writing proofs are as follows:

- Draw the figure that illustrates what is to be proven. The figure may have already been drawn for you, or you may have to draw it yourself.

- List the given statements, and then list the conclusion to be proven. Now you have a beginning and an end to the proof.

- Mark the figure according to what you can conclude about it from the information that is given. This is the step of the proof in which you actually find out how the proof is to be made, and whether you are able to prove what is asked. Mark up all that you are able so that you can see for yourself what you must write in your proof to convince the reader that your conclusion is valid and accurate.

- Write your steps carefully—even the simplest ones. Some of the first steps are often the given statements (but not always), and the last step is the conclusion that is to be proven.

Theorems 2-1 and 2-2 are similar. Study their proofs carefully.

THEOREM 2-1   Theorem of Overlapping Segments
If point *B* is between *A* and *C* and point *C* is between *B* and *D,* then *AB = CD* iff *AC = BD.*

Given $AB = CD$

Prove $AC = BD$

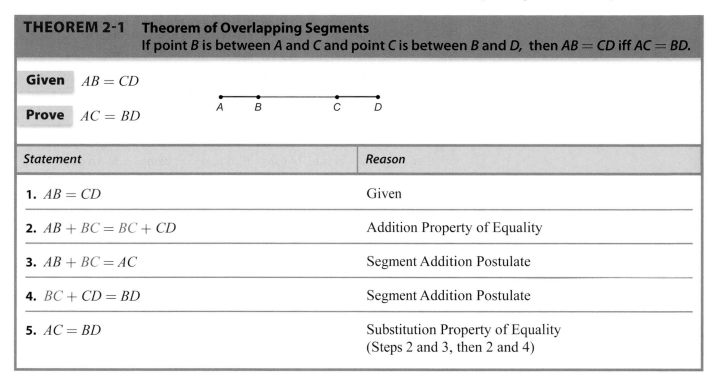

Statement	Reason
1. $AB = CD$	Given
2. $AB + BC = BC + CD$	Addition Property of Equality
3. $AB + BC = AC$	Segment Addition Postulate
4. $BC + CD = BD$	Segment Addition Postulate
5. $AC = BD$	Substitution Property of Equality (Steps 2 and 3, then 2 and 4)

THEOREM 2-2   Theorem of Overlapping Angles
If point *B* lies in the interior of $\angle AWC$ and point *C* lies in the interior of $\angle BWD,$ then $m\angle AWB = m\angle CWD$ iff $m\angle AWC = m\angle BWD.$

Given $m\angle AWB = m\angle CWD$

Prove $m\angle AWC = m\angle BWD$

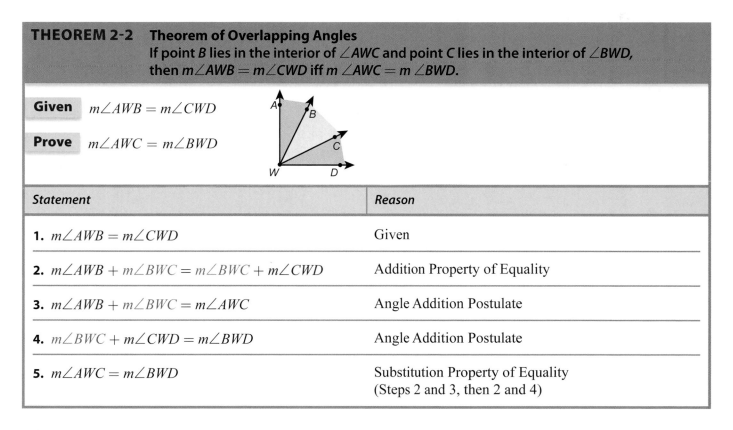

Statement	Reason
1. $m\angle AWB = m\angle CWD$	Given
2. $m\angle AWB + m\angle BWC = m\angle BWC + m\angle CWD$	Addition Property of Equality
3. $m\angle AWB + m\angle BWC = m\angle AWC$	Angle Addition Postulate
4. $m\angle BWC + m\angle CWD = m\angle BWD$	Angle Addition Postulate
5. $m\angle AWC = m\angle BWD$	Substitution Property of Equality (Steps 2 and 3, then 2 and 4)

Sometimes this book will show a third column with a sketch to illustrate each reason. This proof will still be considered a two-column proof.

Summary

- One way to display a proof of a theorem is to use a two-column format.

- In a two-column proof, statements are presented in a list in a column on the left, and reasons are presented in a column on the right. Reasons can include the given, definitions, postulates, theorems already proven, and properties.

Inductive and Deductive Reasoning

Your five-year-old sister notices that every time she throws a ball up into the air, it comes down and hits her on the head. You tell her to do it again, but she says: "No way. I will get hit on the head again!" She is thinking inductively. Your 15-year-old brother says: "That is Newton's law of gravity—what goes up must come down." He is reasoning deductively. Briefly, induction moves from the specific to the general, while deduction progresses from the general to the specific. Assertions that are built on observation and experience are inductive, and reasoning that is based on established principles is deduction. The distinction between the two is the point of view. Remember that deductive reasoning is proof and that observation, measurement, and experimentation are not proof.

KEYWORDS

inductive reasoning   paragraph proof

vertical angles

Sir Isaac Newton

Using Inductive Reasoning

You may recall from Unit 1 that a conjecture is an educated guess. Making a conjecture based on past events or on a pattern is called **inductive reasoning.** Although curiosity, observation, and conjecture have an important role in the proof process, inductive reasoning sometimes fails. Inductive reasoning provides us with a starting point, but it is not proof.

You can use geometry software to emphasize the inductive process, as shown by the following two examples. They demonstrate the process of inductive reasoning, combined with the use of algebra to express geometric ideas.

A reflection across a line and then across a line parallel to the first line is equivalent to a translation of twice the distance between the lines and in a direction perpendicular to the lines.

In this sketch, the triangle was first reflected across the red dashed line. Then it was reflected across the solid blue line. The distance between the red dashed and solid blue lines is two units. The final image is four units away from the original pre-image.

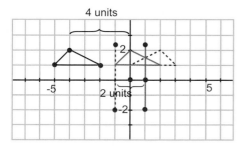

Vertical Angles

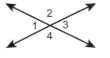

Vertical angles are the two nonadjacent angles formed by intersecting lines. The sides of one angle are the opposite rays to the sides of the other angle. In the diagram, ∠1 and ∠3 form a vertical pair, and ∠2 and ∠4 form another vertical pair.

We can prove that vertical angles are congruent by means of a two-column proof.

THEOREM 2-3	Vertical Angles Theorem

If two angles form a pair of vertical angles, then they are congruent.

Given   ∠1 and ∠3 are vertical angles.

Prove   ∠1 ≅ ∠3

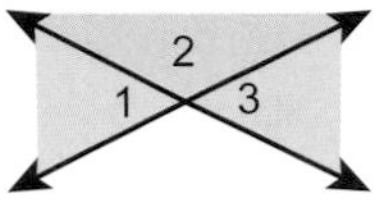

Statement	Reason
1. ∠1 and ∠3 are vertical angles.	Given
2. ∠1 and ∠2 form a linear pair. ∠2 and ∠3 form a linear pair.	Definition of linear pair
3. $m\angle 1 + m\angle 2 = 180°$ $m\angle 2 + m\angle 3 = 180°$	Linear Pair Postulate
4. $m\angle 1 + m\angle 2 = m\angle 2 + m\angle 3$	Substitution Property of Equality
5. $m\angle 1 = m\angle 3$	Subtraction Property of Equality
6. ∠1 ≅ ∠3	Angle Congruence Postulate

You can also write a proof in the form of a paragraph. This is called a **paragraph proof.** A paragraph proof for the Vertical Angles Theorem is shown below. Notice that, similar to the two-column proof, each statement is supported by a reason.

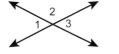

Given   ∠1 and ∠3 are vertical angles.

Prove   ∠1 ≅ ∠3

You are given that ∠1 and ∠3 are vertical angles. Because of the definition of *linear pair*, ∠1 and ∠2 form a linear pair and ∠2 and ∠3 form a linear pair. By the Linear Pair Postulate, $m\angle 1 + m\angle 2 = 180°$ and $m\angle 2 + m\angle 3 = 180°$. By using the Substitution Property of Equality and substituting $m\angle 2 + m\angle 3$ for $180°$ into the first equation, we get $m\angle 1 + m\angle 2 = m\angle 2 + m\angle 3$. By using the Subtraction Property of Equality, we can subtract $m\angle 2$ from both sides to get $m\angle 1 = m\angle 3$. Because of the definition of *congruent*, $\angle 1 \cong \angle 3$.

Most of the time, we will use the two-column format because it is easier to set up and to understand.

Given		Prove	$\angle 1 \cong \angle 4$
$\angle 2 \cong \angle 3$			

Given ıt	Reason	Sketch
1. $\angle 2 \cong \angle 3$	Given	
2. $\angle 1 \cong \angle 2$	Vertical Angles Theorem	
3. $\angle 1 \cong \angle 3$	Substitution Property of Equality	
4. $\angle 3 \cong \angle 4$	Vertical Angles Theorem	
5. $\angle 1 \cong \angle 4$	Substitution Property of Equality	

You can find the measures of all four angles formed by a pair of intersecting lines when you are given just one of the measures.

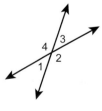

In the diagram, $m\angle 3 = 20°$.
Because $\angle 2$ and $\angle 3$ form a linear pair, then $m\angle 2 = 160°$.
Because $\angle 2$ and $\angle 4$ are vertical angles, $m\angle 4 = 160°$.
Because $\angle 1$ and $\angle 3$ are vertical angles, $m\angle 1 = 20°$.

There are several ways to find the measures of the three angles that are not given. For example, you could have also used the Linear Pair Postulate all around the figure. Similarly, you will find there are sometimes multiple ways to prove a statement. As long as each statement follows logically from previous statements, the proof is valid.

Summary

. . . .

- Inductive reasoning is based on observations of patterns and past events. Inductive reasoning can be used either to make or to support conjectures. It cannot be used to formally prove conjectures.

- A reflection across a line and then across a line parallel to the first line is equivalent to a translation of twice the distance between the lines and in a direction perpendicular to the lines.

- A reflection across two intersecting lines is equivalent to a rotation about the point of intersection through twice the measure of the angle between the lines.

- When two lines intersect, vertical angles are formed. Vertical angles are the nonadjacent angles whose sides are opposite rays.

- The Vertical Angles Theorem states that vertical angles are congruent.

- A paragraph proof is another type of formal proof. Each statement is supported by a reason as in the two-column proof.

UNIT 3   Polygon Basics

The origins of baseball in the United States are not clear, but it is believed that professional baseball began in the mid-1800s. Today's rules of baseball, including the layout of the field, can be traced back to a list of rules compiled in 1845 called *The Knickerbocker Rules*. Many aspects of baseball are geometric. For example:

- Home plate is a pentagon with two pairs of congruent sides.

- The area where the batter stands, called the batter's box, is made up of two congruent rectangles.

- The infield grass is a square.

- First base, second base, and third base are square canvas bags.

- The foul lines separate the foul territory from the fair territory and are perpendicular to each other.

In this unit, you will learn about different types of polygons, including those found on a baseball field.

. . . .

UNIT OBJECTIVES

▶ Define and classify polygons.

▶ Identify and define special quadrilaterals and their properties.

▶ Use properties of parallel lines intersected by a transversal to determine angle measures and recognize the angle measures that produce parallel lines.

▶ Use the Triangle Sum and Exterior Angle Theorems.

▶ Develop and use formulas for finding interior and exterior angle measures of polygons.

▶ Find the lengths of midsegments of triangles and trapezoids.

▶ Find the slope of a line.

▶ Find the midpoint of a line segment.

Polygons and Symmetry

MEMORYTIP

Polygons are named for their number of sides:

Triangle
    three-sided polygon

Quadrilateral
    four-sided polygon

Pentagon
    five-sided polygon

Hexagon
    six-sided polygon

Octagon
    eight-sided polygon

The prefix *poly* means "many," and polygons are many-sided figures. There is no limit to the number of sides a polygon can have. Look at the figures. Can you use inductive reasoning to make a conjecture about what happens to the shape of a regular polygon as the sides increase in number?

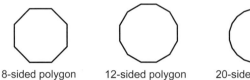

8-sided polygon   12-sided polygon   20-sided polygon

KEYWORDS

axis of symmetry	center of a polygon
central angle	equiangular polygon
equilateral polygon	equilateral triangle
isosceles triangle	polygon
reflection symmetry	regular polygon
rotation symmetry	scalene triangle
side	vertex of a polygon

Polygons

A **polygon** is a closed figure in a plane formed by three or more line segments, such that each line segment intersects exactly two other line segments at their endpoints only.

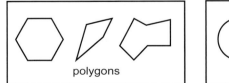

polygons

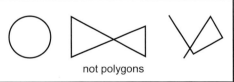

not polygons

The line segments form the **sides** of the polygon. A point where the sides intersect is a **vertex.**

A polygon with all angles congruent is called an **equiangular polygon.**

A polygon with all sides congruent is called an **equilateral polygon.**

A **regular polygon** is both equiangular and equilateral.

Triangles

A triangle is the simplest polygon. You can classify a triangle by its sides. A triangle with no congruent sides is a **scalene triangle.**

A triangle with at least two congruent sides is an **isosceles triangle.**

A triangle with three congruent sides is an **equilateral triangle.** Notice that an equilateral triangle is also an isosceles triangle.

Regular Polygons

Regular polygons have special properties. The **center** is the point inside the polygon that is *equidistant* from each vertex. An angle formed by line segments drawn from the center to two consecutive vertices is called a **central angle.**

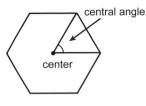

The measure of each central angle of a regular polygon is 360° divided by the number of sides.

For a regular polygon, where m is the measure of the central angle and n is the number of sides,
$$m = \frac{360°}{n}.$$

Symmetry and Regular Polygons

A line drawn through a figure so that one side is a reflection of the image on the opposite side is an **axis of symmetry,** or a *line of symmetry.*

If a figure has **reflection symmetry,** then you can find at least one axis of symmetry in the figure. For figures with reflection symmetry, you can fold the figure along an axis of symmetry and both halves will match up.

If a figure has **rotation symmetry,** then you can rotate it around its center less than one full turn, and the rotated figure looks exactly like the original figure.

All regular polygons have both reflection symmetry and rotation symmetry. The number of axes of symmetry in a regular polygon is equal to its number of sides. The smallest angle by which a regular polygon can be rotated to look exactly like the original polygon is the measure of its central angle.

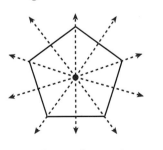

5 axes of symmetry

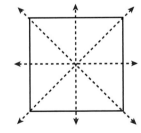

4 axes of symmetry

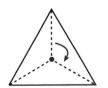

120° angle of rotation

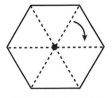

60° angle of rotation

Summary

· ·

- A polygon is a closed figure in a plane formed by three or more line segments, so that each line segment intersects exactly two other line segments at their endpoints only.

- A polygon with congruent sides is equilateral. A polygon with congruent angles is equiangular. A regular polygon is both equilateral and equiangular.

- The center of a regular polygon is the point inside the polygon that is equidistant from each vertex.

- A central angle of a regular polygon is formed by line segments drawn from its center to two consecutive vertices. You can find this measure by dividing the number of sides of the polygon into 360°.

- A regular polygon has reflection symmetry and rotation symmetry. Reflection symmetry means the figure has an axis of symmetry for which one side is a reflection of the other. Rotation symmetry means the figure can be rotated less than one full turn around the center and look exactly like the original figure.

Quadrilaterals and Their Properties

OBJECTIVES

- ▶ Define and identify special quadrilaterals.
- ▶ Identify the properties of special quadrilaterals.
- ▶ Identify the relationships among special quadrilaterals and among their properties.
- ▶ Use properties of special quadrilaterals to solve problems.

The word *diamond* is used loosely to describe a certain four-sided figure. When most people hear the phrase *baseball diamond*, they picture something like the baseball diamond outlined here in red. In reality, the diamond is a square! Do you know the difference between a square and other four-sided shapes? Mathematicians classify special four-sided shapes, each with their own unique side and angle relationships.

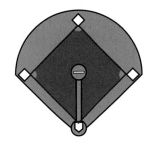

KEYWORDS

parallelogram	quadrilateral
rectangle	rhombus
square	trapezoid

Quadrilaterals

A **quadrilateral** is a four-sided polygon. A quadrilateral is named by writing each vertex in consecutive order. The quadrilateral below could be named *ABCD* or *DABC* or *CBAD*. Some quadrilaterals have special names that are based on their sides and angles.

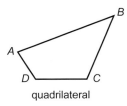

quadrilateral

A **parallelogram** is a quadrilateral with two pairs of parallel sides. The arrows in the diagram show which sides are parallel.

parallelogram

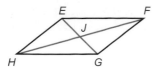

Parallelograms have several properties as shown here.

- The opposite sides are congruent.
  $\overline{EF} \cong \overline{HG}$, $\overline{EH} \cong \overline{FG}$

- The opposite angles are congruent.
  $\angle E \cong \angle G$, $\angle H \cong \angle F$

- The consecutive angles are supplementary.
  $m\angle H + m\angle G = 180°$, $m\angle G + m\angle F = 180°$,
  $m\angle F + m\angle E = 180°$, $m\angle E + m\angle H = 180°$

- The diagonals bisect each other.
  $EJ = JG$, $HJ = JF$

A **rectangle** is a parallelogram with four right angles.

rectangle

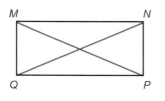

All the properties for a parallelogram are true for a rectangle. But there is an additional property just for rectangles.

- The diagonals are congruent.
  $\overline{MP} \cong \overline{QN}$

A **rhombus** is a parallelogram with four congruent sides.

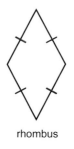

rhombus

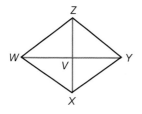

A rhombus has all the properties of a parallelogram plus the following.

- The diagonals are perpendicular.
  $m\angle WVZ = 90°$, $m\angle ZVY = 90°$,
  $m\angle YVX = 90°$, $m\angle XVW = 90°$

- The diagonals bisect the vertices.
  $m\angle WZV = m\angle VZY$, $m\angle ZYV = m\angle VYX$,
  $m\angle YXV = m\angle VXW$, $m\angle XWV = m\angle VWZ$

A **square** is a parallelogram with four congruent sides and four right angles. That means it is both a rectangle and a rhombus. A square has all the properties of a parallelogram, rectangle, and rhombus.

square

A **trapezoid** is a quadrilateral with exactly one pair of parallel sides. A trapezoid is not a parallelogram, so it doesn't have any of its properties.

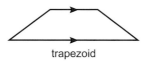
trapezoid

Relationships Among Special Quadrilaterals

We can use Euler diagrams to show the relationships among special quadrilaterals.

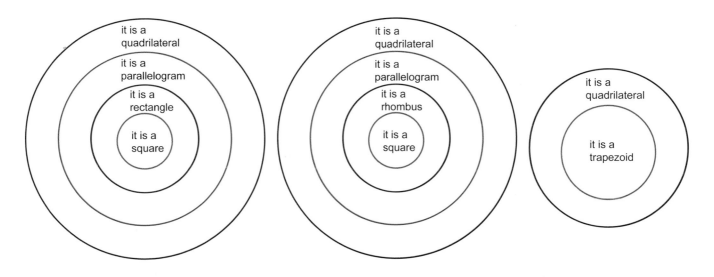

The first diagram allows us to see why it is true to say *If it is a square, then it is a rectangle,* but not true to say *If it is a rectangle, then it is a square.*

Summary

- A quadrilateral is a polygon with four sides. Parallelograms, rectangles, rhombi, squares, and trapezoids are types of quadrilaterals.

- Parallelograms have both pairs of opposite sides parallel. Trapezoids have just one pair of opposite sides parallel.

- Rectangles, rhombi, and squares are types of parallelograms. Rectangles have four right angles, rhombi have four congruent sides, and squares have both four right angles and four congruent sides.

- You can use Euler diagrams to show the relationships among quadrilaterals and to form conditional statements.

Parallel Lines and Transversals

Civil engineers design highways, bridges, buildings, and transit systems. In doing so, they work with parallel and perpendicular lines and angles of varying degrees. Besides constructing new projects, they improve existing structures and systems.

Civil engineers must be skilled in making accurate scale models and drawings. They must know about the environment and geotechnology. Also, they must take into account safety, legal responsibility, expense, and practicality. Most of their time is spent on design, administration, and construction site supervision. For all of their projects, civil engineers need mathematics, science, and a sense of discovery.

KEYWORDS

alternate exterior angles   alternate interior angles

corresponding angles   same-side interior angles

transversal

Parallel Lines and Transversals

Transversals

When a line intersects two or more lines in a plane, we call that line a **transversal.** In the figure at left, line *t* is a transversal. Notice that this intersection creates eight different angles. We give special names to certain pairs of these angles.

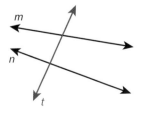

If you think of the eight angles as being split into two different groups of four, one group around line *m* and one group around line *n,* then those angles that "match up" are **corresponding angles.** The corresponding angles in this figure are the angle pairs ∠1 and ∠5, ∠2 and ∠6, ∠3 and ∠7, and ∠4 and ∠8.

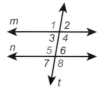

Alternate interior angles are "in between" the two lines that are not the transversal, and are on diagonal opposite sides of the transversal. In this figure, they are the angle pair ∠3 and ∠6 and the angle pair ∠4 and ∠5.

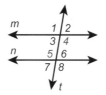

Alternate exterior angles are "outside of" the two lines that are not the transversal, and are on diagonal opposite sides of the transversal. In this figure, they are the angle pair ∠1 and ∠8 and the angle pair ∠2 and ∠7.

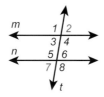

Same-side interior angles are "in between" the two lines that are not the transversal, and are on the same side of the transversal. In this figure, they are the angle pair ∠3 and ∠5 and the angle pair ∠4 and ∠6.

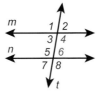

These angle pairs have special relationships. You may have already made some conjectures about them. The following postulates and theorems involve angle pairs formed by two parallel lines intersected by a transversal.

POSTULATE 3-1 Corresponding Angles Postulate

If two parallel lines are intersected by a transversal, then corresponding angles are congruent.

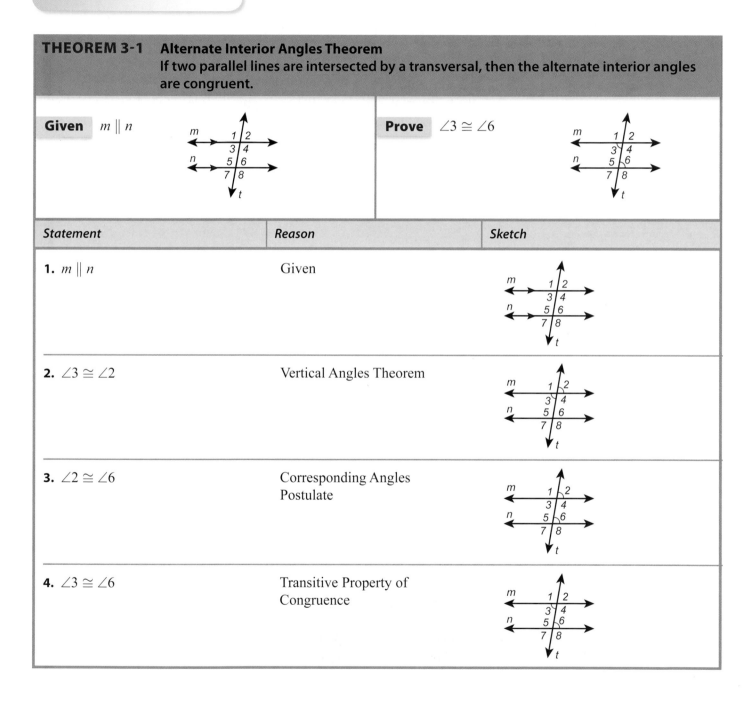

THEOREM 3-1	Alternate Interior Angles Theorem
	If two parallel lines are intersected by a transversal, then the alternate interior angles are congruent.

Given $m \parallel n$

Prove $\angle 3 \cong \angle 6$

Statement	Reason	Sketch
1. $m \parallel n$	Given	
2. $\angle 3 \cong \angle 2$	Vertical Angles Theorem	
3. $\angle 2 \cong \angle 6$	Corresponding Angles Postulate	
4. $\angle 3 \cong \angle 6$	Transitive Property of Congruence	

THEOREM 3-2 Alternate Exterior Angles Theorem

If two parallel lines are intersected by a transversal, then the alternate exterior angles are congruent.

Given $m \parallel n$

Prove $\angle 1 \cong \angle 8$

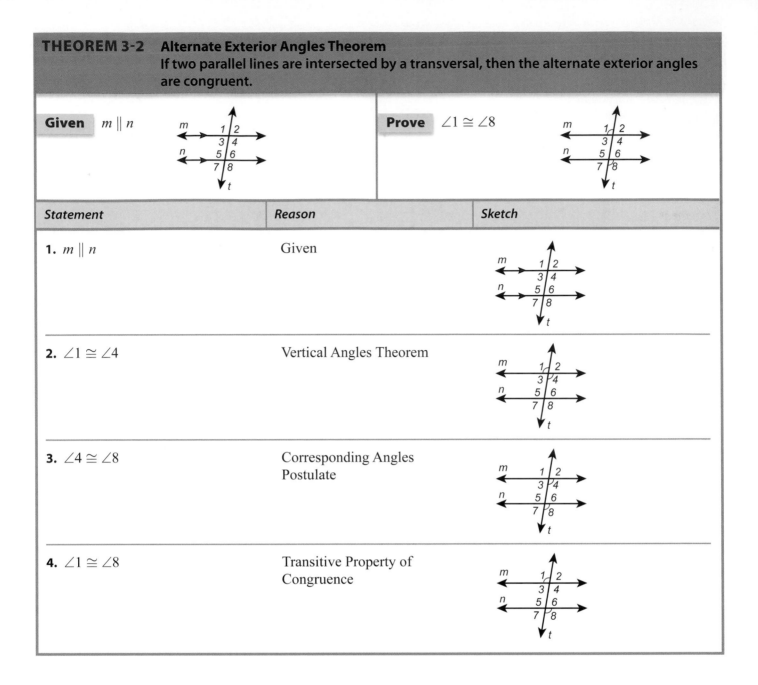

Statement	Reason	Sketch
1. $m \parallel n$	Given	
2. $\angle 1 \cong \angle 4$	Vertical Angles Theorem	
3. $\angle 4 \cong \angle 8$	Corresponding Angles Postulate	
4. $\angle 1 \cong \angle 8$	Transitive Property of Congruence	

THEOREM 3-3 Same-Side Interior Angles Theorem
If two parallel lines are intersected by a transversal, then the same-side interior angles are supplementary.

Given $m \parallel n$

Prove $m\angle 4 + m\angle 6 = 180°$

Statement	Reason	Sketch
1. $m \parallel n$	Given	
2. A linear pair is formed from $\angle 6$ and $\angle 8$.	Definition of a linear pair	
3. $m\angle 6 + m\angle 8 = 180°$	Linear Pair Postulate	
4. $m\angle 4 = m\angle 8$	Corresponding Angles Postulate	
5. $m\angle 4 + m\angle 6 = 180°$	Substitution Property of Equality	

Summary

- A transversal is a line that intersects two or more lines in the same plane.

- When two lines are intersected by a transversal, pairs of corresponding, alternate interior, alternate exterior, and same-side interior angles are formed.

- When two parallel lines are intersected by a transversal:

  - corresponding angles are congruent

  - alternate interior angles are congruent

  - alternate exterior angles are congruent

  - same-side interior angles are supplementary

Converses of Parallel Line Properties

▶ Identify the converses of the transversal postulate and theorems.

▶ Use postulates and theorems about parallel lines to solve probems and complete proofs.

Buildings have a deep influence on our health and inner being. Over time, the geometric form of a structure can either help us feel encouraged, or it can drain us of our motivation. A surrounding environment that supports both our emotional and physical well-being promotes creativity, harmony, and productivity.

Just as architects, engineers, and contractors make buildings pleasing to the eye by using certain shapes and parallel and perpendicular lines, they also make construction strong by exploiting specific forms and arrangements of lines. Cones provide more strength than cylinders; triangles and rectangles are stronger than parallelograms, rhombi, and trapezoids.

The most common shape in building design is the rectangle. Rectangular construction is plain, but it is economical and takes less time to complete than some other designs. Moreover, a rectangular structure, unlike a triangular building, provides maximum functional space, particularly in corners.

In short, a building needs to be balanced. It must be strong while promoting positive feelings as well.

KEYWORD

converse

Using Theorems to Prove Other Theorems

Recall that the **converse** of a conditional statement switches the hypothesis and the conclusion. If a conditional statement is true, its converse may or may not be true. In the previous topic, you proved several theorems about the pairs of angles created when parallel lines are intersected by a transversal. The converses of those theorems, as well as the converse of the Corresponding Angles Postulate, are all true. You now have another postulate and four more theorems that you can use to prove that two lines are parallel.

POSTULATE 3-2   Converse of the Corresponding Angles Postulate

If two coplanar lines are intersected by a transversal and the corresponding angles are congruent, then the lines are parallel.

THEOREM 3-4   Converse of the Alternate Interior Angles Theorem

If two coplanar lines are intersected by a transversal and the alternate interior angles are congruent, then the lines are parallel.

THEOREM 3-5   Converse of the Alternate Exterior Angles Theorem

If two coplanar lines are intersected by a transversal and the alternate exterior angles are congruent, then the lines are parallel.

THEOREM 3-6   Converse of the Same-Side Interior Angles Theorem

If two coplanar lines are intersected by a transversal and the same-side interior angles are supplementary, then the lines are parallel.

Let us take a look at how you can use the new theorems to prove others.

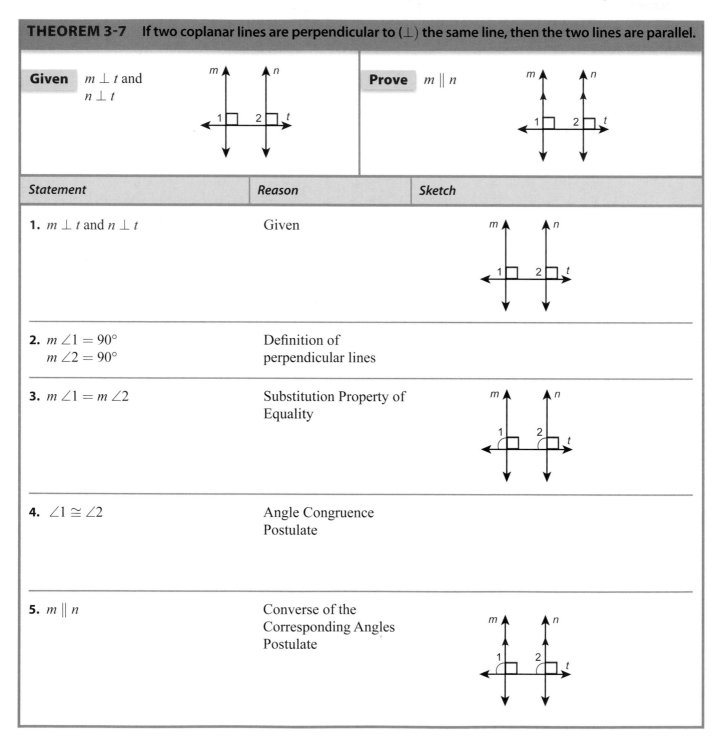

THEOREM 3-7   If two coplanar lines are perpendicular to (⊥) the same line, then the two lines are parallel.

| Given | $m \perp t$ and $n \perp t$ | Prove | $m \parallel n$ |

Statement	Reason	Sketch
1. $m \perp t$ and $n \perp t$	Given	
2. $m \angle 1 = 90°$ $m \angle 2 = 90°$	Definition of perpendicular lines	
3. $m \angle 1 = m \angle 2$	Substitution Property of Equality	
4. $\angle 1 \cong \angle 2$	Angle Congruence Postulate	
5. $m \parallel n$	Converse of the Corresponding Angles Postulate	

THEOREM 3-8 If two coplanar lines are parallel to the same line, then the two lines are parallel.

Given $m \parallel p$ and $n \parallel p$

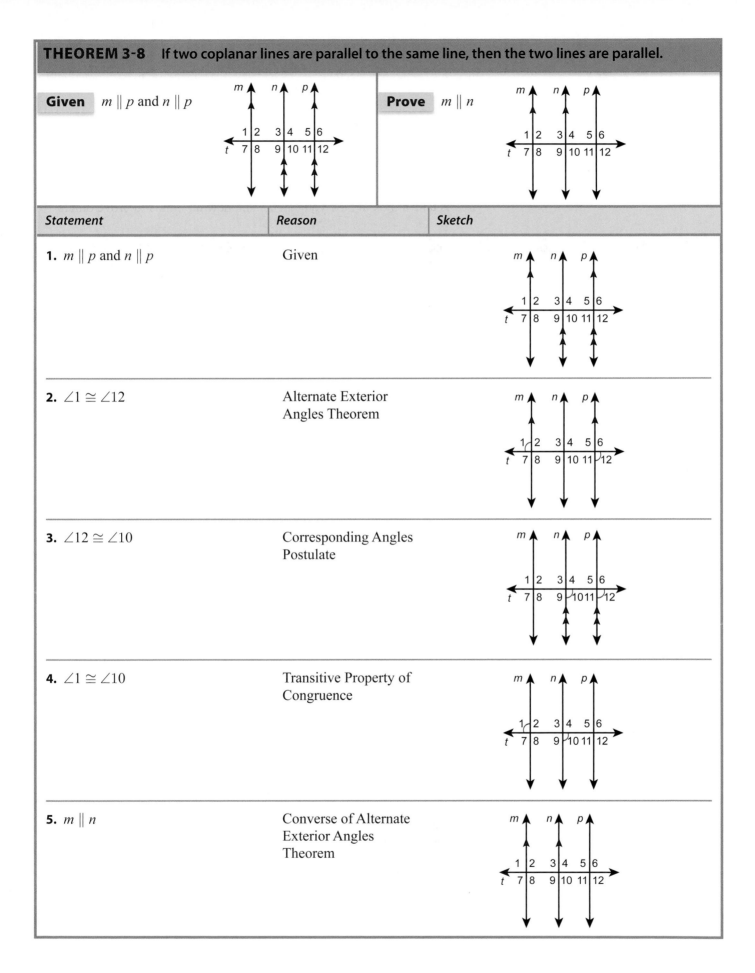

Prove $m \parallel n$

Statement	Reason	Sketch
1. $m \parallel p$ and $n \parallel p$	Given	
2. $\angle 1 \cong \angle 12$	Alternate Exterior Angles Theorem	
3. $\angle 12 \cong \angle 10$	Corresponding Angles Postulate	
4. $\angle 1 \cong \angle 10$	Transitive Property of Congruence	
5. $m \parallel n$	Converse of Alternate Exterior Angles Theorem	

Summary

- The converses of the transversal postulate and theorems are true and can be used to prove that lines are parallel.

- If two coplanar lines are perpendicular to the same line, then the two lines are parallel.

- If two coplanar lines are parallel to the same line, then the two lines are parallel.

The Triangle Sum Theorem

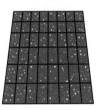 

You often hear about the universe, but no one knows its size or shape. For years, scientists have tried to gain more knowledge about the universe. They have suggested several possibilities for its shape. Two of the possibilities are that it is flat like a sheet of paper or curved like a sphere.

To some extent, its shape depends on its amount of mass. The National Aeronautics and Space Administration is studying a method that uses non-Euclidean geometry to calculate the shape of the universe. It involves measuring the sum of the angles of a huge triangle within the universe, a test that demands a great deal of geometric experience. For now, let's explore the Triangle Sum Theorem in a two-dimensional space.

KEYWORDS

exterior angle   interior angle

remote interior angle

More About Triangles

The **interior angles** of a triangle are the three angles inside the triangle. You can use geometry software to see if there is a relationship among these angles.

Start by drawing a triangle and displaying each angle measure. Then find the sum of the angles. If you select a point and change the shape of the triangle, the sum is still 180°.

You can prove it. But first you need the following postulate.

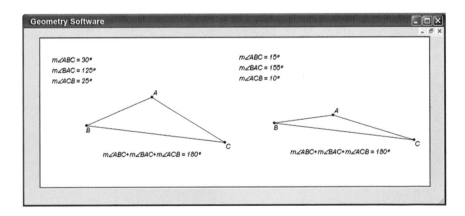

POSTULATE 3-3 Parallel Postulate

Given a line and a point not on the line, there is one and only one line that contains the given point and is parallel to the given line.

In the figure below, you can see that there are an infinite number of lines that pass through point P, but only one, line m, is parallel to line n.

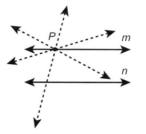

THEOREM 3-9   Triangle Sum Theorem
The sum of the measures of the interior angles of a triangle is 180°.

Given $\triangle ABC$

Prove $m\angle 1 + m\angle 2 + m\angle 3 = 180°$

Statement	Reason	Sketch
1. Draw $\overleftrightarrow{DE} \parallel \overline{AC}$.	Parallel Postulate	
2. $m\angle 4 = m\angle 1$ $m\angle 5 = m\angle 2$	Alternate Interior Angles Theorem	
3. $m\angle 4 + m\angle 3 = m\angle DBC$	Angle Addition Postulate	

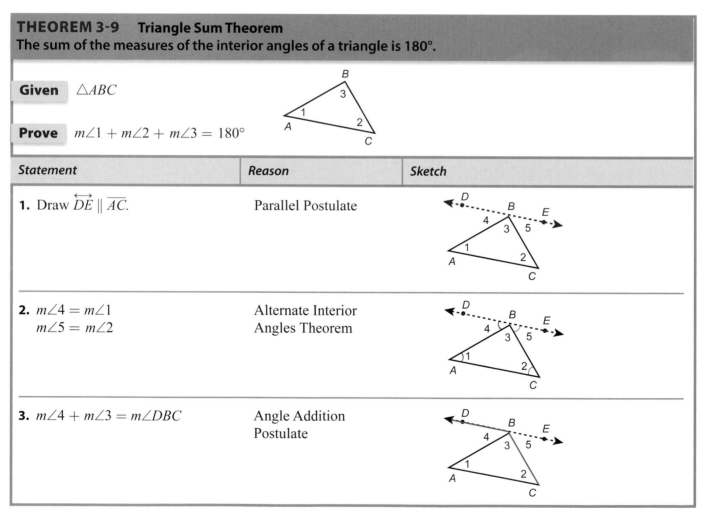

proof continued on next page

Statement	Reason	Sketch
4. $\angle DBC$ and $\angle 5$ form a linear pair.	Definition of a linear pair	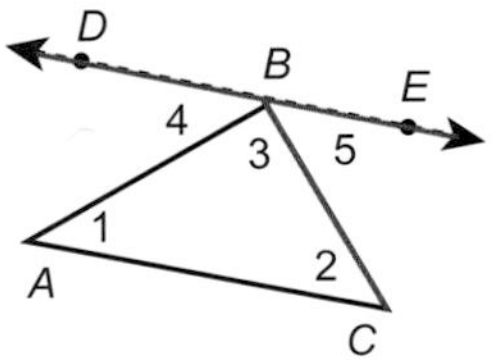
5. $m\angle DBC + m\angle 5 = 180°$	Linear Pair Postulate	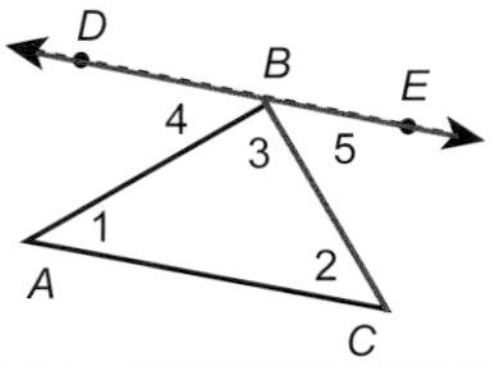
6. $m\angle 4 + m\angle 3 + m\angle 5 = 180°$	Substitution Property of Equality (Steps 3 and 5)	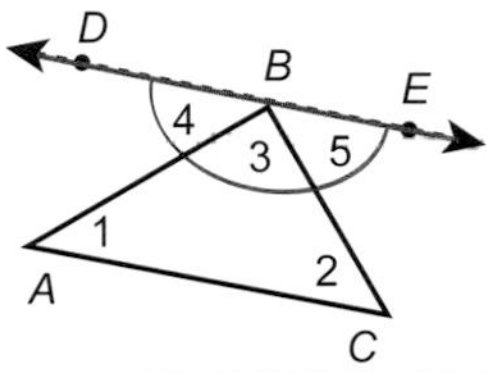
7. $m\angle 1 + m\angle 3 + m\angle 2 = 180°$	Substitution Property of Equality (Steps 2 and 6)	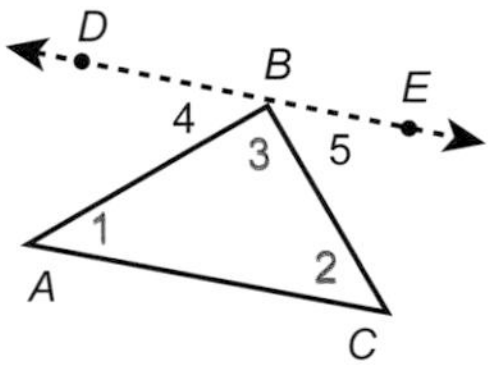

Exterior Angles

An **exterior angle** of a triangle is an angle formed by one side of the triangle and another side of the triangle when it is extended. **Remote interior angles** are the angles that are inside the triangle and are not adjacent to a given exterior angle. In the figure, $\angle 4$ is an exterior angle and $\angle 1$ and $\angle 2$ are the remote interior angles.

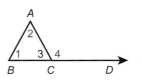

In a triangle, two remote interior angles are related to their exterior angle in a specific way. It is described in the Exterior Angle Theorem.

THEOREM 3-10   **Exterior Angle Theorem**

The measure of an exterior angle of a triangle is equal to the sum of the measures of the remote interior angles.

Given $\angle 4$ is an exterior angle of $\triangle ABC$.

Prove $m\angle 1 + m\angle 2 = m\angle 4$

Statement	Reason	Sketch
1. $\angle 3$ and $\angle 4$ form a linear pair.	Definition of a linear pair	
2. $m\angle 3 + m\angle 4 = 180°$	Linear Pair Postulate	
3. $m\angle 1 + m\angle 2 + m\angle 3 = 180°$	Triangle Sum Theorem	
4. $m\angle 1 + m\angle 2 + m\angle 3 = m\angle 3 + m\angle 4$	Substitution Property of Equality	
5. $m\angle 1 + m\angle 2 = m\angle 4$	Subtraction Property of Equality	

We can use the Triangle Sum Theorem and the Exterior Angle Theorem to find missing angles in figures.

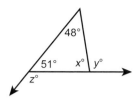

To find the value of *x*, add 51 and 48 and subtract from 180.
$180 - (51 + 48) = 81$

- The value of *x* is 81.

To find the value of *y*, add 48 and 51.
$48 + 51 = 99$

- The value of *y* is 99.

To find the value of *z*, add 48 to the value of *x*.
$48 + 81 = 129$

- The value of *z* is 129.

We can use the Linear Pair Postulate to check our values:
$51° + 129° = 180°$ and $81° + 99° = 180°$

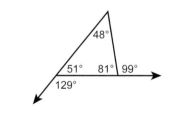

Summary

- The Parallel Postulate states that, given a line and a point not on the line, there is one and only one line that contains the given point and is parallel to the given line.

- The Triangle Sum Theorem states that the sum of the measures of the interior angles of a triangle is 180°.

- An exterior angle of a triangle is an angle formed by one side of the triangle and another side of the triangle that is extended outside the triangle.

- A remote interior angle of a triangle is either of the two interior angles that are not adjacent to a given exterior angle of the triangle.

- The Exterior Angle Theorem states that the measure of an exterior angle of a triangle is equal to the sum of the measures of its two remote interior angles.

Angles in Polygons

OBJECTIVES

- Identify and define convex and concave polygons.
- Find the sum of the measures of interior and exterior angles of a convex polygon.
- Find the measure of each interior and exterior angle of a regular polygon.
- Use properties of polygons to solve problems.

A diamond cutter starts with a raw, uncut stone, and carefully chips away at it to create faces that are polygons. Every face has many angles. When the gem cutter creates a face on a gem, it is important that all the angles be just right. Each angle is an important part of a breathtaking piece of jewelry.

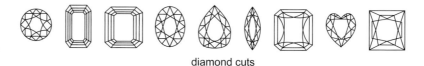

diamond cuts

KEYWORDS

concave polygon	convex polygon
exterior angles of a polygon	interior angles of a polygon

More About Polygons

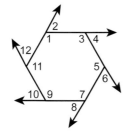

Just as triangles have both interior and exterior angles, other polygons have interior and exterior angles as well. In this diagram, the interior angles are labeled with odd numbers and the exterior angles are labeled with even numbers.

Convex and Concave Polygons

A polygon is **convex** if, for each pair of points inside the polygon, the line segment connecting them lies completely inside the polygon as well.

convex polygons

MEMORYTIP
A concave polygon "caves in" on at least one side.

A polygon is **concave** if at least one line segment connecting any two points inside the polygon does not lie completely inside the polygon.

concave polygons

Interior and Exterior Angles of Polygons

You can use the Triangle Sum Theorem to find the sum of the **interior angle** measures of any convex polygon.

Look at the rectangle. It can be divided into two triangles. The sum of the angles in each triangle is 180°, so the sum of the angles in the rectangle is 180° + 180°, or 360°.

Now look at the pentagon. It can be divided into three triangles. The sum of the angles in each triangle is 180°, so the sum of the angles in the pentagon is 180° + 180° + 180°, or 540°.

A hexagon can be divided into four triangles. So the sum of the angles in a hexagon is 180° + 180° + 180° + 180°, or 720°.

A heptagon can be divided into five triangles. So the sum of the angles in a heptagon is 180° + 180° + 180° + 180° + 180°, or 900°.

Now we will put the information we found above into a table and look for a pattern.

REMEMBER

Drawing conclusions from patterns is inductive reasoning.

Pattern: The number of triangles is always the number of sides minus 2.

Number of Sides	Number of Triangles	Sum of Angle Measures
3	1	180°
4	2	2(180°) = 360°
5	3	3(180°) = 540°
6	4	4(180°) = 720°
7	5	5(180°) = 900°

We can use the pattern to add a row to the table for a polygon with n sides. The right column shows how to get the angle sum (I).

n	$n-2$	$n-2\,(180°) = I$

This is stated in the following formula.

Formula for the Sum of the Interior Angles of a Polygon

Given I = sum of interior angles and n = number of sides:
$$I = (n - 2)(180°)$$

For a *regular polygon,* you can use the formula for the sum of the interior angle measures to find i, the measure of each interior angle. Because all the angles are congruent, you just divide the sum by the number of angles.

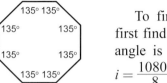

To find the measure of each interior angle of a regular octagon you first find the sum of the angles: $I = 6(180°) = 1080°$. Then, because each angle is the same measure, and there are eight angles, we divide by 8: $i = \dfrac{1080°}{8} = 135°$.

Formula for the Measure of an Interior Angle of a Regular Polygon

Given i = measure of each interior angle and n = number of sides:
$$i = \frac{(n - 2)180°}{n}$$

We will now consider the **exterior angles**. We use E for the sum of the exterior angles and e for the measure of each exterior angle.

Each interior angle of a polygon forms a linear pair with an exterior angle, so the sum of each pair is 180°. The number of linear pairs equals the numbers of sides in the polygon, so the sum of all the interior and exterior angles is $n(180°)$.

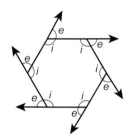

If we subtract the sum of the interior angles from the sum of all the angles, we will be left with the sum of the exterior angles. We will show that the sum of the exterior angles is 360° with an algebraic proof.

This means the sum of the exterior angles for *any* convex polygon is always 360°. To find the measure of each exterior angle of a regular polygon, divide 360° by the number of angles (or sides).

Given	a convex polygon
Prove	$E = 360°$

Statement	Reason
1. $I = (n - 2)(180°)$	Formula for the Sum of the Interior Angles of a Polygon
2. $E = n(180°) - I$	The sum of the exterior angles equals the sum of all the angles minus the sum of the interior angles.
3. $E = n(180°) - [(n - 2)180°]$	Substitution Property of Equality
4. $E = 180°n - [180°n - 360°]$	Distributive Property (180°)
5. $E = 180°n - 180°n + 360°$	Distributive Property (−1)
6. $E = 360°$	Combine like terms.

Formula for the Measure of an Exterior Angle of a Regular Polygon

Given e = measure of each exterior angle and n = number of sides:

$$e = \frac{360°}{n}$$

Summary

- A polygon is convex when a line segment connecting any two points inside the polygon lies completely inside the polygon. A polygon is concave when at least one line segment connecting any two points inside the polygon does not lie completely inside the polygon.

- To find I, the sum of the interior angles of a convex polygon, where n is the number of sides, use the formula $I = (n - 2)(180°)$.

- To find i, the measure of one interior angle of a regular polygon, divide the sum I by the number of sides: $i = \frac{(n - 2)(180°)}{n}$.

- The sum of the exterior angles of any convex polygon is 360°.

- To find e, the measure of one exterior angle of a regular polygon, divide by the number of sides: $e = \frac{360°}{n}$.

Midsegments

OBJECTIVES

- ► Identify the bases, legs, or midsegment of a trapezoid.

- ► Find the length of the midsegment of a trapezoid or triangle.

- ► Solve problems involving the midsegment of a trapezoid or triangle.

Terri Waters, a long-distance swimmer, wants to train at Lake Cougar, but she doesn't know how far her swim will be if she starts at point *A* and goes to point *B* (shown in blue). She and her support crew can drive to points *R* and *T* and walk to the lake. They can't drive across water, but they can easily drive the distances marked in red and green, checking their odometer for the mileage. How much farther does Terri swim than the distance (in red) that the team drives? Study this topic to find out.

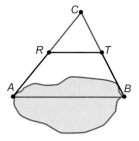

KEYWORDS

bases of a trapezoid

legs of a trapezoid

midsegment of a trapezoid

midsegment of a triangle

Midsegments of Trapezoids

Recall that a trapezoid has one pair of parallel sides. We call these sides the **bases.** The nonparallel sides are called the **legs.**

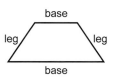

The **midsegment of a trapezoid** is the line segment that connects the midpoints of the legs. The midsegment will *always* be parallel to the bases.

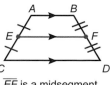

$\overline{EF}$ is a midsegment of *ABDC*.

The length of the midsegment of a trapezoid is one-half the sum of the lengths of the bases. We can write this as the formula $m = \dfrac{b_1 + b_2}{2}$ where m is the length of the midsegment and b_1 and b_2 are the bases.

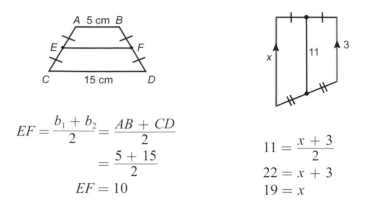

$$EF = \dfrac{b_1 + b_2}{2} = \dfrac{AB + CD}{2}$$
$$= \dfrac{5 + 15}{2}$$
$$EF = 10$$

$$11 = \dfrac{x + 3}{2}$$
$$22 = x + 3$$
$$19 = x$$

Midsegments of Triangles

The **midsegment of a triangle** is the line segment that connects the midpoints of two sides of the triangle. The midsegment will always be parallel to the third side.

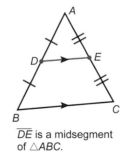

$\overline{DE}$ is a midsegment of $\triangle ABC$.

A triangle can be viewed as a trapezoid with one base equal to 0. When you substitute 0 into the formula for b_1, the formula for the length of the midsegment of a triangle is $m = \dfrac{0 + b_2}{2}$, or $m = \dfrac{b_2}{2}$. This means the length of the midsegment of a triangle is one-half the length of the side parallel to the midsegment.

$$DE = \dfrac{BC}{2}$$
$$= \dfrac{12}{2}$$
$$DE = 6$$

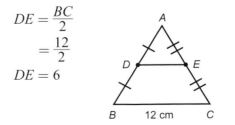

Using Geometry Software to Draw Midsegments

You can use geometry software to draw midsegments of triangles and trapezoids, and to investigate their lengths.

Construct a triangle. Construct the midpoints of any two sides of the triangle. Draw the line segment connecting the two midpoints. Measure and compare the length of the midsegment and the side parallel to it.

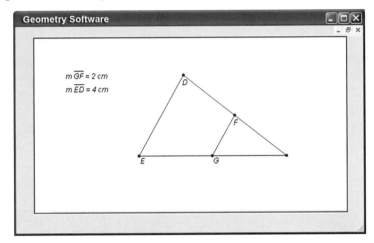

Repeat with a trapezoid. To be certain the bases are truly parallel, either work on a coordinate grid or draw a line parallel to a point not on the line, and then place points on the line. Drag the figures to see that these relationships hold true.

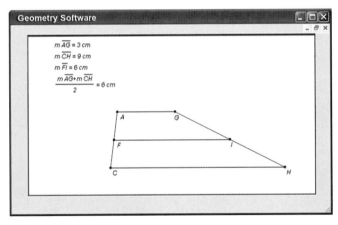

Summary

· ·

- The two parallel sides of a trapezoid are the bases. The other sides are the legs.

- The midsegment of a trapezoid is the line segment that connects the midpoints of the legs of a trapezoid. Its length is one-half the sum of the lengths of the bases.

- The midsegment of a triangle is the line segment that connects the midpoints of two sides of the triangle. This means that the length of the midsegment of a triangle is one-half the length of the triangle's side that is parallel to the midsegment.

Slope

Elevators, ramps, and stairs move us from one level to another or from one height to another. Elevators go straight up and down, but ramps and stairs move on an incline. With each step you take on a ramp or staircase, you travel both a horizontal and a vertical distance. The steepness of the incline depends on the length of those distances. In mathematics, that steepness is called the slope of the incline.

KEYWORDS

rise   run

slope

Right Triangles and Slope
. . . .

The **slope** of a line is a number that describes the steepness of the line. To get from any one point on the line to any other point on the line, you must move a horizontal distance, called the **run,** and a vertical distance, called the **rise.** The slope of the line is equal to the rise divided by the run:

$$\text{slope} = \frac{\text{rise}}{\text{run}}$$

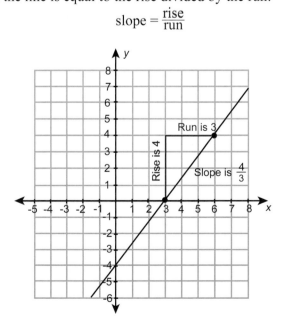

On a coordinate plane, the rise is the difference in the *y*-coordinates and the run is the difference in the *x*-coordinates.

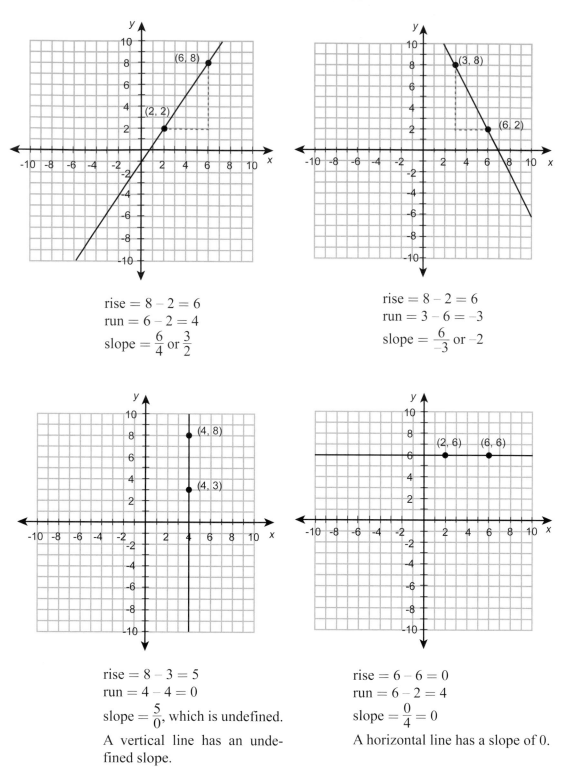

rise = 8 − 2 = 6
run = 6 − 2 = 4
slope = $\frac{6}{4}$ or $\frac{3}{2}$

rise = 8 − 2 = 6
run = 3 − 6 = −3
slope = $\frac{6}{-3}$ or −2

rise = 8 − 3 = 5
run = 4 − 4 = 0
slope = $\frac{5}{0}$, which is undefined.

A vertical line has an undefined slope.

rise = 6 − 6 = 0
run = 6 − 2 = 4
slope = $\frac{0}{4}$ = 0

A horizontal line has a slope of 0.

Between two points (x_1, y_1) and (x_2, y_2), you can write the difference between the y-coordinates as $y_2 - y_1$ and the difference between the x-coordinates as $x_2 - x_1$. Then, instead of writing slope as $\frac{\text{rise}}{\text{run}}$, you can write the following.

Slope Formula

The slope m of a nonvertical line that contains the points

(x_1, y_1) and (x_2, y_2), is $m = \frac{y_2 - y_1}{x_2 - x_1}$.

Parallel and Perpendicular Lines

In the diagram, $p \parallel m$, $s \perp p$, and $s \perp m$.
Using the slope formula, we find the following:

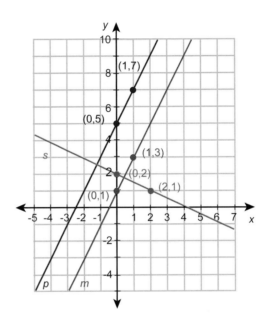

slope of line $p = \frac{7 - 5}{1 - 0} = \frac{2}{1} = 2$

slope of line $m = \frac{3 - 1}{1 - 0} = \frac{2}{1} = 2$

slope of line $s = \frac{1 - 2}{2 - 0} = \frac{-1}{2} = -\frac{1}{2}$

The slopes of the parallel lines (lines p and m) are equal. The slope of line s is the opposite of the reciprocal of lines p and m. In other words, the product of the slopes of the perpendicular lines is -1.

You can use geometry software to investigate this concept further. Construct two parallel line segments, and then construct a line perpendicular to one of the segments. Use your software to measure the slope of each line and line segment. Although the slopes in the diagram below are written in decimal form, remember that $0.25 = \frac{1}{4}$.

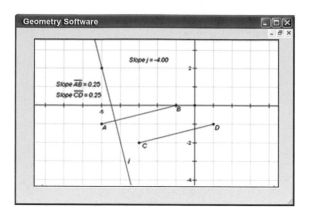

THEOREM 3-11   Parallel Lines Theorem

Two coplanar nonvertical lines are parallel if and only if they have the same slope. Any two vertical lines are parallel.

THEOREM 3-12   Perpendicular Lines Theorem

Two coplanar nonvertical lines are perpendicular if and only if the product of their slopes equals -1. Any vertical line is perpendicular to any horizontal line.

You can use the Parallel Lines Theorem to show that a quadrilateral drawn in the coordinate plane is a parallelogram. Consider $ABCD$ in the figure. You must show that both pairs of opposite sides are parallel. If $\overline{AB}$ and $\overline{DC}$ have equal slopes, and if $\overline{BC}$ and $\overline{AD}$ have equal slopes, the opposite sides are parallel.

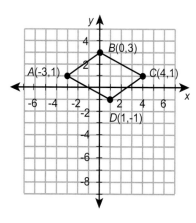

Slope of $\overline{AB} = \dfrac{3-1}{0-(-3)} = \dfrac{2}{3}$

Slope of $\overline{DC} = \dfrac{1-(-1)}{4-1} = \dfrac{2}{3}$

Slope of $\overline{BC} = \dfrac{3-1}{0-4} = \dfrac{2}{-4} = -\dfrac{1}{2}$

Slope of $\overline{AD} = \dfrac{1-(-1)}{-3-1} = \dfrac{2}{-4} = -\dfrac{1}{2}$

Since the opposite sides have equal slopes, $ABCD$ is a parallelogram.

REMEMBER

In a fraction, the negative sign can appear in the numerator, in the denominator, or before the fraction.

$\dfrac{-1}{2} = \dfrac{1}{-2} = -\dfrac{1}{2}$

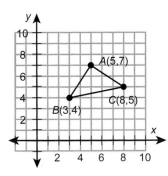

You can use the Perpendicular Lines Theorem to show that a triangle in a coordinate plane is a right triangle. Consider $\triangle ABC$ in the figure. All you need to do is show that one of the angles of the triangle is a right angle. If two sides have slopes with a product of -1, the angle formed by those sides is a right angle. Begin by finding the slopes of each side.

Slope of $\overline{AB} = \dfrac{7-4}{5-3} = \dfrac{3}{2}$

Slope of $\overline{AC} = \dfrac{7-5}{5-8} = \dfrac{2}{-3} = -\dfrac{2}{3}$

Slope of $\overline{BC} = \dfrac{5-4}{8-3} = \dfrac{1}{5}$

Since the product of the slopes of $\overline{AB}$ and $\overline{AC}$ is -1, $\overline{AB} \perp \overline{AC}$ and $\triangle ABC$ is a right triangle.

The Midpoint Formula

Recall that the *midpoint* of a line segment divides the line segment into two congruent parts. To find the midpoint of a line segment on a number line, you could add the coordinates of the endpoints and then divide by 2. The midpoint of the segment with endpoints 3 and 7 is $\dfrac{3+7}{2} = \dfrac{10}{2} = 5$.

To find the midpoint of a line segment on a coordinate plane, use the Midpoint Formula.

Midpoint Formula

The coordinates of the midpoint of a line segment with endpoints (x_1, y_1) and (x_2, y_2), are

$$\left(\dfrac{x_1 + x_2}{2}, \dfrac{y_1 + y_2}{2} \right).$$

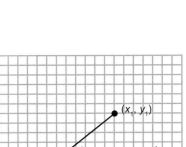

To find the midpoint of $\overline{AB}$, use the Midpoint Formula.

$$\left(\dfrac{x_1 + x_2}{2}, \dfrac{y_1 + y_2}{2} \right)$$

$$\left(\dfrac{2+8}{2}, \dfrac{3+5}{2} \right)$$

$$\left(\dfrac{10}{2}, \dfrac{8}{2} \right)$$

$$(5, 4)$$

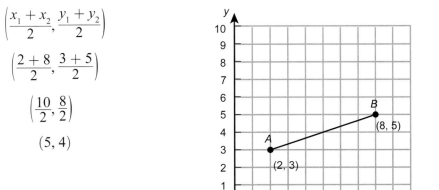

Summary

- The slope m of a line describes the steepness of the line.

- The slope of a nonvertical line that contains the points (x_1, y_1) and (x_2, y_2) is $m = \dfrac{y_2 - y_1}{x_2 - x_1}$.

- A vertical line has an undefined slope. A horizontal line has a slope of 0.

- Two nonvertical lines are parallel if and only if they have the same slope. Any two vertical lines are parallel.

- Two nonvertical lines are perpendicular if and only if the product of their slopes equals -1. Any vertical line is perpendicular to any horizontal line.

- The coordinates of the midpoint of a line segment on the coordinate plane with endpoints (x_1, y_1) and (x_2, y_2) are $\left(\dfrac{x_1 + x_2}{2}, \dfrac{y_1 + y_2}{2} \right)$.

UNIT 4

Congruent Polygons and Special Quadrilaterals

Congruent shapes sometimes occur where you least expect them. For instance, in apartment buildings, the floor plans of the apartments are often identical, especially when units are directly above or below each other. You could view the outlines of these apartments as congruent polygons. Sometimes apartments are reflections of each other, with the hallway between them acting as a mirror. The room sizes and shapes are still the same. This congruence is used for several reasons: it makes the apartment building pleasing to the eye, it makes rent prices fair, and it makes the wiring and plumbing more cost-effective.

In this unit, you will learn about congruence of polygons and ways to prove congruence in geometric figures.

. . . .

UNIT OBJECTIVES

▶ Identify congruent polygons and corresponding parts of congruent polygons.

▶ Use postulates and theorems to prove triangles congruent.

▶ Write two-column proofs to prove triangles congruent.

▶ Identify and use the properties of isosceles triangles.

▶ Use congruent triangles to prove properties of special quadrilaterals.

▶ Determine when a parallelogram is a rectangle, rhombus, or square, based on its properties.

▶ Prove that rotations, reflections, and translations preserve congruence.

▶ Develop and use the Triangle Inequality Theorem.

Congruent Polygons and Their Corresponding Parts

OBJECTIVES

▶ Identify congruent polygons and corresponding parts of congruent polygons.

▶ Use the Polygon Congruence Postulate.

A person who restores automobiles must use exact replacement parts to take the place of rusted or worn-out parts. A manufacturer of vehicle parts must ensure that each type of vehicle part is the exact same size and shape. Both of those people are working with parts that are congruent. If the types of parts are congruent, the vehicle owners will know that their car or truck will operate properly.

KEYWORDS

congruent polygons

corresponding angles

corresponding sides

Congruence

Congruent polygons are the same size and shape. In the diagram, $ABCD \cong FGHI$. If one is placed on top of the other, they match exactly. $\overline{AB}$ is an exact match with $\overline{FG}$ and $\angle A$ is an exact match with $\angle F$.

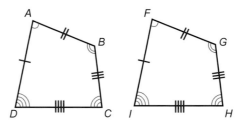

The word *corresponding* refers to angles or sides that lie in the same position in a pair of figures. Congruent polygons have **corresponding sides** and **corresponding angles** that are congruent to each other. Mathematicians use tick marks to indicate congruent sides, and multiple arcs or arcs with tick marks to indicate congruent angles.

POSTULATE 4-1 Polygon Congruence Postulate

Two polygons are congruent if and only if there is a correspondence between their sides and angles so that all pairs of corresponding angles are congruent and all pairs of corresponding sides are congruent.

This postulate lets us make the following statements about polygons *ABCD* and *FGHI:*

$$\angle A \cong \angle F \qquad \angle B \cong \angle G \qquad \angle C \cong \angle H \qquad \angle D \cong \angle I$$

$$\overline{AB} \cong \overline{FG} \qquad \overline{BC} \cong \overline{GH} \qquad \overline{CD} \cong \overline{HI} \qquad \overline{DA} \cong \overline{IF}$$

ABCD $\cong$ *FGHI* is called a *congruence statement.* When you write a congruence statement, list the vertices so that corresponding angles match. This allows you to identify corresponding parts of a figure even when one of the figures is rotated.

These two triangles are congruent. They are not positioned the same way, but the congruence statement written under the triangles tells you that $\angle R$ corresponds to $\angle X$ because they are both listed first, $\angle S$ corresponds to $\angle Y$ because they are both listed second, and so on. You can also identify corresponding sides. The endpoints will be in the same position in the congruence statement. $\overline{RT}$ corresponds to $\overline{XZ}$ because the endpoints of each one are written in the same order.

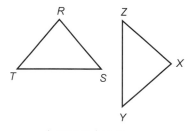

$\triangle RST \cong \triangle XYZ$

Using Geometry Software to Explore Congruent Polygons

The congruent polygons shown in the sketch below were constructed with geometry software. You can create a copy of a figure by translating it. If you display all the side and angle measures of both polygons, you can see that corresponding angles are congruent and corresponding sides are congruent .

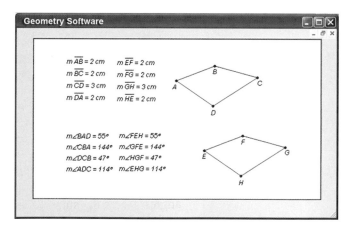

RECONNECT TO THE BIG IDEA

Remember Isometric transformations do not change distances, angles, or areas.

You can translate, reflect, or rotate one of the polygons and see that the orientations of the figures do not change their congruence. The measures of the sides and angles remain the same.

Summary

- Congruent polygons have the same size and shape. Corresponding sides and angles are those that "match up."

- The Polygon Congruence Postulate states that two polygons are congruent if and only if there is a correspondence between their sides and angles so that all pairs of corresponding angles are congruent and all pairs of corresponding sides are congruent.

- Congruent polygons may or may not have the same orientation. For example, one figure may need to be rotated so that they look exactly the same.

- A congruence statement can be used to determine which sides and angles of a polygon are congruent.

Triangle Congruence: SSS, SAS, and ASA

OBJECTIVES

▸ Identify included angles and included sides in triangles.

▸ Identify and use the Side-Side-Side, Side-Angle-Side, and Angle-Side-Angle Congruence Postulates.

Some bridges are more than a mile long. How are engineers, architects, and contractors able to create such magnificent structures?

Rectangles, arches, and triangles are the most common shapes used in construction. Under a heavy load, a rectangle distorts easily. When cross braces are placed diagonally, rectangles are divided into triangles that are significantly stronger because the cross braces distribute the weight load equally. A network of triangular braces and constraints makes structures stronger and more flexible. As a result, structures are able to better handle hurricane-force winds and earthquakes.

KEYWORDS

included angle   included side

Congruent Triangles

From the Polygon Congruence Postulate, you know that two polygons are congruent if and only if all corresponding angles and sides are congruent.

Although this postulate is useful for polygons in general, you actually need less information if you want to prove two triangles are congruent. Recall that, by definition, the sides of a polygon must meet only at their endpoints. If you are given three sides of a set length and can join them only at their endpoints, a triangle of only one size can be formed.

POSTULATE 4-2   Side-Side-Side (SSS) Congruence Postulate

If the three sides of one triangle are congruent to the three sides of another triangle, then the two triangles are congruent.

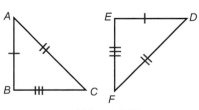

$\triangle ABC \cong \triangle DEF$

Included Sides and Angles

Before we look at more ways to show two triangles congruent, we must introduce two new terms: included angle and included side.

The angle formed by two sides of a triangle is an **included angle.** For example, in $\triangle ABC$, $\angle A$ is the included angle between $\overline{AC}$ and $\overline{AB}$.

An **included side** lies between two specific angles. In $\triangle ABC$, $\overline{AC}$ is the included side between $\angle A$ and $\angle C$.

Suppose you are given two segments of a set length and told to connect them at a given angle. Then suppose you must form a triangle with a third piece. There is only one length that will work. This is the basis for the next postulate.

POSTULATE 4-3   Side-Angle-Side (SAS) Congruence Postulate

If two sides and the included angle in one triangle are congruent to two sides and the included angle in another triangle, then the two triangles are congruent.

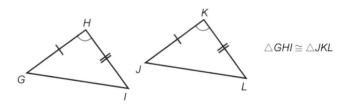

Now suppose you are told to form a triangle and are given one segment of a set length. This segment is an included side between two angles whose measures you are also given. To get the endpoints of the other two segments to join at the third vertex, you will find that there is only one pair of segments that will create the triangle. This idea leads to the following postulate.

POSTULATE 4-4   Angle-Side-Angle (ASA) Congruence Postulate

If two angles and the included side in one triangle are congruent to two angles and the included side in another triangle, then the two triangles are congruent.

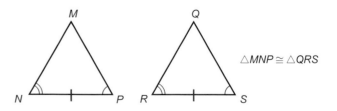

Sometimes, congruent sides and angles are not marked as such, but we know they are congruent from previous properties, postulates, theorems, or definitions.

Given $\overline{AD} \perp \overline{BC}$ D is the midpoint of $\overline{BC}$. **Prove** $\triangle BDA \cong \triangle CDA$		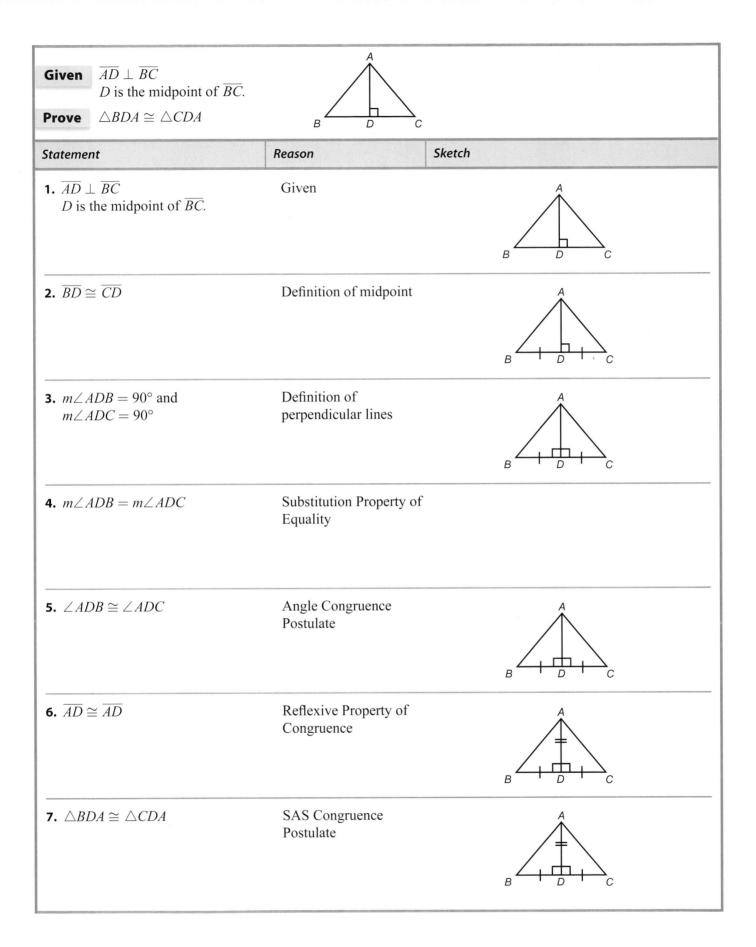

Statement	Reason	Sketch
1. $\overline{AD} \perp \overline{BC}$ D is the midpoint of $\overline{BC}$.	Given	
2. $\overline{BD} \cong \overline{CD}$	Definition of midpoint	
3. $m\angle ADB = 90°$ and $m\angle ADC = 90°$	Definition of perpendicular lines	
4. $m\angle ADB = m\angle ADC$	Substitution Property of Equality	
5. $\angle ADB \cong \angle ADC$	Angle Congruence Postulate	
6. $\overline{AD} \cong \overline{AD}$	Reflexive Property of Congruence	
7. $\triangle BDA \cong \triangle CDA$	SAS Congruence Postulate	

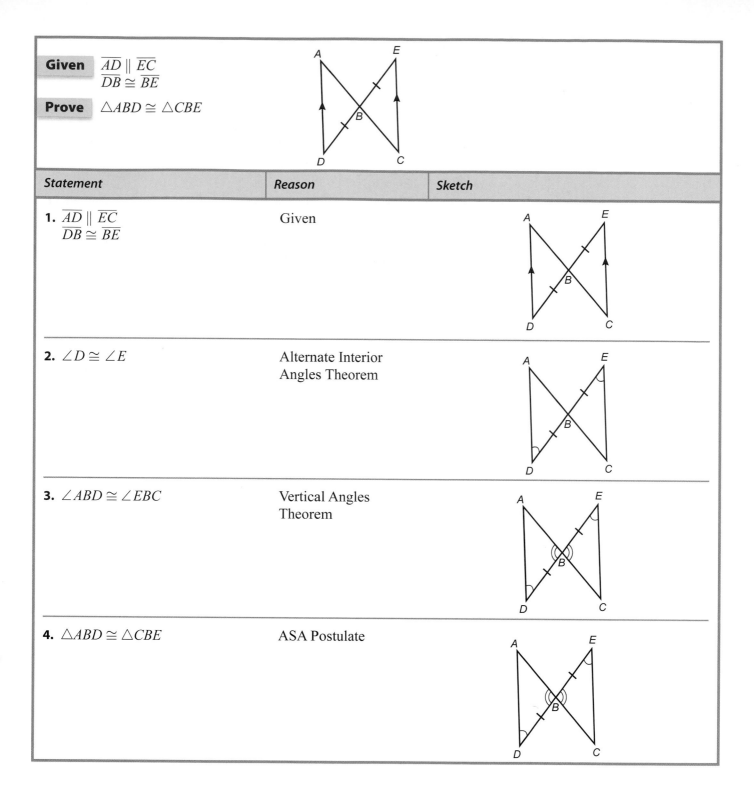

Given $\overline{AD} \parallel \overline{EC}$
          $\overline{DB} \cong \overline{BE}$

Prove $\triangle ABD \cong \triangle CBE$

Statement	Reason	Sketch
1. $\overline{AD} \parallel \overline{EC}$ $\overline{DB} \cong \overline{BE}$	Given	
2. $\angle D \cong \angle E$	Alternate Interior Angles Theorem	
3. $\angle ABD \cong \angle EBC$	Vertical Angles Theorem	
4. $\triangle ABD \cong \triangle CBE$	ASA Postulate	

Summary

You can use the SSS, SAS, and ASA Congruence Postulates to prove two triangles congruent:

- If the sides of one triangle are congruent to the sides of another triangle, then the two triangles are congruent.

- If two sides and the included angle in one triangle are congruent to two sides and the included angle in another triangle, then the two triangles are congruent.

- If two angles and the included side in one triangle are congruent to two angles and the included side in another triangle, then the two triangles are congruent.

Isosceles Triangles and Corresponding Parts

Domes, although they are thin, are among the strongest and most rigid structures in existence. Originally they were made of stone, but they were heavy and started to crack. American architect and engineer Buckminster Fuller radically changed the design of domes in the 1950s with his invention of the geodesic dome—a partial sphere shape structured from a series of congruent triangles. Modern engineers design geodesic domes in all shapes and sizes. One of the most famous is at the Epcot Center in Orlando, Florida.

KEYWORDS

base   base angle
CPCTC   legs of an isosceles triangle
vertex angle

Isosceles Triangles

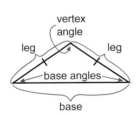

A triangle with at least two congruent sides is an isosceles triangle. The two congruent sides are the **legs of the isosceles triangle**. The two angles opposite the legs are the **base angles.** The included side is the **base.** The angle opposite the base is the **vertex angle.**

Properties of Isosceles Triangles

If you draw a few examples of isosceles triangles, you might notice that the base angles seem to be congruent in each case. You could also construct an isosceles triangle in The Geometer's Sketchpad and measure the base angles. However many examples you look at, you will see that the base angles of an isosceles triangle are always congruent. This seems like a good candidate for a theorem, but until we prove it, it is just a conjecture.

RECONNECT TO THE BIG IDEA

Remember   A theorem is not deemed true unless it is proven.

Before we prove it, we must learn the meaning of CPCTC. **CPCTC** stands for "**c**orresponding **p**arts of **c**ongruent **t**riangles are **c**ongruent." Once we prove that two triangles are congruent by using the triangle congruence postulates and theorems, we can use CPCTC to say the angles and sides we didn't use to prove congruence are congruent.

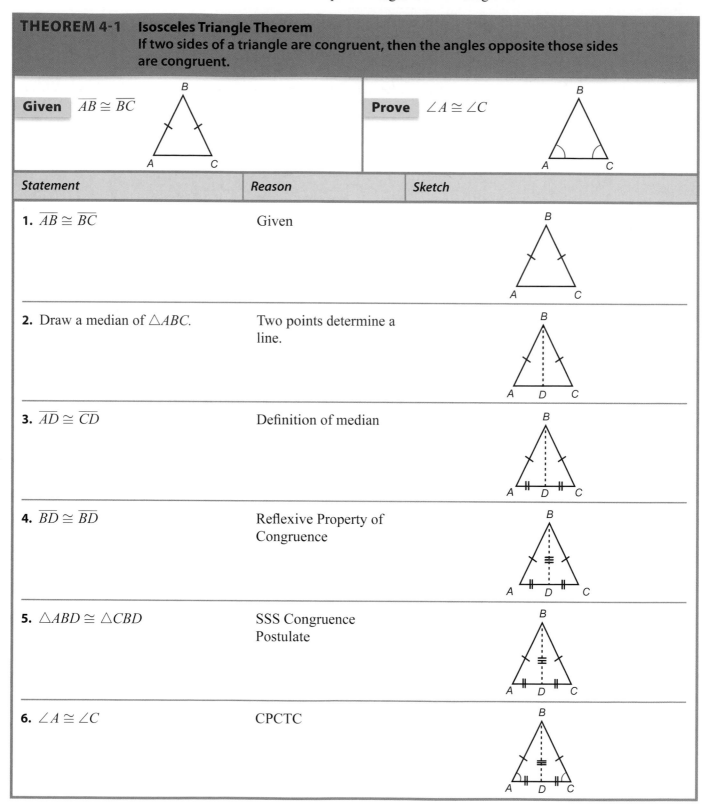

THEOREM 4-1   Isosceles Triangle Theorem
If two sides of a triangle are congruent, then the angles opposite those sides are congruent.

Given $\overline{AB} \cong \overline{BC}$

Prove $\angle A \cong \angle C$

Statement	Reason	Sketch
1. $\overline{AB} \cong \overline{BC}$	Given	
2. Draw a median of $\triangle ABC$.	Two points determine a line.	
3. $\overline{AD} \cong \overline{CD}$	Definition of median	
4. $\overline{BD} \cong \overline{BD}$	Reflexive Property of Congruence	
5. $\triangle ABD \cong \triangle CBD$	SSS Congruence Postulate	
6. $\angle A \cong \angle C$	CPCTC	

The converse of the Isosceles Triangle Theorem is also true.

THEOREM 4-2   Converse of the Isosceles Triangle Theorem

If two angles of a triangle are congruent, then the sides opposite those angles are congruent.

Equilateral Triangles

Because equilateral triangles are also isosceles, we can use the Isosceles Triangle Theorem to prove that the measure of each angle of an equilateral triangle is 60°.

Given $\triangle DEF$ is an equilateral triangle.	
Prove $m\angle D = 60°, m\angle E = 60°,$ and $m\angle F = 60°$	

Statement	Reason
1. $\triangle DEF$ is an equilateral triangle.	Given
2. $\overline{DE} \cong \overline{FE}$ $\overline{EF} \cong \overline{DF}$	Definition of equilateral triangle
3. $\angle F \cong \angle D, \angle D \cong \angle E$	Isosceles Triangle Theorem
4. $m\angle F = m\angle D, m\angle D = m\angle E$	Angle Congruence Postulate
5. $m\angle D + m\angle E + m\angle F = 180°$	Triangle Sum Theorem
6. $m\angle D + m\angle D + m\angle D = 180°$	Substitution Property of Equality
7. $3(m\angle D) = 180°$	Meaning of multiplication
8. $m\angle D = 60°$	Division Property of Equality
9. $m\angle E = 60°$ and $m\angle F = 60°$	Substitution Property of Equality

A polygon with congruent angles is equiangular. So any equilateral triangle is also equiangular.

Vertex Angles of Isosceles Triangles

You can use Sketchpad to see what happens when the vertex angle of an isosceles triangle is bisected. If you draw the angle bisector of the vertex angle and measure the angles formed at the base, the angles that are formed each measure 90°. You will find that the two line segments formed by the intersection of the angle bisector with the base are congruent.

The bisector of the vertex angle of an isosceles triangle is the perpendicular bisector of the base. This next proof proves the base is bisected. You can prove the angle bisector is perpendicular to the base in a separate proof.

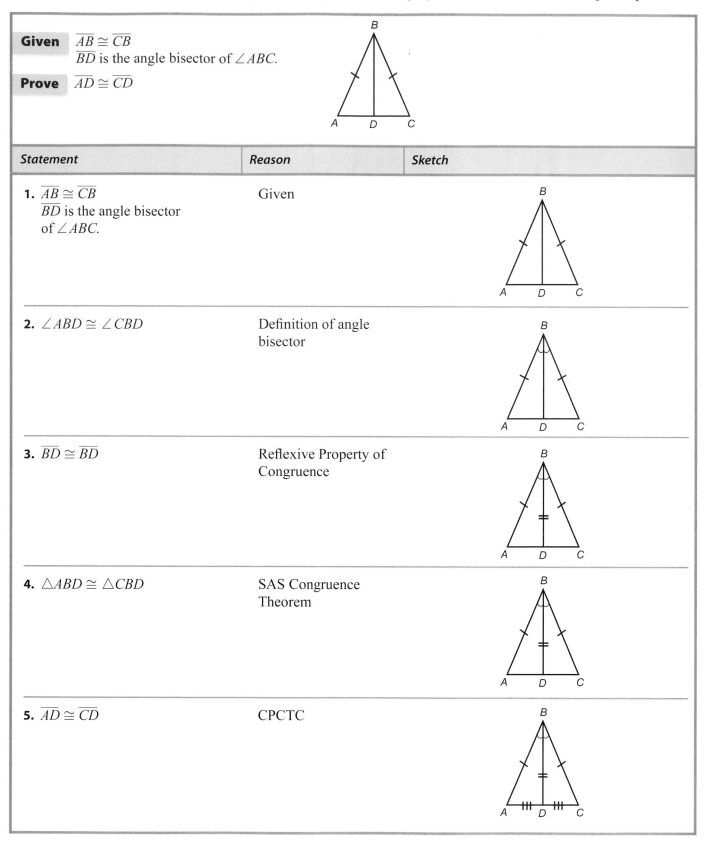

Given $\overline{AB} \cong \overline{CB}$
$\overline{BD}$ is the angle bisector of $\angle ABC$.

Prove $\overline{AD} \cong \overline{CD}$

Statement	Reason	Sketch
1. $\overline{AB} \cong \overline{CB}$ $\overline{BD}$ is the angle bisector of $\angle ABC$.	Given	
2. $\angle ABD \cong \angle CBD$	Definition of angle bisector	
3. $\overline{BD} \cong \overline{BD}$	Reflexive Property of Congruence	
4. $\triangle ABD \cong \triangle CBD$	SAS Congruence Theorem	
5. $\overline{AD} \cong \overline{CD}$	CPCTC	

Summary

· ·

- The two congruent sides of an isosceles triangle are called the legs. The two angles opposite the legs are the base angles. The included side is called the base. The angle opposite the base is the vertex angle.

- Two sides of a triangle are congruent if and only if the angles opposite those sides are congruent.

- The measure of each angle of an equilateral triangle is 60°.

- The bisector of the vertex angle of an isosceles triangle is the perpendicular bisector of the base.

Triangle Congruence: AAS and HL

A football team is running on the field. Some players are running from point A to point B to point C, and then back to point A. Other players are running from point C to point D to point A, and then back to point C. Read on to know why the routes are the same length.

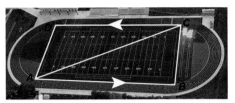

More Congruence in Triangles

The following theorem is another way to prove that two triangles are congruent.

THEOREM 4-3	Angle-Angle-Side (AAS) Congruence Theorem
	If two angles and a non-included side of one triangle are congruent to the corresponding angles and non-included side of another triangle, then the two triangles are congruent.

Given $\angle A \cong \angle X$
$\angle B \cong \angle Y$
$\overline{AC} \cong \overline{XZ}$

Prove $\triangle ABC \cong \triangle XYZ$

Statement	Reason
1. $\angle A \cong \angle X$ $\angle B \cong \angle Y$ $\overline{AC} \cong \overline{XZ}$	Given
2. $m\angle A + m\angle B + m\angle C = 180°$ $m\angle X + m\angle Y + m\angle Z = 180°$	Triangle Sum Theorem
3. $m\angle A + m\angle B + m\angle C = m\angle X + m\angle Y + m\angle Z$	Substitution Property of Equality
4. $m\angle A + m\angle B + m\angle C = m\angle A + m\angle B + m\angle Z$	Substitution Property of Equality (Steps 1 and 3)
5. $m\angle C = m\angle Z$	Subtraction Property of Equality
6. $\angle C \cong \angle Z$	Angle Congruence Postulate
7. $\triangle ABC \cong \triangle XYZ$	ASA Congruence Postulate

A Congruence Theorem for Right Triangles Only

The following theorem is a way to prove that two right triangles are congruent.

REMEMBER

The hypotenuse is the side opposite the right angle. The other sides are the legs.

THEOREM 4-4 Hypotenuse-Leg (HL) Congruence Theorem

If the hypotenuse and a leg of one right triangle are congruent to the hypotenuse and corresponding leg of another right triangle, then the two triangles are congruent.

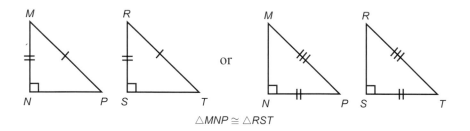

$$\triangle MNP \cong \triangle RST$$

Combinations That Do Not Prove Congruence

Now that we have seen some theorems we can use to prove that two triangles are congruent, let's take a look at two situations that do not prove congruence.

Proving that the three angles of one triangle are congruent to three angles of another triangle (AAA) does not prove that the two triangles are congruent. Look at these two triangles. They have the same shape but not the same size. Congruent triangles must have both the same shape and the same size. Therefore, AAA does *not* prove triangle congruence.

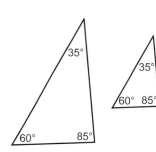

What if two sides and a non-included angle of two triangles (SSA) are congruent? Look at the triangles below.

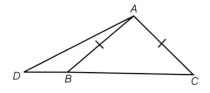

$\triangle DAB$ and $\triangle DAC$ have two pairs of congruent sides, $\overline{DA} \cong \overline{DA}$ and $\overline{AB} \cong \overline{AC}$, and a congruent angle, $\angle D$, which is not the included angle. It is apparent the triangles are not congruent because the third sides, $\overline{DB}$ and $\overline{DC}$, are not congruent.

Therefore, SSA does not prove triangle congruence.

Given	*ABCD* is a parallelogram. $\overline{DB}$ bisects $\overline{AC}$.	
Prove	$\triangle ABE \cong \triangle CDE$	

Statement	Reason	Sketch
1. *ABCD* is a parallelogram. $\overline{DB}$ bisects $\overline{AC}$.	Given	
2. $\overline{AB} \parallel \overline{DC}$	Definition of parallelogram	
3. $\angle BAC \cong \angle DCA$	Alternate Interior Angles Theorem	
4. $\angle ABD \cong \angle CDB$	Alternate Interior Angles Theorem	
5. $\overline{AE} \cong \overline{CE}$	Definition of segment bisector	
6. $\triangle ABE \cong \triangle CDE$	AAS Congruence Theorem	

Sometimes the triangles you need to prove congruent will overlap. When this happens, you may find it easier to redraw the figure with the two triangles separated.

Given $\angle A$ and $\angle F$ are right angles. $\overline{CB} \cong \overline{DE}$ $\overline{AC} \cong \overline{FD}$	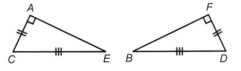
Prove $\triangle DFB \cong \triangle CAE$	

Statement	Reason
1. $\angle A$ and $\angle F$ are right angles. $\overline{CB} \cong \overline{DE}$ $\overline{AC} \cong \overline{FD}$	Given
2. $CB = DE$	Segment Congruence Postulate
3. $CE = DB$	Theorem of Overlapping Segments
4. $\overline{CE} \cong \overline{DB}$	Segment Congruence Postulate
5. $\triangle DFB \cong \triangle CAE$	HL Congruence Theorem

The original triangles in the diagram above, when moved apart, look like this.

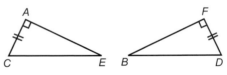

After the third sides are proved congruent, they look like this.

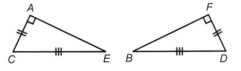

Summary

- You can use the AAS and HL Congruence Theorems to prove two triangles are congruent.

  - If two angles and a non-included side of one triangle are congruent to the corresponding angles and non-included side of another triangle, then the two triangles are congruent.

  - If the hypotenuse and a leg of one right triangle are congruent to the hypotenuse and corresponding leg of another right triangle, then the two triangles are congruent.

- AAA and SSA cannot be used to prove triangles congruent.

Using Triangles to Understand Quadrilaterals

Skyscrapers and towers are exposed to dead and live weight loads. Dead loads include steel columns, beams, concrete, and glass—the building's structure —while live loads encompass people, furniture, and materials that are moved into the structure. Other significant weight loads that affect buildings are wind force, compression, and tension. Steel columns, beams, and steel-reinforced concrete provide strength to withstand compression and tension. Diagonal supports play a major role in making the structure rigid, preventing it from leaning in the wind. The diagonal supports join with the horizontal and vertical components to form triangles, which create stability and dissipate force.

KEYWORD

kite

Properties of Special Quadrilaterals

A parallelogram is a quadrilateral with two sets of parallel sides. You can use a diagonal to divide a parallelogram into two triangles, and then use ASA Congruence to prove that opposite sides of a parallelogram are congruent.
A rhombus is a quadrilateral with all four sides congruent. This proof uses SSS Congruence to prove that a rhombus is a parallelogram.

Given	ABCD is a parallelogram.

Prove $\overline{CD} \cong \overline{AB}$ and $\overline{AD} \cong \overline{BC}$

Statement	Reason	Sketch
1. ABCD is a parallelogram.	Given	
2. $\overline{AD} \parallel \overline{BC}$ and $\overline{CD} \parallel \overline{AB}$	Definition of a parallelogram	
3. $\angle DAC \cong \angle BCA$ $\angle DCA \cong \angle BAC$	Alternate Interior Angles Theorem	
4. $\overline{AC} \cong \overline{CA}$	Reflexive Property of Congruence	
5. $\triangle DAC \cong \triangle BCA$	ASA Congruence Postulate	
6. $\overline{CD} \cong \overline{AB}$ and $\overline{AD} \cong \overline{CB}$	CPCTC	

A rhombus is a quadrilateral with all four sides congruent. This proof uses SSS Congruence to prove that a rhombus is a parallelogram.

Given	$DEFG$ is a rhombus.	
Prove	$DEFG$ is a parallelogram.	

Statement	Reason	Sketch
1. $DEFG$ is a rhombus.	Given	
2. $\overline{DE} \cong \overline{EF} \cong \overline{GF} \cong \overline{DG}$	Definition of a rhombus	
3. $\overline{GE} \cong \overline{EG}$	Reflexive Property of Congruence	
4. $\triangle DEG \cong \triangle FGE$	SSS Congruence Postulate	
5. $\angle DEG \cong \angle FGE$ $\angle EGD \cong \angle GEF$	CPCTC	
6. $\overline{DE} \parallel \overline{GF}$ and $\overline{DG} \parallel \overline{EF}$	Converse of Alternate Interior Angles Theorem	
7. $DEFG$ is a parallelogram.	Definition of a parallelogram	

Using SAS Congruence, prove that the diagonals of a rectangle are congruent.

Given $ABCD$ is a rectangle.

Prove $\overline{AC} \cong \overline{BD}$

Statement	Reason	Sketch
1. $\overline{AD} \cong \overline{BC}$	Opposite sides of a parallelogram are congruent.	
2. $\overline{DC} \cong \overline{CD}$	Reflexive Property of Congruence	
3. $m\angle ADC = 90°$ $m\angle BCD = 90°$	Definition of rectangle	
4. $m\angle ADC = m\angle BCD$	Substitution Property of Equality	
5. $\angle ADC \cong \angle BCD$	Angle Congruence Postulate	
6. $\triangle ADC \cong \triangle BCD$	SAS Congruence Postulate	
7. $\overline{AC} \cong \overline{BD}$	CPCTC	

Another Special Quadrilateral

The **kite** is a special quadrilateral with exactly two pairs of congruent, consecutive sides. A kite is not a parallelogram, so it does not have the same properties of a parallelogram. A property that a kite does have is that its diagonals are perpendicular.

kite

Summary

- Because quadrilaterals can be broken into triangles, the triangle congruence postulates and theorems can be used to prove many of the properties of parallelograms, rectangles, rhombi, squares, and kites.

- A kite is a quadrilateral with exactly two pairs of congruent consecutive sides. The diagonals of a kite are perpendicular.

Types of Quadrilaterals

► Explain what is required for a quadrilateral to be a parallelogram and what is required for a parallelogram to be a rectangle or rhombus.

Builders use the properties of diagonals to "square up" rectangular shapes, such as patios or pools. They locate the corners of the objects with the help of two theorems: (1) If the diagonals of a quadrilateral bisect each other, then the quadrilateral is a parallelogram. (2) If the diagonals of a parallelogram are congruent, then the parallelogram is a rectangle. Builders then cut two equal lengths of twine to represent the diagonals of the rectangular structure, connecting them at their midpoints. When the builders pull the pieces of twine straight and tight, the ends will be at the corners of the patio or pool.

When Is It a Parallelogram?

Recall that a parallelogram is a quadrilateral whose opposite sides are parallel. We have three theorems that can be used to prove that a quadrilateral is a parallelogram. The first is proven below.

THEOREM 4-5   If two pairs of opposite sides of a quadrilateral are congruent, then the quadrilateral is a parallelogram.

Given $\overline{AB} \cong \overline{DC}$
         $\overline{AD} \cong \overline{BC}$

Prove $ABCD$ is a parallelogram.

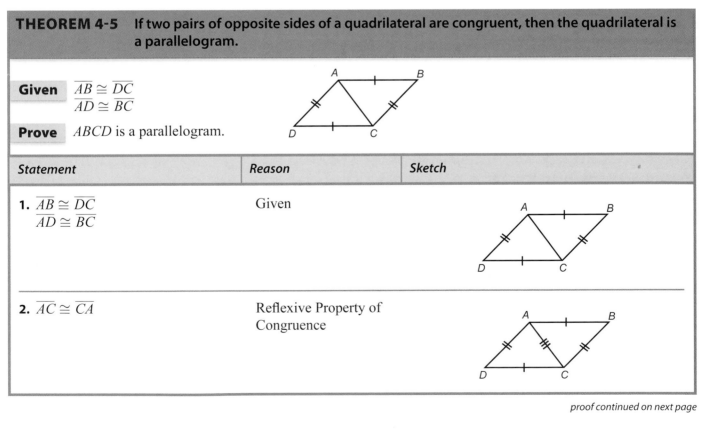

Statement	Reason	Sketch
1. $\overline{AB} \cong \overline{DC}$ $\overline{AD} \cong \overline{BC}$	Given	
2. $\overline{AC} \cong \overline{CA}$	Reflexive Property of Congruence	

proof continued on next page

3. $\triangle ADC \cong \triangle CBA$	SSS Congruence Postulate	
4. $\angle DAC \cong \angle BCA$ $\angle ACD \cong \angle CAB$	CPCTC	
5. $\overline{DC} \parallel \overline{AB}$ $\overline{BC} \parallel \overline{AD}$	Converse of Alternate Interior Angles Theorem	
6. $ABCD$ is a parallelogram.	Definition of a parallelogram	

Here are the other theorems that describe ways to prove a quadrilateral is a parallelogram.

THEOREM 4-6 If two opposite sides of a quadrilateral are parallel and congruent, then the quadrilateral is a parallelogram.

THEOREM 4-7 If the diagonals of a quadrilateral bisect each other, then the quadrilateral is a parallelogram.

REMEMBER

The definition of a rectangle is a parallelogram with four right angles.

What Type of Parallelogram Is It?

There are several theorems that can be used to prove that a parallelogram is a special type of parallelogram, specifically a rectangle or rhombus. One of the theorems is proven below.

THEOREM 4-8 If one angle of a parallelogram is a right angle, then the parallelogram is a rectangle.

Given $ABCD$ is a parallelogram. $\angle D$ is a right angle.

Prove $ABCD$ is a rectangle.

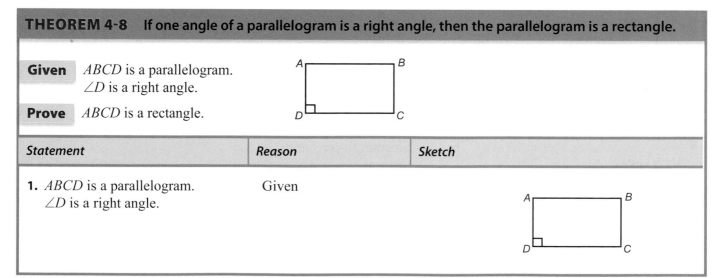

Statement	Reason	Sketch
1. $ABCD$ is a parallelogram. $\angle D$ is a right angle.	Given	

proof continued on next page

2. $m\angle D = 90°$	Definition of a right angle	
3. $\overline{AB} \parallel \overline{DC}$ $\overline{AD} \parallel \overline{BC}$	Definition of a parallelogram	
4. $\angle A \cong \angle D$ $\angle C \cong \angle D$	Converse of the Same-Side Interior Angles Theorem	
5. $m\angle A = m\angle D$ $m\angle C = m\angle D$	Angle Congruence Postulate	
6. $m\angle A = 90°$ $m\angle C = 90°$	Substitution Property of Equality	
7. $m\angle B = 90°$	Converse of the Same-Side Interior Angles Theorem	
8. $ABCD$ is a rectangle.	Definition of a rectangle	

The next theorem is another way to prove that a parallelogram is a rectangle.

THEOREM 4-9 If the diagonals of a parallelogram are congruent, then the parallelogram is a rectangle.

These theorems tell when a parallelogram is a rhombus.

THEOREM 4-10 If the diagonals of a parallelogram are perpendicular, then the parallelogram is a rhombus.

REMEMBER

The definition of a rhombus is a parallelogram with four congruent sides.

THEOREM 4-11   If two adjacent sides of a parallelogram are congruent, then the parallelogram is a rhombus.

THEOREM 4-12   If the diagonals of a parallelogram bisect the angles of the parallelogram, then the parallelogram is a rhombus.

Summary

- A quadrilateral is a parallelogram if the following are true:
    - Two pairs of opposite sides are congruent.
    - Two opposite sides are congruent and parallel.
    - The diagonals bisect each other.
- A parallelogram is a rectangle if the following are true:
    - One angle is a right angle.
    - The diagonals are congruent.
- A parallelogram is a rhombus if the following are true:
    - The diagonals are perpendicular.
    - Two adjacent sides are congruent.
    - The diagonals bisect the angles of the parallelogram.

Constructions with Polygons

OBJECTIVE

▶ Use compass and straightedge or technology to construct segments, angles, perpendicular lines, parallel lines, angle bisectors, triangles, and hexagons.

Many artists look at balance and symmetry when they work with patterns and relationships. Materials such as paper, wood, plastic, and metal can be formed into any number of geometric shapes to make a sculptor's vision into a work of art. Geometric shapes also can help illustrators create artistic representations that are realistic or abstract. You can create your own art by constructing colorful regular polygons and other geometric shapes.

KEYWORDS

central angle
regular hexagon

Constructing a Regular Hexagon

A **regular hexagon** is a six-sided polygon with congruent sides and congruent angles. You can construct a regular hexagon with geometry software using rotations. First you need to determine the measure of each **central angle.** You may recall that the measure of each central angle of a regular polygon is 360° divided by the number of its sides: $360° \div 6 = 60°$.

To start, create a point that will be the center of the hexagon. Then create another point that will be one of its vertices. Since each central angle in a regular hexagon measures 60°, the first vertex should be rotated around the center point by 60° until all the vertices are displayed.

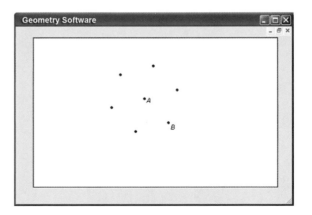

The hexagon is complete once the vertices are joined by segments.

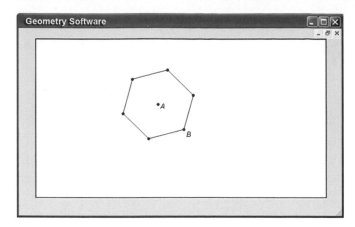

Because it is a regular hexagon, all the sides and angles should be congruent. You can check this by displaying all the measurements. Even if you drag the hexagon and increase the lengths of its sides, the six sides are still congruent and each of the six interior angles measures 120°.

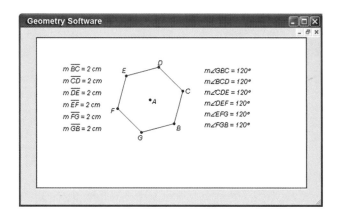

If you construct the angle bisector of each of the interior angles, you will notice that each bisector intersects the center of the hexagon.

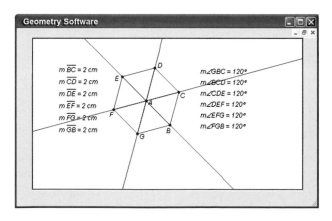

Continue to explore the hexagon by measuring the angles and sides of the triangles formed by the intersection of the angle bisectors. You can make and test conjectures about the congruence of these triangles.

You can also make a regular hexagon by constructing equilateral triangles. One way to make an equilateral triangle is to construct a circle and its radius, and then rotate the radius 60° about the center point. Construct a segment between the two points on the circle. Rotate this triangle 60° until a hexagon is formed. If desired, hide all but the sides of the hexagon.

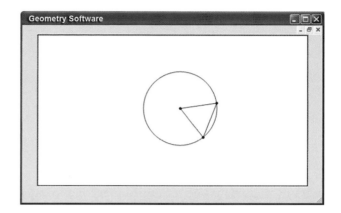

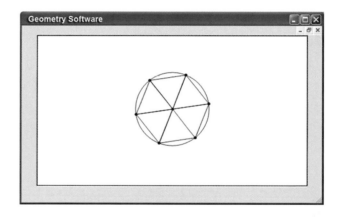

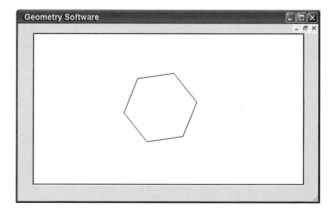

Summary

- Regular hexagons are formed by six congruent equilateral triangles. Each central angle measures 60° and each interior angle measures 120°.

- There is more than one way to construct a regular hexagon.

Transformations and Triangle Inequality

OBJECTIVES

► Define and recognize an isometry.

► Prove that translations, rotations, and reflections preserve shape, size, and accompanying properties.

► Describe and use the Triangle Inequality Theorem.

Versailles is a large, fine palace outside Paris, France. King Louis XIV moved his court from Paris to the palace in 1682. Now it is a historical museum that visitors can tour. In addition, important meetings involving international treaties have been held at Versailles over the years. The palace has many geometrical features, including floors, walls, and ceilings that make use of repeated patterns and symmetry.

KEYWORD

isometry

Revisiting Transformations

An **isometry** is a transformation that preserves the size and shape of an object's original image, also known as the pre-image. Reflections, rotations, and translations are isometric because, in each transformation, the image is congruent to the pre-image.

Recall that when you translate a figure, you slide it along a straight path. Imagine each point of the figure sliding along parallel paths, where each path is the same length.

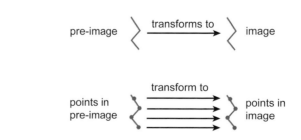

RECONNECT TO THE BIG IDEA

Remember A transformation is a rule that maps one set of points to another set of points.

You can use what you have learned about triangle congruence and special quadrilaterals to mathematically prove that a translation of a triangle is isometric.

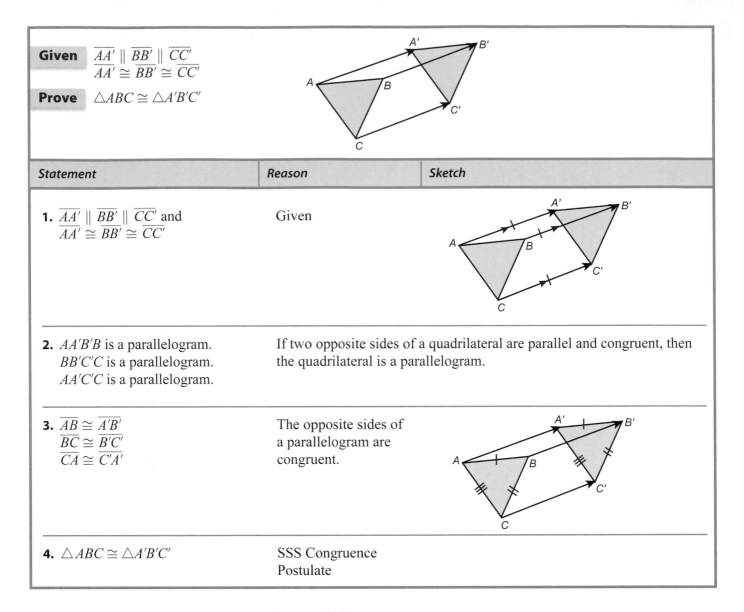

Given $\overline{AA'} \parallel \overline{BB'} \parallel \overline{CC'}$
$\overline{AA'} \cong \overline{BB'} \cong \overline{CC'}$

Prove $\triangle ABC \cong \triangle A'B'C'$

Statement	Reason	Sketch
1. $\overline{AA'} \parallel \overline{BB'} \parallel \overline{CC'}$ and $\overline{AA'} \cong \overline{BB'} \cong \overline{CC'}$	Given	
2. $AA'B'B$ is a parallelogram. $BB'C'C$ is a parallelogram. $AA'C'C$ is a parallelogram.	If two opposite sides of a quadrilateral are parallel and congruent, then the quadrilateral is a parallelogram.	
3. $\overline{AB} \cong \overline{A'B'}$ $\overline{BC} \cong \overline{B'C'}$ $\overline{CA} \cong \overline{C'A'}$	The opposite sides of a parallelogram are congruent.	
4. $\triangle ABC \cong \triangle A'B'C'$	SSS Congruence Postulate	

Inequalities

THEOREM 4-13 In a triangle, the angle opposite the longer side is greater than the angle opposite the shorter side.

In $\triangle XYZ$, if $ZY > XY$ then $m\angle X > m\angle Z$.

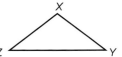

THEOREM 4-14 In a triangle, the side opposite the greater angle is longer than the side opposite the lesser angle.

In $\triangle ABC$, if $m\angle A > m\angle B$ then $BC > AC$.

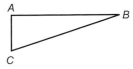

You can explore these theorems by drawing a triangle and then analyzing the side and angle measures as you change the shape of the triangle.

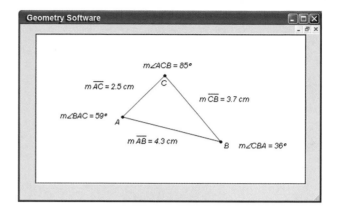

Comparison Property of Inequality

The Comparison Property of Inequality states that if $a = b + c$ and $c > 0$, then $a > b$.

In the diagram below,
$m\angle ABD = m\angle ABC + m\angle CBD$.

By the Comparison Property of Inequality,
$m\angle ABD > m\angle ABC$. Also, $m\angle ABD > m\angle CBD$.

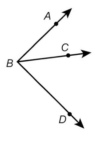

The Triangle Inequality Theorem

Three sides of any length don't always meet to form a triangle. Imagine one side is 12 inches long and the other sides are just 2 inches long. When you join the segments, they would look something like the figure below. The short sides are unable to join together.

The sum of the lengths of any two sides of a triangle is greater than the length of the third side. This is the Triangle Inequality Theorem. Use the inequality information you just learned to prove this theorem.

THEOREM 4-15 Triangle Inequality Theorem
The sum of the lengths of any two sides of a triangle is greater than the length of the third side.

Given $\triangle ABC$

Prove $BA + AC > BC$

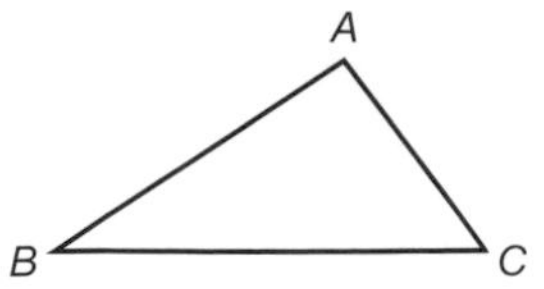

Statement	Reason	Sketch
1. $\triangle ABC$	Given	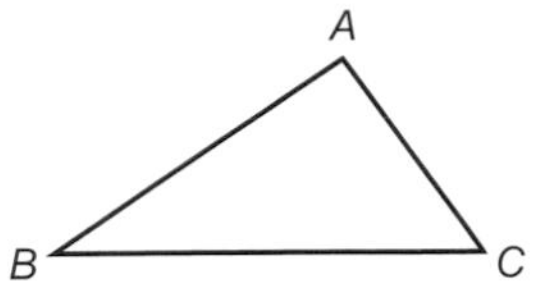
2. Construct $\overline{AD}$ so that $AD = AC$.	Ruler Postulate	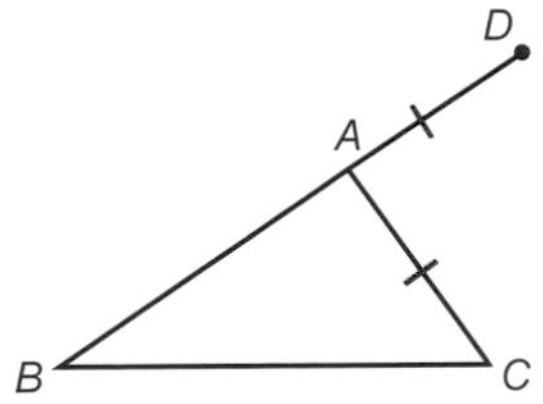
3. Construct $\overline{DC}$.	Two points determine a line.	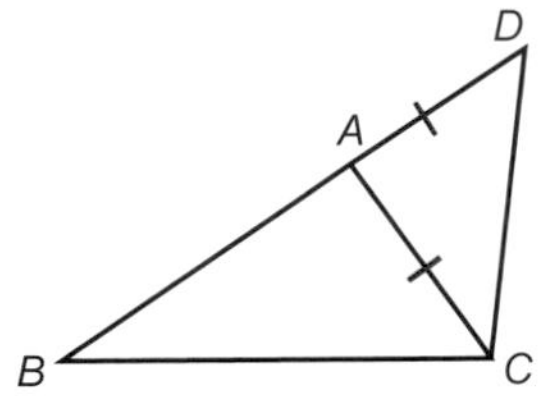
4. $\angle ADC \cong \angle ACD$	Isosceles Triangle Theorem	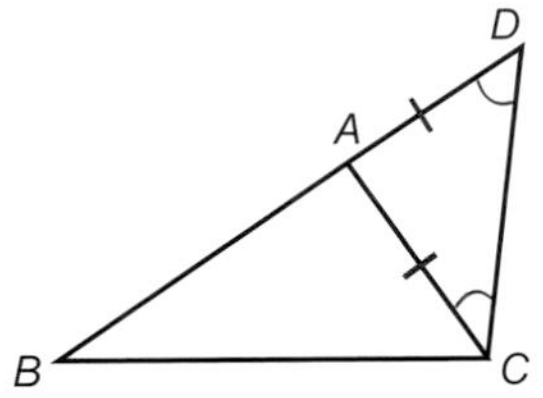
5. $m\angle BCD = m\angle BCA + m\angle ACD$	Angle Addition Postulate	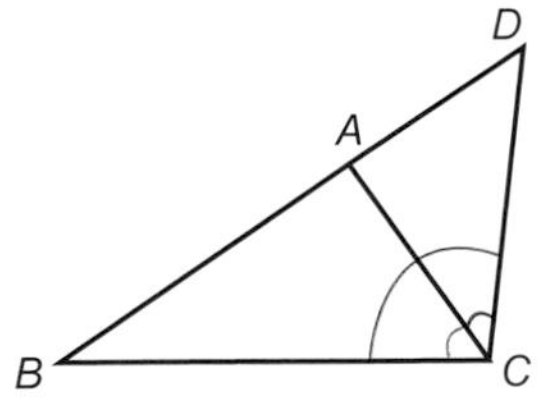
6. $m\angle BCD > m\angle ACD$	Comparison Property of Inequality	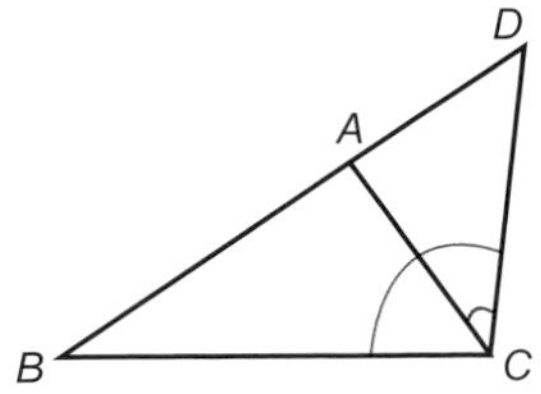

proof continued on next page

7. $m\angle ADC = m\angle ACD$	Angle Congruence Postulate	
8. $m\angle BCD > m\angle ADC$	Substitution (Steps 4 and 7)	
9. $BD > BC$	The side opposite the greater angle is longer than the side opposite the lesser angle.	
10. $BA + AD = BD$	Segment Addition Postulate	
11. $BA + AD > BC$	Substitution (Steps 9 and 10)	
12. $BA + AC > BC$	Substitution (Steps 2 and 11)	

Summary

- An isometry is a transformation that preserves the size and shape of the pre-image. Reflections, rotations, and translations are isometries.

- In a triangle, the angle opposite the longer side is greater than the angle opposite the shorter side. Likewise, the side opposite the greater angle is longer than the side opposite the lesser angle.

- The Comparison Property of Inequality states that if $a = b + c$ and $c > 0$, then $a > b$.

- The Triangle Inequality Theorem states that the sum of the lengths of any two sides of a triangle is greater than the length of the third side.

UNIT 5

Perimeter, Area, and Right Triangles

Formulas for areas of triangles, quadrilaterals, and circles are some of the most commonly used formulas in mathematics. They are even used by people who don't regularly use mathematics on the job. Day-to-day living creates circumstances in which you need to know how much space a region occupies. For example, if you decide to mow lawns for a summer job, you may need to know the square footage of each lawn to determine how much to charge your customers.

Later in life, you may want to buy carpet or tile for your home and will need to know how much to buy. You might want to brighten the walls—and there you go—you'll be using area formulas to determine how much paint or wallpaper you need. You might work on your garden: topsoil and mulch are sold in bags that cover a given area.

In this unit, you will learn how to find the perimeters and areas of polygons and circles.

· ·

UNIT OBJECTIVES

▶ Develop and use formulas to find the areas and perimeters of rectangles, parallelograms, triangles, and trapezoids.

▶ Develop and use formulas to find the areas and circumferences of circles.

▶ Use the Pythagorean Theorem to find lengths of missing sides of right triangles.

▶ Determine if triangles are right, acute, or obtuse by studying the lengths of their sides.

▶ Find the lengths of missing sides in 45°-45°-90° and 30°-60°-90° triangles.

▶ Find the areas of regular polygons.

Perimeter and Area

One night the sheriff's dispatcher in South Ridge received a call from a woman who said she was lost. Sheriff's officers were able to narrow her location to a specific region. They needed to figure out how long a border and how large a search area they needed to cover. For those calculations, they needed geometry.

KEYWORDS

area	base	circumference
height	nonoverlapping regions	perimeter

Perimeter and Area

You are probably used to seeing the dimensions of a rectangle referred to as length and width, but you can also refer to them as **base b** and **height h.**

In geometric figures, the base refers to "the bottom side." But figures can be rotated, so in the case of a rectangle, the base could actually be any side of the figure.

The height of a geometric figure is perpendicular to the base. In a rectangle, the height is either of the sides perpendicular to the base. Later, you will see that sometimes the height of a figure is not a side, but lies in the interior or exterior of the figure.

Perimeter

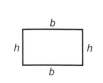

Perimeter is the distance around a figure. It measures the boundary of a region. The perimeter of a circle is called **circumference.**

The perimeter of a polygon is the sum of the lengths of its sides. Because the opposite sides of a rectangle are congruent, the perimeter of a rectangle can be written as $P = b + b + h + h$. This can be written more simply as $P = 2b + 2h$.

Perimeter of a Rectangle

The perimeter P of a rectangle with base b and height h is

$$P = 2b + 2h$$

The perimeter of this rectangle is found by substituting values for b and h into the formula:

$$\begin{aligned} P &= 2b + 2h \\ &= 2(4.2) + 2(1.8) \\ &= 8.4 + 3.6 \\ &= 12 \end{aligned}$$

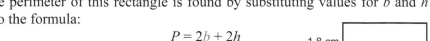

The perimeter of the rectangle is 12 cm.

Area

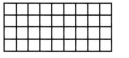

Area is the number of square units contained in the interior of a figure. It measures the region of a polygon.

The rectangle at left is broken into square units. To find the number of square units, you can count them, or better yet, multiply the number of columns by the number of rows. The number of columns is the base and the number of rows is the height, so the area of a rectangle can be written as $A = bh$.

Area of a Rectangle

The area A of a rectangle with base b and height h is
$$A = bh$$

To find the area, substitute values for b and h:

$$\begin{aligned} A &= bh \\ A &= (9)(4) \\ A &= 36 \end{aligned}$$

The area of the rectangle is 36 square units. This can also be written as 36 units^2. If the dimensions of the rectangle were given in inches, the area would be 36 square inches, or 36 inches^2, or abbreviated as 36 in^2.

Sometimes you can use the formula for the area of a rectangle to find the areas of other polygons. The hexagon below can be viewed as two nonoverlapping regions, both of which are rectangles. In **nonoverlapping regions,** a point in the interior of one region is not in the interior of another region.

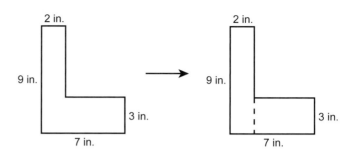

POSTULATE 5-1   Area Sum Postulate

If a figure is made up of nonoverlapping regions, then the area of the figure is the sum of the areas of the regions.

According to the Area Sum Postulate, the area of the hexagon is the sum of the area of the two rectangles:

Area of left rectangle = (9)(2) = 18
+ Area of right rectangle = (5)(3) = 15
Area of hexagon   = 33

The area of the hexagon is 33 in².

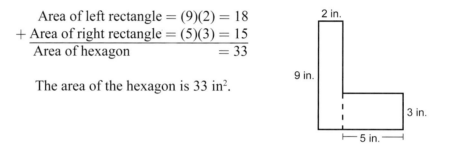

Summary

- Perimeter is the distance around a figure. The perimeter of a polygon is the sum of the lengths of its sides. You can find the perimeter of a rectangle by using the formula $P = 2b + 2h$.

- Area is the number of square units in a figure. You can find the area of a rectangle by using the formula $A = bh$.

- If a figure is made up of nonoverlapping regions, then the area of the figure is the sum of the areas of the regions.

Areas of Triangles and Quadrilaterals

OBJECTIVES

▶ Define altitude.

▶ Identify altitudes and bases of triangles, parallelograms, and trapezoids.

▶ Develop and use the area formulas for triangles, parallelograms, and trapezoids.

One of the most enduring stories of the sea is that of the Bermuda Triangle. According to legend, unexplained things happen there, including the disappearance of many airplanes and ships over the years. The U.S. Coast Guard believes there are explanations, including the fact that a magnetic compass in the Bermuda Triangle behaves unlike the way it behaves in almost all other places on earth. Other explanations include that the weather can be more unpredictable than in other regions.

Where is the Bermuda Triangle? Start at the southern tip of Florida, go northeast to Bermuda, go south to Puerto Rico, and go back to Florida and you've covered the boundaries. It's an area of about 500,000 square miles. How was that number calculated? Read on to find out.

KEYWORDS

altitude of a parallelogram	altitude of a trapezoid
altitude of a triangle	base of a parallelogram
base of a triangle	bases of a trapezoid
height	

Areas of Triangles, Parallelograms, and Trapezoids

An **altitude** is a perpendicular line segment that measures the **height** of a geometric figure. The height is the shortest distance between the base of the figure and its opposite side or vertex. In a triangle, an altitude is the perpendicular distance from a vertex to its opposite side, which is called the **base**. Any side of a triangle can be the base, so all triangles have three altitudes. An altitude can lie inside, on, or outside of the triangle. The three altitudes of $\triangle ABC$ are shown in red below.

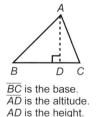

$\overline{BC}$ is the base.
$\overline{AD}$ is the altitude.
AD is the height.

$\overline{AC}$ is the base.
$\overline{BE}$ is the altitude.
BE is the height.

$\overline{AB}$ is the base.
$\overline{CF}$ is the altitude.
CF is the height.

In a quadrilateral with at least one pair of parallel sides, the parallel sides are the bases and the altitude measures the distance between them. An **altitude of a parallelogram** is always perpendicular to both bases. Parallelograms have two pairs of parallel sides, so the height depends on which sides are considered the bases. As shown below, the altitudes may or may not be drawn from a vertex.

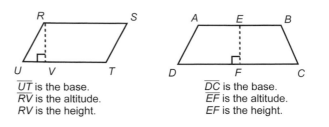

$\overline{UT}$ is the base.
$\overline{RV}$ is the altitude.
RV is the height.

$\overline{DC}$ is the base.
$\overline{EF}$ is the altitude.
EF is the height.

Area of a Parallelogram

Study the figures below. They show that a rectangle can be formed by cutting part of a parallelogram and moving it to the other side.

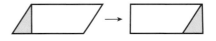

The parallelogram was reshaped into a rectangle without changing its area. Therefore the formula for the area of a parallelogram is the same as that of a rectangle.

Formula for the Area of a Parallelogram

The area A of a parallelogram with base b and height h is
$$A = bh$$

To find the area of the parallelogram, substitute for b and h.

$$A = bh$$
$$= 9(2)$$
$$= 18$$

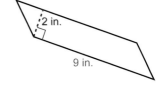

The area of the parallelogram is 18 in².

Area of a Triangle

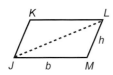

Any parallelogram can be divided into two congruent triangles by drawing a diagonal from one of its vertices. Therefore the area of either $\triangle JKL$ or $\triangle LMJ$ is half the area of the parallelogram.

Since the area of a parallelogram is $A = bh$, the area of a triangle can be found by multiplying bh by $\frac{1}{2}$ as follows.

Formula for the Area of a Triangle

The area A of a triangle with base b and height h is

$$A = \frac{1}{2}bh$$

To find the area of the triangle, substitute for b and h.

$$
\begin{aligned}
A &= \frac{1}{2}bh \\
&= \frac{1}{2}(12)(7) \\
&= \frac{1}{2}(84) \\
&= 42
\end{aligned}
$$

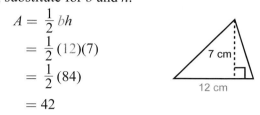

The area of the triangle is 42 cm².

Area of a Trapezoid

A parallelogram can be divided into two congruent trapezoids, as shown below. Because the **bases of the trapezoid** are different lengths, they are referred to as b_1 and b_2.

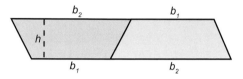

The area of the parallelogram is $A = (b_1 + b_2)h$. The area of one of the trapezoids is half the area of the parallelogram. The formula below shows this.

Formula for the Area of a Trapezoid

The area A of a trapezoid with bases b_1 and b_2 and height h is

$$A = \frac{1}{2}(b_1 + b_2)h$$

To find the area of the trapezoid, substitute for b_1, b_2, and h.

$$
\begin{aligned}
A &= \frac{1}{2}(b_1 + b_2)h \\
&= \frac{1}{2}(4 + 8)3 \\
&= \frac{1}{2}(12)3 \\
&= \frac{1}{2}(36) \\
&= 18
\end{aligned}
$$

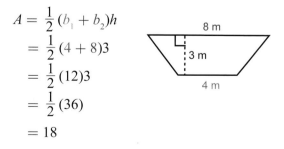

The area of the trapezoid is 18 m².

Summary

- An altitude is a perpendicular line segment that measures the height of a figure.

- In a triangle, an altitude is the perpendicular distance from a vertex to its corresponding base. A triangle has three altitudes, one from each vertex.

- In a quadrilateral with at least one pair of parallel sides, the parallel sides are the bases, and the altitude measures the distance between them.

- The formula for the area of a triangle with base b and height h is $A = \frac{1}{2}bh$.

- The formula for the area of a parallelogram with base b and height h is $A = bh$.

- The formula for the area of a trapezoid with bases b_1 and b_2 and height h is $A = \frac{1}{2}(b_1 + b_2)h$.

Circumference and Area of Circles

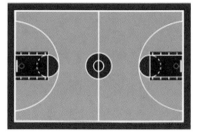

OBJECTIVES

▶ Define circle, radius, diameter, sector, and pi.

▶ Find the circumference and area of circles.

Several geometric shapes appear on a basketball court, including three circles. One of those circles is at center court and the other two are at the free throw lines.

Think about a painter who has the job of painting a basketball court. He has to paint different parts of the court in certain colors. Knowing formulas for areas of different shapes, including circles, helps him determine how many gallons of paint to buy.

KEYWORDS

circle	center of a circle
diameter	pi (π)
radius	sector

Circles

. . . .

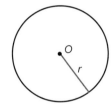

A **circle** is the set of all points on a plane that are the same distance r from a given point in the plane known as the **center** of the circle, where r is the radius of the circle. A circle is named by its center, so circle O is the circle you see here. In the definition for a circle, radius is defined as a length, but it can also be a segment. A **radius** of a circle is a line segment that connects the center of the circle to a point on the circle. The plural form of the word *radius* is *radii*. All radii of a circle are the same length.

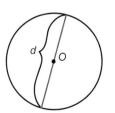

A **diameter** d of a circle is a line segment that connects two points on the circle and contains the center of the circle. All diameters of a circle are the same length. In a given circle, the length of any diameter is twice the length of the radius, $d = 2r$.

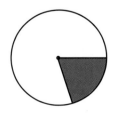

A **sector** of a circle is a region whose boundaries are two radii and part of the circle. The shaded region in the diagram is a sector.

Circumference of a Circle

Recall that circumference is the perimeter of a circle. The circumference C of any circle, divided by its diameter, always equals **pi,** which is represented by the Greek letter π. In other words, $\pi = \frac{C}{d}$. We can multiply both sides of this equation by d to write a formula for the circumference of a circle: $C = \pi d$. Since $d = 2r$, the formula can also be written as shown below.

Formula for the Circumference of a Circle

The circumference C of a circle with radius r is

$$C = 2\pi r$$

The number π is an irrational number, which means it never repeats and never ends. If you do not have a π button on your calculator, you can approximate it as 3.14. Calculations with pi are approximate ones unless you leave the pi symbol as part of the calculation. That's why you see the "is approximately" sign ($\approx$)—rather than the equals sign—used here when computing a circumference or area.

The circumference of this circle is exactly 12π feet, which is approximately 37.7 feet.

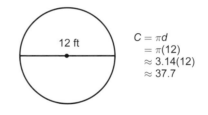

$$C = \pi d$$
$$= \pi(12)$$
$$\approx 3.14(12)$$
$$\approx 37.7$$

12 ft

Area of a Circle

Suppose a circle is divided into eight equal sectors—you might think of a pizza divided into eight equal slices. If you arrange the sectors as shown below, you see that they almost form a parallelogram. The two bases of the figure came from the pizza's circumference, so the length of each base is one-half of the circumference, or one-half of πd, which is the same as πr. The height is the radius of the pizza, r. The area of a parallelogram is base times height, so the area of the pizza is close to πr^2.

πr

r

As the number of sectors increases, the bases become "straighter" and come closer to forming a parallelogram.

Formula for the Area of a Circle

The area A of a circle with radius r is

$$A = \pi r^2$$

The area of this circle is exactly 36π square feet, which is approximately 113 square feet.

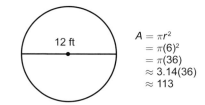

$A = \pi r^2$
$ = \pi(6)^2$
$ = \pi(36)$
$ \approx 3.14(36)$
$ \approx 113$

Approximating Circles with Polygons

You can approximate the area and circumference of a circle with regular polygons inscribed in a circle. The greater the number of sides, the better the approximations because there is less space in the interior of the circle not covered by the polygon. The diagrams, from left to right, show an inscribed triangle, square, and hexagon.

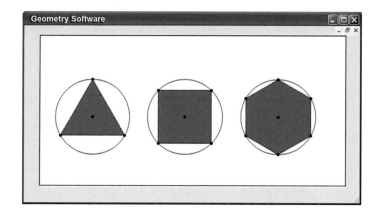

Summary

• A circle is the set of all points in a plane that are the same distance r from a given point in the plane known as the center of the circle, where r is the radius of the circle.

• A radius of a circle is a line segment that connects the center of the circle to a point on the circle.

• A diameter of a circle is a line segment that connects two points on the circle and contains the center of the circle.

• The formula for the circumference of a circle is $C = \pi d$ or $C = 2\pi r$.

• The formula for the area of a circle is $A = \pi r^2$.

• The area and circumference of a circle can be approximated with regular polygons inscribed in the circle. The greater the number of sides in the polygon, the better the approximation.

The Pythagorean Theorem

You have been waiting eagerly for the mail carrier because you ordered a game and you expect it today. You hear the mail carrier's truck and dash out of the house. But when you come back with your game, you find that you have locked yourself out and no one is inside.

There is an open window, but it's on the second floor. You can borrow a ladder from one of the neighbors, but you have to know the minimum length of the ladder you need. It's not the height of the window because bushes prevent you from leaning the ladder right up against the house. The geometry in this lesson will come in handy on a day like today!

KEYWORDS

acute triangle	hypotenuse
leg of a right triangle	obtuse triangle
Pythagorean triple	right triangle

The Pythagorean Theorem

Earlier, you learned that triangles are classified by their number of congruent sides. Triangles are also classified by the measures of their angles.

A triangle with an obtuse angle is called an **obtuse triangle.** This triangle is obtuse because the measure of angle B is greater than 90°.

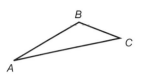

A triangle with three acute angles is an **acute triangle.** Angles D, E, and F all have measures less than 90°.

A triangle with a right angle is a **right triangle.** The side opposite the right angle in a right triangle is the **hypotenuse.** The other two sides are the **legs of the right triangle.**

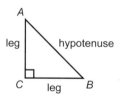

There is a special relationship among the sides of a right triangle. It is stated in the Pythagorean Theorem below.

THEOREM 5-1   The Pythagorean Theorem

For all right triangles, the square of the length of the hypotenuse c equals the sum of the squares of the lengths of the legs a and b:

$$c^2 = a^2 + b^2$$

You can explore the relationships of the sides using geometry software. Construct a right triangle and then construct squares adjacent to the sides of the right triangle. Measure the areas of the three squares. Notice that the sum of the areas of the smaller squares equals the area of the larger square. See that this remains true even as you change the lengths of the sides.

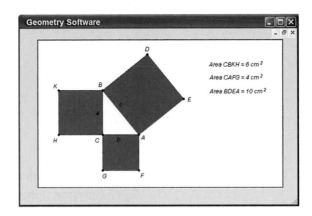

REMEMBER

The hypotenuse is always the longest side of a right triangle. If it is not, you know you made a mistake.

You can use the Pythagorean Theorem to find missing sides of right triangles. The legs a and b are interchangeable, but c must be the hypotenuse.

$$c^2 = 9^2 + 10^2$$
$$c^2 = 81 + 100$$
$$c^2 = 181$$
$$c = \sqrt{181}$$
$$c \approx 13.45$$

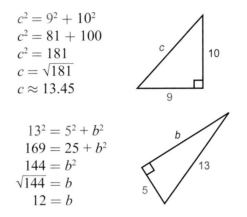

$$13^2 = 5^2 + b^2$$
$$169 = 25 + b^2$$
$$144 = b^2$$
$$\sqrt{144} = b$$
$$12 = b$$

The converse of the Pythagorean Theorem is also true.

THEOREM 5-2   The Converse of the Pythagorean Theorem

If the square of the length of the longest side of a triangle equals the sum of the squares of the lengths of the other two sides, then the triangle is a right triangle.

You can use the converse to determine if a triangle is a right triangle when you are given only its side lengths. Substitute the measures of the legs for a and b, and the measure of the hypotenuse for c in $c^2 = a^2 + b^2$. If the resulting statement is true, the triangle is a right triangle. If the measures are integers as well, the three integers are called a **Pythagorean triple.**

Is a triangle with side lengths of 3, 4, and 5 a right triangle?

$$5^2 \overset{?}{=} 3^2 + 4^2$$
$$25 \overset{?}{=} 9 + 16$$
$$25 = 25$$

Yes. Side lengths of 3, 4, and 5 form a right triangle.
3-4-5 is a Pythagorean triple.

Is a triangle with side lengths of 4, 6, and 7 a right triangle?

$7^2 \overset{?}{=} 4^2 + 6^2$

$49 \overset{?}{=} 16 + 36$

$49 \neq 52$

No. Side lengths of 4, 6, and 7 do not form a right triangle. 4-6-7 is *not* a Pythagorean triple.

The Pythagorean Inequalities

If $c^2 \neq a^2 + b^2$, we know the triangle is not a right triangle. If a triangle is not right, it must be acute or obtuse. The list below summarizes all the side relationships for a right triangle.

For any $\triangle ABC$, with c as the length of the longest side:
  If $c^2 = a^2 + b^2$, then $\triangle ABC$ is a right triangle.

  If $c^2 > a^2 + b^2$, then $\triangle ABC$ is an obtuse triangle.

  If $c^2 < a^2 + b^2$, then $\triangle ABC$ is an acute triangle.

Summary

- An acute triangle has three acute angles. An obtuse triangle has one obtuse angle. A right triangle has one right angle.

- The Pythagorean Theorem states that for all right triangles, the square of the length of the hypotenuse c equals the sum of the squares of the lengths of the legs a and b: $c^2 = a^2 + b^2$.

- For any $\triangle ABC$, with c as the length of the longest side:
  - If $c^2 = a^2 + b^2$, then $\triangle ABC$ is a right triangle.
  - If $c^2 > a^2 + b^2$, then $\triangle ABC$ is an obtuse triangle.
  - If $c^2 < a^2 + b^2$, then $\triangle ABC$ is an acute triangle.

Areas of Special Triangles and Regular Polygons

Stephanie wants to store a lamp, so she starts looking for a box. She finds a cube-shaped box whose side lengths are just slightly shorter than the height of the lamp. Is there a chance the lamp will fit in this box? Learn about special triangles to find out.

KEYWORDS

30°-60°-90° triangle

45°-45°-90° triangle

apothem

Special Right Triangles

A **45°-45°-90° triangle** is a triangle with angle measures of 45°, 45°, and 90°. Because two angles are congruent, two sides are congruent, so it can also be defined as an isosceles right triangle.

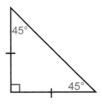

There is a relationship between the sides of a 45°-45°-90° triangle. You can use the Pythagorean Theorem to derive it.

Because the legs are congruent, we will use a to represent each of them, and c to represent the hypotenuse.

According to the Pythagorean Theorem,

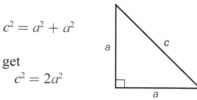

$$c^2 = a^2 + a^2$$

After combining like terms, we get

$$c^2 = 2a^2$$

By taking the square root of each side, and rearranging the factors, the equation becomes

$$c = a\sqrt{2}$$

This equation states that the hypotenuse is the product of the length of a leg and the square root of 2. This is the next theorem.

THEOREM 5-3   45°-45°-90° Triangle Theorem

In any 45°-45°-90° triangle, the length of the hypotenuse is $\sqrt{2}$ times the length of a leg.

The square root of 2 is an irrational number. It never repeats or ends. It is approximately equal to 1.41. You can use this theorem to find the lengths of missing sides. In the following examples, see the given lengths for the 45°-45°-90° triangles and how the missing lengths were found.

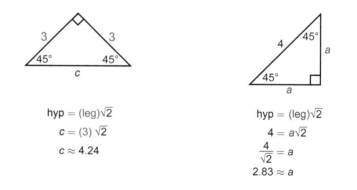

$$\text{hyp} = (\text{leg})\sqrt{2}$$
$$c = (3)\sqrt{2}$$
$$c \approx 4.24$$

$$\text{hyp} = (\text{leg})\sqrt{2}$$
$$4 = a\sqrt{2}$$
$$\frac{4}{\sqrt{2}} = a$$
$$2.83 \approx a$$

30°-60°-90° Triangles

A **30°-60°-90° triangle** is a triangle with angle measures of 30°, 60°, and 90°. The leg opposite the 30° angle is the shorter leg, and the leg opposite the 60° angle is the longer leg.

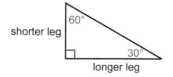

There are relationships among the sides of a 30°-60°-90° triangle. We will again use the Pythagorean Theorem to find them.

First you form two congruent 30°-60°-90° triangles by drawing an altitude of an equilateral triangle. Because the sides of the triangle are congruent, we will use s to represent their length. This makes the bases of the right triangles $\frac{s}{2}$. The variable a represents the altitude.

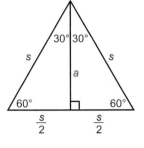

According to the Pythagorean Theorem,

$$s^2 = a^2 + \left(\frac{s}{2}\right)^2$$

Simplify the power to get

$$s^2 = a^2 + \frac{s^2}{4}$$

Then solve for a.

$$a^2 = s^2 - \frac{s^2}{4}$$

$$a^2 = \frac{4s^2}{4} - \frac{s^2}{4}$$

$$a^2 = \frac{3s^2}{4}$$

$$a = \frac{s\sqrt{3}}{2}$$

Looking back at the original triangle, the short side was half the hypotenuse, or $\frac{s}{2}$, and the equation we just found gives the long side as the square root of 3 times the short side. This is the next theorem.

THEOREM 5-4   30°-60°-90° Triangle Theorem

In any 30°-60°-90° triangle, the length of the hypotenuse is 2 times the length of the shorter leg, and the length of the longer leg is $\sqrt{3}$ times the length of the shorter leg.

The square root of 3 is an irrational number. It never repeats or ends. It is approximately equal to 1.73. You can use this theorem to find the lengths of missing sides. In the following example, one side's length is given as 6.

hyp = 2 (shorter leg)	longer leg = (shorter leg)$\sqrt{3}$
$c = 2\,(6)$	$b = (6)\sqrt{3}$
$c = 12$	$b \approx 10.4$

Regular Polygons

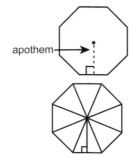

apothem

The **apothem** of a regular polygon is a line segment drawn from the center of the polygon perpendicular to one of its sides.

If you draw central angles to divide this octagon into congruent triangles, the apothem would be the height of each triangle. The sides of the octagon are the bases of each triangle. Because you have the base and height, you can find the area of each triangle.

Area of a Regular Polygon

Let's use a regular octagon to find a formula for the area of a regular polygon. A regular octagon consists of eight congruent triangles, each with base b and height h.

Using the formula for the area of a triangle, you can write the area of the octagon

$$A = 8\left(\frac{1}{2}\right)bh$$

Because the hexagon is regular, its perimeter P equals $8b$. By substitution,

$$A = P\left(\frac{1}{2}\right)h$$

When we replace the height h with the apothem a, we get the equation in the next theorem.

> **REMEMBER**
>
> The formula for the area of a triangle is $A = \frac{1}{2}bh$.

THEOREM 5-5   Area of a Regular Polygon Theorem

The area A of a regular polygon with apothem a and perimeter P is

$$A = \frac{1}{2}aP$$

To find the area of the hexagon at left, first find the length of the apothem. You can find this length by dividing the hexagon into congruent triangles that have central angles of 60°. As shown below, the apothem splits each triangle into two 30°-60°-90° triangles. The shorter side of the 30°-60°-90° triangle is one-half the length of a side of the hexagon, or 3 cm.

6 cm

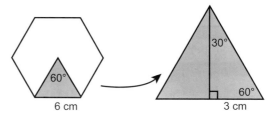

The apothem is the longer leg of the triangle, which is $\sqrt{3}$ times the shorter side, or $3\sqrt{3}$. The perimeter of the hexagon is $6 \cdot 6$, or 36.

Now substitute these values for a and P into the formula for the area of a regular polygon.

$$A = \frac{1}{2}aP$$
$$= \frac{1}{2}(3\sqrt{3})(36)$$
$$= 54\sqrt{3}$$

The area of the hexagon is $54\sqrt{3}$ cm².

Summary

- In any 45°-45°-90° triangle, the length of the hypotenuse is $\sqrt{2}$ times the length of a leg.

- In any 30°-60°-90° triangle, the length of the hypotenuse is 2 times the length of the shorter leg, and the length of the longer leg is $\sqrt{3}$ times the length of the shorter leg.

- The apothem of a regular polygon is a line segment drawn from the center of the polygon perpendicular to one of its sides.

- The area A of a regular polygon with apothem a and perimeter P is $A = \frac{1}{2}aP$.

Using the Distance Formula

OBJECTIVES

▶ Use the Pythagorean Theorem to develop the Distance Formula.

▶ Use the Distance Formula to find the distance between two points in a coordinate plane.

▶ Estimate the area of irregular figures on a coordinate plane.

In this scale figure of a car, each interval represents a certain number of inches. If you know that the bottom of the front bumper is at (2, 4) and the bottom of the rear bumper is at (12, 2), you can find the length of the car from bumper to bumper.

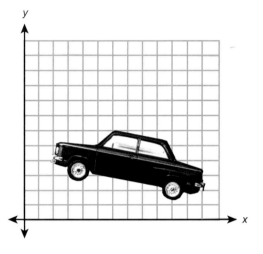

Distance

Suppose you want to find the distance between the points (2, 4) and (12, 2). The length of the run is the difference between the x-coordinates of the two points,

$$12 - 2, \text{ or } 10.$$

The length of the rise is the difference between the two y-coordinates,

$$4 - 2, \text{ or } 2.$$

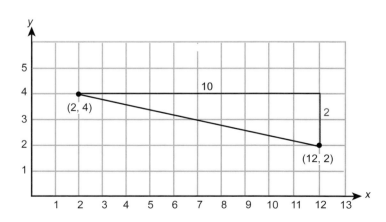

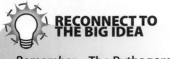

RECONNECT TO THE BIG IDEA

Remember The Pythagorean Theorem is a fundamental tool in geometry.

These two values are the lengths of the legs of a right triangle. You can find the length of the hypotenuse by using the Pythagorean Theorem:

$$c^2 = a^2 + b^2$$
$$c^2 = (10)^2 + (2)^2$$
$$c^2 = 100 + 4$$
$$c^2 = 104$$
$$c \approx 10.2$$

The distance between points $(2, 4)$ and $(12, 2)$ is about 10.2 units.

Calculating Distance

You can use the same steps to find the distance between any two points (x_1, y_1) and (x_2, y_2) on the coordinate plane.

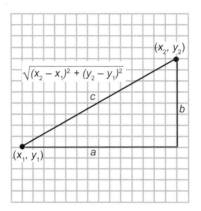

The length of side a is $x_2 - x_1$ and the length of side b is $y_2 - y_1$. So,

$$c^2 = (x_2 - x_1)^2 + (y_2 - y_1)^2$$
$$\sqrt{c^2} = \sqrt{(x_2 - x_1)^2 + (y_2 - y_1)^2}$$
$$c = \sqrt{(x_2 - x_1)^2 + (y_2 - y_1)^2}$$

This is known as the Distance Formula.

The Distance Formula

In a coordinate plane, the distance d between any two points (x_1, y_1) and (x_2, y_2) is

$$d = \sqrt{(x_2 - x_1)^2 + (y_2 - y_1)^2}$$

To find the distance between $(3, -1)$ and $(5, 0)$:

$$d = \sqrt{(x_2 - x_1)^2 + (y_2 - y_1)^2}$$
$$= \sqrt{(5 - 3)^2 + (0 - (-1))^2}$$
$$= \sqrt{(5 - 3)^2 + (0 + 1)^2}$$
$$= \sqrt{2^2 + 1^2}$$
$$= \sqrt{5}$$
$$\approx 2.24$$

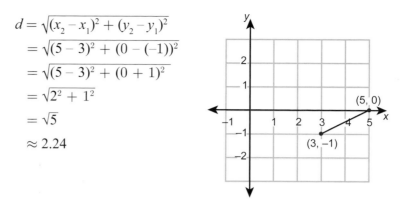

The distance between $(3, -1)$ and $(5, 0)$ is approximately 2.24 units.

Estimating Area

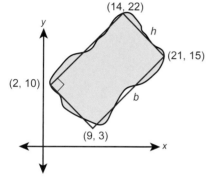

You can use the Distance Formula to estimate areas of irregular figures. To estimate the area of the lake shown at left, you can draw a rectangle that roughly outlines the perimeter of the lake. Then use the vertices of the rectangle to find its base and height. In this example, each unit on the coordinate plane is one mile.

$$\text{base} = \sqrt{(21 - 9)^2 + (15 - 3)^2} \qquad \text{height} = \sqrt{(2 - 9)^2 + (10 - 3)^2}$$
$$= \sqrt{12^2 + 12^2} \qquad\qquad\qquad = \sqrt{(-7)^2 + (7)^2}$$
$$= \sqrt{144 + 144} \qquad\qquad\qquad = \sqrt{49 + 49}$$
$$= \sqrt{288} \qquad\qquad\qquad\qquad = \sqrt{98}$$
$$\approx 17 \qquad\qquad\qquad\qquad\quad \approx 9.9$$

$$A \approx (17)(9.9)$$
$$\approx 168$$

The area of the lake is approximately 168 mi².

Summary

- The Distance Formula is derived from the Pythagorean Theorem and states that the distance d between any two points (x_1, y_1) and (x_2, y_2) is $d = \sqrt{(x_2 - x_1)^2 + (y_2 - y_1)^2}$.

- You can use the Distance Formula when estimating areas of irregular figures.

Proofs and Coordinate Geometry

To this point, you have proven theorems directly by using two forms of proofs—paragraph and two-column. Also, you have verified theorems indirectly through the process of proof by contradiction. Now you will prove theorems in yet another way—through coordinate proofs. When you construct a coordinate proof, you combine the laws of the coordinate plane, algebra, and geometry.

Coordinate Proofs

In coordinate proofs, you start by placing a figure on the coordinate plane. Do not haphazardly place it anywhere. Place it in a way that your calculations will be as simple as possible. The following guidelines help you do that.

- Place the entire figure in the first quadrant.

- Place at least one side of the polygon on either the *x*- or *y*-axis.

- Place a center or vertex at the origin.

The examples below show wise placement of three figures and how their coordinates are named.

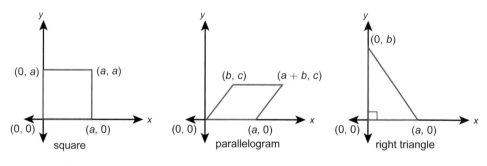

square   parallelogram   right triangle

Proofs

The midsegment of a triangle is a line segment that connects the midpoints of two sides of the triangle. The following proof shows that a midsegment is always parallel to the third side and that it is half the length of the third side.

Given G is the midpoint of $\overline{DF}$.

H is the midpoint of $\overline{EF}$.

Prove $\overline{GH} \parallel \overline{DE}$ and $GH = \frac{1}{2} DE$

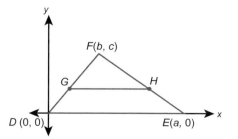

First find the coordinates of G and H by using the Midpoint Formula:

Point G: $\left(\dfrac{0 + b}{2}, \dfrac{0 + c}{2}\right) = \left(\dfrac{b}{2}, \dfrac{c}{2}\right)$

Point H: $\left(\dfrac{a + b}{2}, \dfrac{0 + c}{2}\right) = \left(\dfrac{a + b}{2}, \dfrac{c}{2}\right)$

Next, prove $\overline{GH} \parallel \overline{DE}$ by showing that the lines have the same slope.

Slope of $\overline{GH} = \dfrac{\dfrac{c}{2} - \dfrac{c}{2}}{\dfrac{a + b}{2} - \dfrac{b}{2}} = \dfrac{0}{\dfrac{a}{2}} = 0$

Slope of $\overline{DE} = \dfrac{0 - 0}{a - 0} = \dfrac{0}{a} = 0$

Since both slopes are zero, they are equal and the segments are parallel. Now use the Distance Formula to find GH and DE.

$GH = \sqrt{\left(\dfrac{a + b}{2} - \dfrac{b}{2}\right)^2 + \left(\dfrac{c}{2} - \dfrac{c}{2}\right)^2} = \sqrt{\left(\dfrac{a}{2}\right)^2 + 0} = \dfrac{a}{2} = \dfrac{1}{2}a$

$DE = \sqrt{(a - 0)^2 + (0 - 0)^2} = \sqrt{a^2} = a$

Therefore, $GH = \dfrac{1}{2} DE$.

This next coordinate proof proves that the diagonals of a parallelogram bisect each other.

Given Parallelogram $QRST$ with diagonals $\overline{QS}$ and $\overline{RT}$

Prove $\overline{QS}$ and $\overline{RT}$ bisect each other.

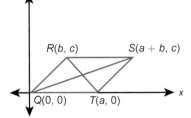

Prove $\overline{QS}$ and $\overline{RT}$ bisect each other by finding the midpoints of $\overline{QS}$ and $\overline{RT}$ and showing the midpoints are the same.

Midpoint of $\overline{QS} = \left(\dfrac{a + b + 0}{2}, \dfrac{c + 0}{2}\right) = \left(\dfrac{a + b}{2}, \dfrac{c}{2}\right)$

Midpoint of $\overline{RT} = \left(\dfrac{a + b}{2}, \dfrac{0 + c}{2}\right) = \left(\dfrac{a + b}{2}, \dfrac{c}{2}\right)$

So, $\overline{QS}$ and $\overline{RT}$ bisect each other.

Reflecting Over the Line y = x

If a point (x, y) is reflected across the line $y = x$, then its image is the point (y, x). For example, if the point whose coordinates are $(3, 4)$ is reflected over $y = x$, its image coordinates will be $(4, 3)$.

By coordinate proof you can prove that when a point is reflected over the line $y = x$, the line is the perpendicular bisector of the segment whose endpoints are the pre-image and image points.

Given J is the image of K reflected over $y = x$.

Prove $\overleftrightarrow{LM}$ is the perpendicular bisector of $\overline{JK}$.

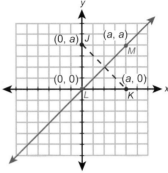

You begin by finding slopes.

Slope of $\overline{JK} = \dfrac{a-0}{0-a} = \dfrac{a}{-a} = -1$

Slope of $\overleftrightarrow{LM} = \dfrac{a-0}{a-0} = \dfrac{a}{a} = 1$

The product of the slopes is -1, so the line and segment are perpendicular. Now you just need to prove that the reflection line bisects the segment. You find the coordinates of the segment's midpoint: $\left(\dfrac{a+0}{2}, \dfrac{0+a}{2}\right) = \left(\dfrac{a}{2}, \dfrac{a}{2}\right)$. This point is on the line $y = x$, so your proof is complete.

Connecting the Midpoints of a Rectangle

You can use a coordinate proof to prove that the figure formed by the midpoints of a rectangle is a rhombus.

On a grid, place a rectangle as shown. Label in multiples of 2 to avoid fractions in the midpoints.

Given E, F, G, and H are the midpoints of $\overline{AB}$, $\overline{BC}$, $\overline{CD}$, and $\overline{DA}$ respectively.

Prove $EFGH$ is a rhombus.

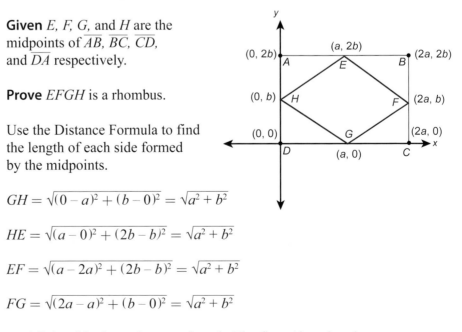

Use the Distance Formula to find the length of each side formed by the midpoints.

$GH = \sqrt{(0-a)^2 + (b-0)^2} = \sqrt{a^2 + b^2}$

$HE = \sqrt{(a-0)^2 + (2b-b)^2} = \sqrt{a^2 + b^2}$

$EF = \sqrt{(a-2a)^2 + (2b-b)^2} = \sqrt{a^2 + b^2}$

$FG = \sqrt{(2a-a)^2 + (b-0)^2} = \sqrt{a^2 + b^2}$

All the sides have the same length. The figure is a rhombus.

Summary

• You can use the coordinate plane and algebra to prove theorems. These proofs are called coordinate proofs.

• When you place images on a coordinate plane, choose points that will make calculations simple. The best way is to put the figure in Quadrant I, placing at least one side on an axis and using the origin as a center point or vertex.

• If a point (x, y) is reflected across the line $y = x$, then its image is the point (y, x).

• The quadrilateral formed by connecting consecutive midpoints of a rectangle is a rhombus.

UNIT 6

Three-Dimensional Figures and Graphs

We live in a three-dimensional world that is often represented on a two-dimensional plane. Drawings, paintings, and maps are some of the two-dimensional representations of our world.

Artists were not always able to accurately represent three dimensions on a flat surface. In the fifteenth century, Filippo Brunelleschi, an Italian sculptor and architect with an interest in mathematics, was the first to conduct experiments that led to an understanding of one-point perspective. To create the illusion of depth on a two-dimensional surface, he demonstrated that lines that are parallel in the real world should be drawn as meeting at a single vanishing point. In this unit, you will extend your geometric knowledge and skills to three-dimensional figures.

. . . .

UNIT OBJECTIVES

▶ Draw basic three-dimensional figures as well as two-dimensional views of three-dimensional figures.

▶ Define polyhedron and identify the faces, edges, and vertices of polyhedra.

▶ Define prism and the parts of a prism.

▶ Classify prisms.

▶ Find the surface area of prisms.

▶ Find the volume of prisms.

▶ Locate and plot points in a three-dimensional coordinate system.

▶ Use the Distance and Midpoint Formulas for three dimensions.

▶ Use intercepts to graph planes in space.

▶ Use parametric equations to plot lines in space.

Solid Shapes and Three-Dimensional Drawing

OBJECTIVES

▶ Define three-dimensional drawing and depth.

▶ Use isometric grid paper to show how three-dimensional figures can be drawn.

▶ Draw two-dimensional views of three-dimensional figures.

▶ Interpret a three-dimensional drawing.

▶ Solve problems involving surface area and volume.

During the Renaissance, artists started using perspective to represent the three-dimensional world on their two-dimensional canvases. Notice how the painting on the right has depth and looks more realistic than the one on the left.

KEYWORDS

depth	isometric drawing
orthographic views	perspective drawing
solids	surface area
three-dimensional drawing	volume

Figures in Three Dimensions

Polygons are two-dimensional figures. They are flat and lie on a single plane. **Solids** are three-dimensional figures. Three-dimensional figures have the additional dimension of depth. **Depth** is a measure of the length of a figure from the front of the figure to the back.

Drawing Three-Dimensional Figures

A **three-dimensional drawing** represents a three-dimensional figure on a two-dimensional plane. The three-dimensional drawings shown below are called **perspective drawings** because the objects appear true-to-life, as they would if you were actually looking at them.

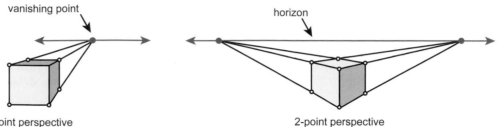

1-point perspective   2-point perspective

You can draw a cube in one-point perspective by first drawing a square, a line called the horizon, and a point on the horizon called the vanishing point. This square is the front of the cube. Draw straight lines from the vertices of the square to the vanishing point. Draw the back face of the cube so that its vertices are on the lines leading to the vanishing point. You may find it easiest to draw the top horizontal segment first. Because it is a cube, locate the points so that all sides appear to be the same length. Connect the front and back squares by tracing over the segments between them.

To draw a cube in two-point perspective, start with the horizon, two vanishing points, and a vertical line segment that will be the front edge of the cube. Draw lines from the front segment's endpoints to each vanishing point and use those to draw the left and right vertical sides of the cube. Join the top of each edge to its opposite vanishing point to form the top face of the cube.

Look carefully at the sides and angles of each cube in the diagrams. Some sides that should be parallel are not drawn parallel, and some angles do not actually measure 90°.

Isometric Drawings of Three-Dimensional Figures

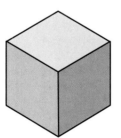

Another type of three-dimensional drawing is called an **isometric drawing**. Isometric drawings show three sides of a solid figure from a corner view. Notice in the diagram at left that the parallel lines are drawn parallel and the right angles on the top face are drawn as 120° and 60° angles. This is one way isometric drawings differ from perspective drawings.

You can use isometric grid paper to help you draw three-dimensional figures.

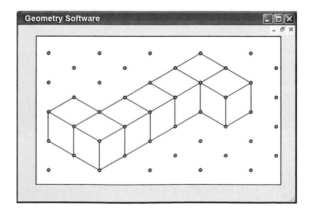

Orthographic Views

Orthographic views of a three-dimensional figure show the front, back, top, bottom, left side, and right side views of the figure. The orthographic views of a square pyramid are shown in the diagram.

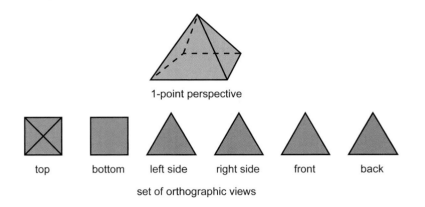

1-point perspective

top   bottom   left side   right side   front   back

set of orthographic views

To draw a top view, imagine flying above the object and looking straight down on it. If you flew above the pyramid and looked down, you would see more than just the top point. You would see the outline of the base of the figure as well as the four edges that lead to the corners of the base. For a bottom view, imagine lying below the object and looking straight up. For side views, imagine floating around the figure and recording what you see when you face each side directly.

The orthographic views of a previous drawing are shown below. Notice that in the left side, right side, front, and back views, the depth of each block is irrelevant. If you can see a block from that side, regardless of its depth, a square is included in the orthographic view.

Just a couple of views of a figure do not tell you what the figure looks like. Though three views are sufficient for some figures, other figures require as many as six views to get an accurate view of what the figure looks like.

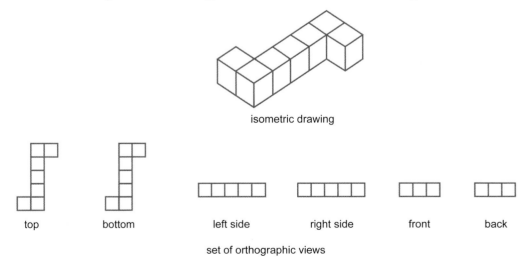

isometric drawing

top   bottom   left side   right side   front   back

set of orthographic views

Surface Area and Volume

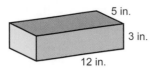

5 in.
3 in.
12 in.

The **surface area** of a figure is the amount of space that covers the figure. To find the surface area of a solid, find the sum of the areas of its outer surfaces.

Compare the area calculations below with the three-dimensional figure above.

top	$12 \times 5 = 60$
bottom	$12 \times 5 = 60$
left side	$3 \times 5 = 15$
right side	$3 \times 5 = 15$
front	$12 \times 3 = 36$
+ back	$12 \times 3 = 36$
	222

The surface area of the three-dimensional figure is 222 in².

The **volume** of a solid is the amount of space inside the figure, measured in cubic units. If it's a small rectangular figure, you may be able to count the cubes. This is normally not possible, however, because of either the size or shape of the figure.

In a three-dimensional figure like the prism at left, you can multiply or count to find the area of one "layer" of cubes and multiply by the number of layers. Because each layer in this figure is a rectangle, you can find its volume by multiplying its dimensions.

$$V = 3 \times 5 \times 4$$
$$= 60$$

The volume of the figure is 60 cm³.

RECONNECT TO THE BIG IDEA

Remember Measurement is the process of using a unit to determine how much of something you have.

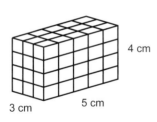

4 cm
3 cm
5 cm

Summary

- Perspective drawings show three-dimensional objects as they appear in real life. To draw in perspective, use a horizon and vanishing points.

- Isometric drawings show three sides of a solid figure from a corner view.

- Orthographic views of a three-dimensional figure show the front, back, top, bottom, left side, and right side views of the figure.

- The surface area of a solid is the amount of space that covers the figure.

- The volume of a solid is the amount of space inside the figure.

Lines, Planes, and Polyhedra

OBJECTIVES

▶ Identify and define skew lines, half-planes, and dihedral angles.

▶ Define polyhedron.

▶ Identify the faces, edges, and vertices of polyhedra.

▶ Create a figure from its net, and draw nets of polyhedra.

A globe is a fair representation of the earth—it is a three-dimensional model representing a three-dimensional shape. However, flat maps of earth, called map projections, distort earth's shape. Projecting a curved figure onto a flat surface always creates some type of deformation. Unlike the shape of earth, many other three-dimensional shapes can be created accurately from two-dimensional models.

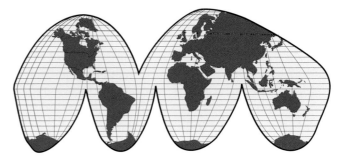

KEYWORDS

dihedral angle	edge
face	half-plane
net	parallel planes
polyhedron	skew lines
vertex of a polyhedron	

Lines and Planes in Space

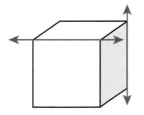

If two lines lie on the same plane, then those lines either intersect or are parallel. If two lines lie in different planes, there is another possibility. The lines can be askew. **Skew lines** are two lines that do not intersect but are not parallel. The blue lines in the diagram are skew lines.

Parallel planes are planes that do not intersect. For instance, the top and bottom faces of a cube lie on parallel planes.

A line that lies in a plane separates the plane into two **half-planes**. A half-plane consists of all the points on either side of the line.

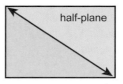

half-plane

If two planes intersect, they form four angles and four half-planes. Each angle is called a dihedral angle. A **dihedral angle** is formed by two non-coplanar half-planes and their line of intersection.

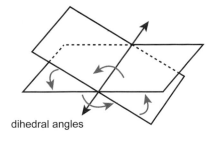

dihedral angles

Polyhedra

A solid is a three-dimensional figure. A **polyhedron** is a solid enclosed by polygons. So, although a sphere is a solid, it is not a polyhedron. Note that the two plurals of *polyhedron* are *polyhedra* and *polyhedrons*.

The flat surfaces of a polyhedron are called the **faces**. The faces meet to form the **edges** of the polyhedron. The vertices of the faces meet to form the **vertices** of the polyhedron. The number of faces, edges, and vertices of three polyhedra are shown below.

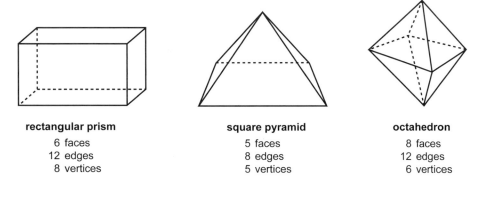

rectangular prism
6 faces
12 edges
8 vertices

square pyramid
5 faces
8 edges
5 vertices

octahedron
8 faces
12 edges
6 vertices

Nets of Polyhedra

A **net** is what a solid looks like if you unfold it. You can think of a net as a pattern for making a solid, much in the same way that a pattern is used to sew pieces of clothing together. Nets are often used to find surface area.

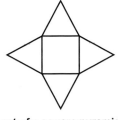

net of a square pyramid

To create the net of an octahedron with geometry software, create an equilateral triangle, and then use rotations and reflections to create the net in the diagram. If you like, you can add color. Once you have created your net, you can print it and fold it to create the polyhedron.

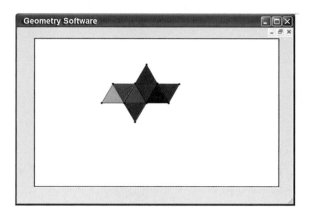

You can use grid paper to create a net. To make sure the figure folds up properly, be sure the top and bottom faces are congruent and that the height for the front and back is the same as for the top and bottom.

Summary

- Skew lines do not lie in the same plane and do not intersect.

- Parallel planes are planes that do not intersect.

- A line in a plane separates the plane into two half-planes.

- An angle formed by the intersection of two planes is called a dihedral angle.

- A polyhedron is a solid enclosed by polygons. Each polygon is called a face. The faces intersect at edges. The vertices of the faces meet to form the vertices of the polyhedron.

- A net shows what a solid looks like when the solid has been unfolded. A net can also serve as a pattern for a solid.

Prisms

OBJECTIVES

► Define prism and the parts of a prism.

► Classify prisms.

► Solve problems that involve the diagonal of a right prism.

► Find the surface area and volume of prisms.

In the picture, a triangular prism is dispersing light into all of its different colors. Prisms that reflect, refract, and disperse light are called optical prisms. Optical prisms come in many shapes and sizes. You will learn about various kinds of prisms in geometry and how to measure them.

KEYWORDS

base area of a prism   diagonal of a polyhedron

lateral edge   lateral face

oblique prism   prism

right prism

Types of Prisms

A **prism** is a polyhedron with two parallel, congruent faces called **bases**. We call the other faces **lateral faces**. Notice that lateral faces are parallelograms formed by parallel segments that connect corresponding vertices of the bases. These parallel segments are called the **lateral edges**. Prisms are classified by the shapes of their bases. If the bases of a prism are triangles, we call it a triangular prism; if the bases are hexagons, we call it a hexagonal prism, and so on.

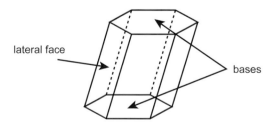

lateral face

bases

hexagonal prism

A prism whose lateral edges are perpendicular to the bases is a **right prism**.

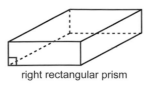

right rectangular prism

If a prism is not a right prism, it is an **oblique prism**. The lateral faces of an oblique prism are not perpendicular to the bases.

oblique triangular prism

Diagonals

A **diagonal of a polyhedron** is a line segment that joins two vertices that are in different faces. Like diagonals of polygons, they do not overlap the sides of the figure itself. A diagonal of a right rectangular prism is shown in red at left.

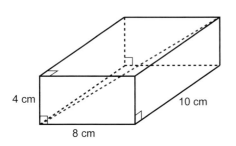

4 cm

10 cm

8 cm

Formula for the Diagonal of a Right Rectangular Prism

The length of a diagonal d of a right rectangular prism is

$$d = \sqrt{l^2 + w^2 + h^2}$$

For the right rectangular prism at left:

$$d = \sqrt{10^2 + 8^2 + 4^2}$$
$$= \sqrt{100 + 64 + 16}$$
$$= \sqrt{180}$$
$$\approx 13.42$$

The length of the diagonal is approximately 13.42 cm.

Surface Area of Prisms

Recall that surface area tells how much space covers a figure. The surface area of a prism is the sum of the areas of the bases and the lateral faces. The area of one base is defined as B. The sum of the areas of the lateral faces is defined as L. Because the bases are congruent, we write the sum of the bases as $2B$.

Formula for the Surface Area of a Prism

The surface area S of a prism, where B is the area of
one base and L is the sum of the areas of the lateral faces, is
$$S = 2B + L$$

Follow the steps to find the surface area of the right triangular prism below.

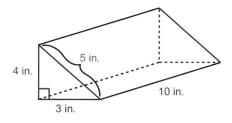

Step 1: Find B and $2B$ by using the formula for the area of a triangle.

$$A = \frac{1}{2}bh$$
$$= \frac{1}{2}(3)(4)$$
$$= 6$$

The area of one base is 6 in². So $2B$ is $2(6 \text{ in}^2) = 12 \text{ in}^2$.

Step 2: Find L. There are three lateral faces.

$A = bh$	$A = bh$	$A = bh$
$= 10(3)$	$= 10(4)$	$= 10(5)$
$= 30$	$= 40$	$= 50$

$$L = 30 + 40 + 50 = 120$$

Step 3: Find S.

$$S = 2B + L$$
$$= 12 + 120$$
$$= 132$$

The surface area of the prism is 132 in².

Volume of Prisms

Recall that volume is the amount of space inside a figure. The volume of a prism can be found by multiplying the area of a base B by its height h. The height of a prism is the perpendicular distance between the bases. When the prism is oblique, the height will be different from the length of a lateral edge.

Formula for the Volume of a Prism

The volume V of a prism, where B is the area of one base and h is the height of the prism, is

$$V = Bh$$

To find the volume of the same right triangular prism for which you just found the surface area, see the following steps.

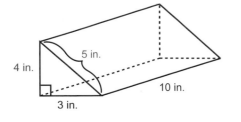

Step 1: Find B.

$$A = \frac{1}{2}bh$$

$$= \frac{1}{2}(3)(4)$$

$$= 6$$

The area of a base is 6 in².

Step 2: Identify h. The height is the distance between the bases. In this figure it is 10 inches.

Step 3: Find V.

$$V = Bh$$
$$= 6(10)$$
$$= 60$$

The volume of the prism is 60 in³.

Summary

REMEMBER

Area is measured in square units. Volume is measured in cubic units.

- A prism is a polyhedron with two parallel, congruent bases and lateral faces that are parallelograms formed by the parallel segments that connect corresponding vertices of the bases.

- A prism whose lateral edges are perpendicular to the bases is a right prism. A prism whose lateral edges are not perpendicular to the bases is an oblique prism.

- The diagonal of a polyhedron is a line segment that joins two vertices that are in different faces.

- The length of a diagonal d of a right rectangular prism can be found by using the formula $d = \sqrt{l^2 + w^2 + h^2}$.

- The surface area S of a prism, where B is the area of one base and L is the sum of the areas of the lateral faces, is $S = 2B + L$.

- The volume V of a prism, where B is the area of one base and h is the height of the prism, is $V = Bh$.

Coordinates in Three Dimensions

Architects, interior designers, and radiologists are just a few of the professionals that have benefited from three-dimensional computer imaging technology. Architects use computer software to create three-dimensional computer models of buildings. Interior designers create virtual rooms where a client can change wall color or floor tiling with the click of a mouse. Radiologists use computer imaging to "see" inside the human body, using a three-dimensional view, and are able to detect medical conditions at a much earlier stage. This lesson introduces you to a three-dimensional coordinate system.

KEYWORDS

coordinate plane	first octant
octant	ordered triple
right-handed system	three-dimensional coordinate system

The Three-Dimensional Coordinate System

The **coordinate plane** you are familiar with is formed by the intersection of an x-axis and a y-axis. Each point in the coordinate plane is represented by an ordered pair of real numbers (x, y). You can locate and plot a point by first starting at the origin, then moving left or right according to the x-coordinate, and finally moving up or down according to the y-coordinate. Remember that the positive x-direction points to the right, and the positive y-direction points upward.

Plotting points in three dimensions can be accomplished using a similar method. First, we must add a third axis to the system, the z-axis, which will correspond to the third dimension. To visualize the addition of this axis, imagine the ordinary xy-plane lying flat on a table, with the positive x-direction pointing toward you and the positive y-direction pointing to the right, as shown in the figure.

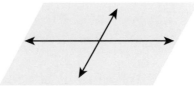

Now imagine a third axis, the *z*-axis, which is perpendicular to both the *x*- and *y*-axes. The positive direction for this new axis will point upward. By adding this axis, we have formed a **three-dimensional coordinate system**.

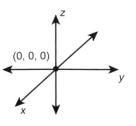

Notice that in forming this coordinate system, we could have chosen the positive *z*-direction to point downward. By instead choosing it to point upward, we have defined a **right-handed system**. This name comes from the so-called "right-hand rule": If you imagine wrapping your right hand around the *z*-axis, with your fingers curling from the positive *x*-direction axis toward the positive *y*-direction, as shown in the figure, then your thumb will point in the positive *z*-direction.

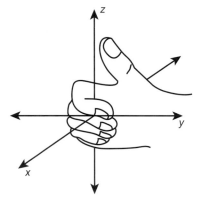

Had we chosen the positive *z*-direction to point downward, we would have formed a left-handed system. In most applications, however, right-handed systems are used.

In a three-dimensional coordinate system, the intersection of the *x*-, *y*-, and *z*-axes creates three intersecting planes, the *xy*-, *yz*- and *xz*-planes. These planes divide the system into eight parts. Each part is called an **octant.** In the **first octant** the values of *x, y,* and *z* are all positive.

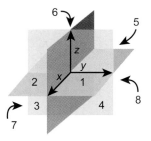

Each point in a three-dimensional coordinate system is associated with a unique **ordered triple** of real numbers having the form (*x, y, z*). Given an ordered triple, you can locate and plot the corresponding point using the following method. First, start at the origin. Then move forward or backward according to the *x*-coordinate. Next, move left or right according to the *y*-coordinate. Finally, move up or down according to the *z*-coordinate.

For example, to plot the point (3, 4, 4), begin at the origin, and then move 3 units in a positive direction (forward) along the *x*-axis. Then move 4 units in a positive direction (right) along the *y*-axis. To help show perspective, you can draw a rectangle in the *xy*-plane having one corner at the origin and another corner at (3, 4, 0). Finally, after drawing the rectangle, move 4 units in a positive direction (up) along the *z*-axis.

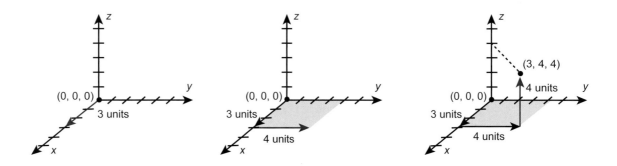

Finding the Distance Between Points

Finding the distance between two points in space is similar to finding the distance between two points on a plane.

Distance Formula for Three Dimensions

The distance d between the points (x_1, y_1, z_1) and (x_2, y_2, z_2) in space is

$$d = \sqrt{(x_2 - x_1)^2 + (y_2 - y_1)^2 + (z_2 - z_1)^2}$$

The following is how you would find the distance between (4, 4, 3) and (5, 0, 6):

$$d = \sqrt{(x_2 - x_1)^2 + (y_2 - y_1)^2 + (z_2 - z_1)^2}$$

$$= \sqrt{(5 - 4)^2 + (0 - 4)^2 + (6 - 3)^2}$$

$$= \sqrt{(1)^2 + (-4)^2 + (3)^2}$$

$$= \sqrt{1 + 16 + 9}$$

$$= \sqrt{26}$$

$$\approx 5.10$$

Finding the Midpoint of a Line Segment

The formula for the midpoint of a line segment in space is an extension of the formula for the midpoint of a line segment in the coordinate plane.

Midpoint Formula in Three Dimensions

The midpoint of a segment with endpoints (x_1, y_1, z_1) and (x_2, y_2, z_2) in space has these coordinates:

$$\left(\frac{x_1 + x_2}{2}, \frac{y_1 + y_2}{2}, \frac{z_1 + z_2}{2} \right)$$

The following is how you would find the midpoint of a line segment with endpoints $(8, 5, 2)$ and $(4, 6, 0)$:

$$\left(\frac{x_1 + x_2}{2}, \frac{y_1 + y_2}{2}, \frac{z_1 + z_2}{2} \right)$$

$$\left(\frac{8 + 4}{2}, \frac{5 + 6}{2}, \frac{2 + 0}{2} \right)$$

$$\left(6, 5\frac{1}{2}, 1 \right)$$

Summary

$\cdots\cdots\cdots\cdots\cdots\cdots\cdots\cdots\cdots\cdots\cdots\cdots\cdots\cdots\cdots\cdots\cdots\cdots\cdots$

- A coordinate system has three axes—an x-axis, a y-axis, and a z-axis.

- Points in space are named by the use of ordered triples.

- The axes form an xy-plane, a yz-plane, and an xz-plane, which divide the coordinate system into octants.

- To find the distance between two points in space, (x_1, y_1, z_1) and (x_2, y_2, z_2), use the Distance Formula for Three Dimensions: $d = \sqrt{(x_2 - x_1)^2 + (y_2 - y_1)^2 + (z_2 - z_1)^2}$.

- The coordinates of the midpoint of a line segment in space with endpoints (x_1, y_1, z_1) and (x_2, y_2, z_2), are $\left(\frac{x_1 + x_2}{2}, \frac{y_1 + y_2}{2}, \frac{z_1 + z_2}{2} \right)$.

Equations of Lines and Planes in Space

OBJECTIVES

▶ Use intercepts to graph a plane in space.

▶ Define trace and find the equations of traces given the equation of a plane.

▶ Use parametric equations to plot lines in space.

▶ Define the equation of a plane in space.

When Lydia went hiking, she took her Global Positioning System (GPS) device and marked the parking lot as her first waypoint. After a few hours of hiking up steep hills and across streams, she realized that she didn't know the way back. She looked at her GPS device, chose the first waypoint, and selected "Go to." Easy! The only problem came when the route took her off the trail and straight into some poison ivy.

The GPS device determined a line between Lydia, who was standing on a steep hill, and the parking lot. If she could imagine the route from her point on the hill down to the parking lot, she would be imagining a line in space.

KEYWORDS
  intercept
  parametric equation
  trace

Equations in Space

On the coordinate plane, an intercept is where a line crosses an axis. In space, an **intercept** is a point where a *plane* crosses an axis. You can use the x-, y-, and z-intercepts to help you sketch a plane in space.

Equation of a Plane in Space

Given that A, B, C, and D are real numbers not all equal to zero and A is nonnegative, the equation of a plane in space is

$$Ax + By + Cz = D$$

Let us sketch the plane $2x + 6y + 4z = 12$.

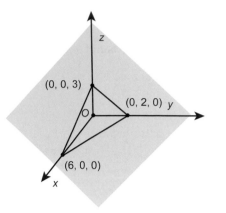

To find the **x-intercept**, substitute 0 for y and z.

$$2x + 6(0) + 4(0) = 12$$
$$2x = 12$$
$$x = 6$$

- The x-intercept is the point (**6, 0, 0**).

To find the **y-intercept**, substitute 0 for x and z.

$$2(0) + 6y + 4(0) = 12$$
$$6y = 12$$
$$y = 2$$

- The y-intercept is the point (**0, 2, 0**).

To find the **z-intercept**, substitute 0 for x and y.

$$2(0) + 6(0) + 4z = 12$$
$$4z = 12$$
$$z = 3$$

- The z-intercept is the point (**0, 0, 3**).

To sketch the plane, plot the intercepts, draw the triangle connecting these points, and shade the plane. Remember—a plane extends forever on all sides.

Similarly, if you have the graph of a plane, you can work backward to find an equation from its intercepts. For example, consider the plane with an x-intercept of (10, 0, 0), a y-intercept of (0, 5, 0), and a z-intercept of (0, 0, 2). Each of these points gives values of x, y, and z that satisfy the equation $Ax + By + Cz = D$. Substitute these values into the equation and solve for A, B, C, and D.

Substituting 10 for x, 0 for y, and 0 for z gives:
$$A(10) + B(0) + C(0) = D$$
$$10A = D$$
$$A = \frac{D}{10}$$

Substituting 0 for x, 5 for y, and 0 for z gives:
$$A(0) + B(5) + C(0) = D$$
$$5B = D$$
$$B = \frac{D}{5}$$

Substituting 0 for x, 0 for y, and 2 for z gives:
$$A(0) + B(0) + C(2) = D$$
$$2C = D$$
$$C = \frac{D}{2}$$

When we put these values back into $Ax + By + Cz = D$ we get:

$$\frac{D}{10}x + \frac{D}{5}y + \frac{D}{2}z = D$$

Because the plane does not pass through the origin, D is not zero, so we can divide both sides by D.

$$\frac{x}{10} + \frac{y}{5} + \frac{z}{2} = 1.$$

Once you multiply the equation by the least common denominator of 10, you have the equation in standard form, where A, B, C, and D are all integers.

$$x + 2y + 5z = 10$$

The plane graphed below has an x-intercept at $(4, 0, 0)$ and a z-intercept at $(0, 0, 1)$, but it has no y-intercept. This plane is parallel to the y-axis.

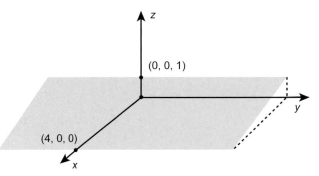

You can still find an equation for this plane by eliminating the y term from the equation $Ax + By + Cz = D$ and solving as before. The equation becomes $Ax + Cz = D$. Substituting $(4, 0, 0)$ and $(0, 0, 1)$ gives:

$$A(4) + C(0) = D \qquad\qquad A(0) + C(1) = D$$
$$4A = D \qquad\qquad\qquad\quad C = D$$
$$A = \frac{D}{4}$$

So $\frac{x}{4} + z = 1$, or $x + 4z = 4$, is an equation for this plane.

Finally, consider the plane shown below. It is perpendicular to the z-axis, so it has neither an x-intercept nor a y-intercept, but it has a z-intercept at $(0, 0, 5)$.

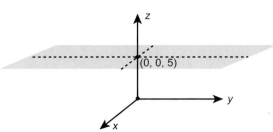

In this case, eliminate both the x- and y-terms from $Ax + By + Cz = D$. This gives $Cz = D$. Substituting $(0, 0, 5)$ gives $5C = D$, which gives $\frac{z}{5} = 1$. This is the same as $z = 5$.

Equations of Traces

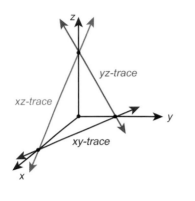

You learned previously that the intersection of the three axes creates three coordinate planes, the xy-, yz-, and xz-planes. A **trace** is the intersection of a plane with one of the coordinate planes. Remember that two planes intersect in a line.

- An xy-trace is the line formed by the intersection of a plane with the xy-plane. The points on an xy-trace all have a z-coordinate of 0, so to find the equation of the trace, you set z to 0 in the equation of the plane.

- A yz-trace is the line formed by the intersection of a plane with the yz-plane. The points on a yz-trace all have an x-coordinate of 0, so to find the equation of the trace, you set x to 0 in the equation of the plane.

- An xz-trace is the line formed by the intersection of a plane with the xz-plane. The points on an xz-trace all have a y-coordinate of 0, so to find the equation of the trace, you set y to 0 in the equation of the plane.

Suppose you want to find the equations of the traces for the plane given by $5x + 6y - 2z = 30$.

To find the xy-trace, substitute 0 for z.

$$5x + 6y - 2(0) = 30$$
$$5x + 6y = 30$$

- The equation of the xy-trace is $5x + 6y = 30$.

To find the yz-trace, substitute 0 for x.

$$5(0) + 6y - 2z = 30$$
$$6y - 2z = 30$$
$$3y - z = 15$$

- The equation of the yz-trace is $3y - z = 15$.

To find the xz-trace, substitute 0 for y.

$$5x + 6(0) - 2z = 30$$
$$5x - 2z = 30$$

- The equation of the xz-trace is $5x - 2z = 30$.

Parametric Equations and Equations of Lines

Parametric equations express variables in terms of another variable, called the *parameter*. The variable t is usually the variable used to represent the parameter. In this book, parametric equations will be used to describe the equation of a line in three dimensions. Later in your math and science studies, you may use parametric equations to represent time and motion.

Suppose we want to graph the line whose parametric equations are as follows:

$$x = 6t + 1 \qquad y = t - 1 \qquad z = 3t + 1$$

First, make a table and choose values for t.

t	x	y	z	ordered triple
0				
1				
2				

Second, substitute a value into each parametric equation to find the corresponding values for x, y, and z.

When $t = 0$,

$$\begin{aligned} x &= 6(0) + 1 & y &= (0) - 1 & z &= 3(0) + 1 \\ &= 1 & &= -1 & &= 1 \end{aligned}$$

When $t = 1$,

$$\begin{aligned} x &= 6(1) + 1 & y &= (1) - 1 & z &= 3(1) + 1 \\ &= 7 & &= 0 & &= 4 \end{aligned}$$

When $t = 2$,

$$\begin{aligned} x &= 6(2) + 1 & y &= (2) - 1 & z &= 3(2) + 1 \\ &= 13 & &= 1 & &= 7 \end{aligned}$$

t	x	y	z	ordered triple
0	1	−1	1	$(1, -1, 1)$
1	7	0	4	$(7, 0, 4)$
2	13	1	7	$(13, 1, 7)$

Finally, plot the points $(1, -1, 1)$, $(7, 0, 4)$, and $(13, 1, 7)$ and draw the line connecting them.

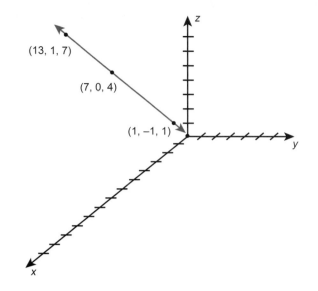

Summary

- In space, an intercept is a point where a plane crosses an axis. The x-, y-, and z-intercepts can help you sketch a plane.

- The equation of a plane is $Ax + By + Cz = D$, where A, B, C, and D are real numbers not all equal to zero and A is nonnegative.

- A trace is the intersection of a plane with one of the coordinate planes.

- Parametric equations express variables in terms of another variable called the parameter.

- You can use parametric equations to graph a line in space.

UNIT 7   Surface Area and Volume

Managers of companies that produce food products must decide how to package their goods, which is not as simple as you might think. Many factors play into the decision of the size and shape of a food container, such as volume—or "How much will it hold?"—and surface area—or "How much will it cost to wrap the item this way?" The managers also consider how the individual containers will fit into larger boxes for shipping to stores. Other considerations are the dimensions of grocery store shelves and whether or not the product is flat on at least one side and can be stacked. And managers never forget about their customers. They think about the appearance of the package and its practicality. They ask, "Will a customer be attracted to this?" and "Is this container easy to carry?"

This unit is about the surface area and volume of solids. As you study each solid, you will recognize some of them as the shapes of certain food containers.

. . . .

UNIT OBJECTIVES

► Identify these figures and their parts: prisms, pyramids, cylinders, cones, and spheres.

► Find the surface area and volume of a prism.

► Find the surface area and volume of a pyramid.

► Find the surface area and volume of a cylinder.

► Find the surface area and volume of a cone.

► Find the surface area and volume of a sphere.

► Transform figures in three-dimensional space.

► Describe how a solid of revolution is generated.

► Identify planes of symmetry for solid figures.

Surface Area and Volume

OBJECTIVES

- ▶ Use formulas to calculate the surface areas of right rectangular prisms and cubes.

- ▶ Use formulas to calculate the volumes of right rectangular prisms and cubes.

- ▶ Find the surface area to volume ratios of figures.

- ▶ Solve problems using the ratio of surface area to volume.

- ▶ Determine the changes in perimeter, area, surface area, and volume in common geometric figures or solids when the value of one or more lengths has changed.

A company that manufactures baseballs wants to find the least expensive way to ship 1000 boxes of its product. There are many ways to decrease the cost of shipping. Two of them involve calculating the surface area and volume of the shipping boxes. If the company can increase the number of baseballs that fit into a shipping box, without increasing the cost of shipping the box, then the company will save money. Similarly, if the same number of baseballs can be shipped in a box with less surface area, the company will save money on the cost of the boxes. The company needs to maximize the volume of the shipping boxes while minimizing the surface area.

KEYWORDS

cube

surface area

surface area to volume ratio

volume

Right Rectangular Prisms

Recall that the **surface area** of a solid is the sum of the areas of the outer surfaces of the figure. You can use the net of a right rectangular prism to develop a formula for finding its surface area. In the sketch below, the area of each face is written as a product of its dimensions (length, width, and height), with the sum written to the right. Notice that there are three pairs of congruent faces.

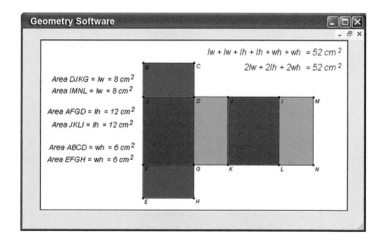

Formula for the Surface Area of a Right Rectangular Prism

The formula for the surface area S of a right rectangular prism of length l, width w, and height h is
$$S = 2lw + 2lh + 2wh$$

The calculator screen below shows how to find the surface area of the prism displayed in the previous sketch.

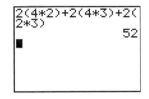

Recall that the **volume** of a solid is the number of unit cubes inside the figure. You can use transformations or isometric dots to draw the prism of the net in the previous sketch. The number of unit cubes that fills the figure is equal to the product of the length, width, and height of the prism.

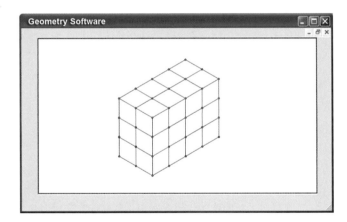

Formula for the Volume of a Right Rectangular Prism

The formula for the volume V of a right rectangular prism of length l, width w, and height h is
$$V = lwh$$

The volume of the prism in the diagram above is $4 \cdot 2 \cdot 3$, or 24 cm³.

Surface Area and Volume of Cubes

When every face of a right rectangular prism is a square, the prism is called a **cube**. Because a square has sides of equal length, we call each side s.

The area of every face of a cube is the same. That means it is possible to find a cube's surface area by multiplying the area of just one face by 6.

Formula for the Surface Area of a Cube

The formula for the surface area S of a cube of side s is
$$S = 6s^2$$

The calculator screen shows how to use this formula to find the surface area of a cube with a side length of 2 units.

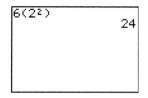

By substituting s for l, w, and h, in the formula for the volume of a right rectangular prism, the formula for the volume a cube can be derived.

Formula for the Volume of a Cube

The formula for the volume V of a cube of side s is
$$V = s^3$$

To cube a number on a graphing calculator, use the caret key (^). The display shows that a cube with a side length of 2 units has a volume of 8 cubic units.

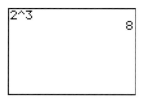

Changing Attributes of Figures

Below, the length of a rectangle is doubled. Notice that by doubling one dimension, the area doubles.

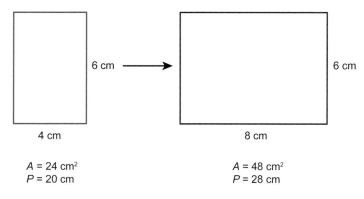

6 cm

4 cm

A = 24 cm²
P = 20 cm

6 cm

8 cm

A = 48 cm²
P = 28 cm

If you tripled one dimension, the area would also triple. Now what if both dimensions were doubled?

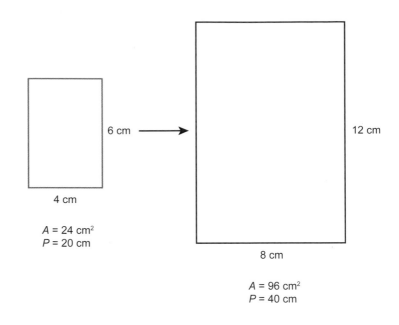

When both dimensions were doubled, the area quadrupled. In other words, it was doubled twice. The perimeter doubled as well.

We now turn to solids. This time, the length of a cube is doubled. The figure becomes a rectangular prism, and the volume doubles as well.

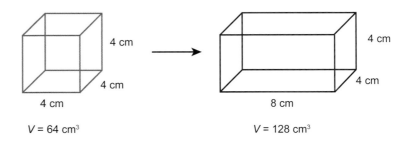

If you tripled one dimension, the volume would triple as well. Consider what happens when two dimensions and three dimensions are doubled.

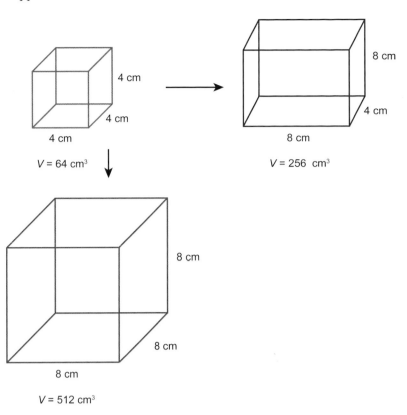

V = 64 cm³

V = 256 cm³

V = 512 cm³

When two dimensions were doubled, the volume quadrupled, or doubled twice. When three dimensions were doubled, the volume became eight times greater, which is the same as being doubled three times.

REMEMBER

A ratio is a comparison of two quantities by division.

Surface Area to Volume Ratio

The **surface area to volume ratio** of a figure plays a large role in the sciences, such as in studying the cooling rates of animals. An animal with a greater surface area to volume ratio will lose heat more quickly than an animal with a smaller surface area to volume ratio.

The ratio is found by simply dividing the surface area of a figure by its volume. The surface area to volume ratio of a cube is:

$$\frac{\text{surface area of a cube}}{\text{volume of a cube}} = \frac{6s^2}{s^3} = \frac{6}{s}$$

Compare the ratios for cubes with side lengths of 2, 3, and 6:

side length of cube, s	2	3	6
surface area to volume ratio of a cube, $\frac{6}{s}$	$\frac{6}{(2)} = 3$	$\frac{6}{(3)} = 2$	$\frac{6}{(6)} = 1$

Notice that as the side length *increased,* the surface area to volume ratio *decreased.* This is true for any solid: The surface area to volume ratio is *inversely proportional* to the size of the solid.

Maximizing Volume and Minimizing Surface Area

A common dilemma in manufacturing is determining how to maximize the volume of a box while minimizing its surface area. In this sketch, the yellow area is a net of a box without a top. You can increase or decrease the length of the sides of the squares in white to change the volume and surface area of the yellow box until you are content with the measurements.

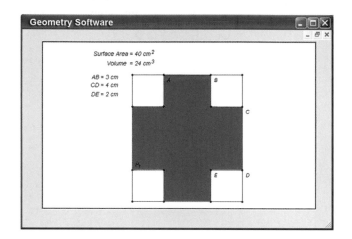

Summary

- The formula for finding the surface area S of a right rectangular prism with length l, width w, and height h is $S = 2lw + 2lh + 2wh$. The formula for the volume V of a right rectangular prism is $V = lwh$.

- A cube is a right rectangular prism whose every face is a square. With a side length s, $S = 6s^2$ and $V = s^3$.

- Doubling one dimension of a plane figure doubles the area; doubling two dimensions quadruples the area and doubles the perimeter.

- Doubling one dimension of a solid figure doubles the volume; doubling two dimensions quadruples the volume; and doubling all three dimensions makes the volume eight times greater.

- The surface area to volume ratio of a solid is inversely proportional to the size of the solid.

Surface Area and Volume of Prisms

OBJECTIVES

▶ Define and identify parts of a prism.

▶ Develop and use the formula for the surface area of a right prism.

▶ Develop and use Cavalieri's Principle.

▶ Find the volume of any prism.

Many buildings are built in the shape of a prism. If an entire building is not a prism, then usually at least a part of it is. Homeowners may calculate surface area when determining how much paint they need to paint the exterior of their home. They may calculate volume when choosing what size air conditioner they need to buy to effectively cool a room. Now you will learn how to calculate the surface area and volume of any prism.

KEYWORDS

altitude   bases of a prism

base area   cross section

height   lateral area

lateral face

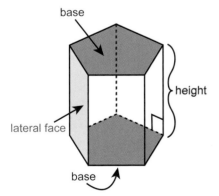

Prisms

Recall that a prism is a polyhedron with two parallel, congruent faces called **bases**. The other faces of the prism are called **lateral faces**. An **altitude** of a prism is a perpendicular line segment that joins the planes of the bases. An altitude may lie inside, on, or outside the solid. The **height** of a prism is the length of an altitude.

Surface Area of a Prism

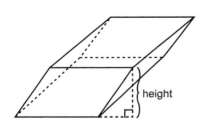

You know that surface area is found by calculating the sum of the areas of every face in a solid. For a right prism, there is another way. As shown in the following sketches, the lateral faces of any right prism "unfold" to form a rectangle. The length of the base of the rectangle equals the perimeter of the base of the prism and the width of the rectangle equals the height. **Lateral area L** denotes this area of the rectangle, because it is the sum of the areas of the lateral faces.

These are nets of two right prisms. The lateral areas are shown in blue.

This is the net of a right rectangular prism.

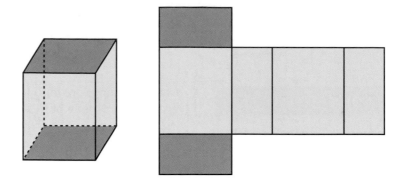

This is the net of a right triangular prism.

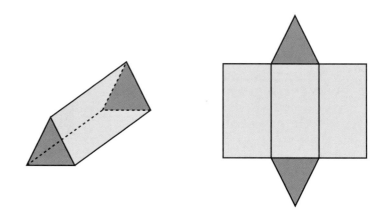

Because the blue areas are rectangles, their areas can be found by multiplying the length, which is the perimeter P of the base, by the width, which is the height h of the prism. The expression is hP. To then find the surface area of the entire prism, add the **base areas** to the expression. Each base area is B, so $2B$ is added to the lateral area, hP.

Formula for Surface Area of a Right Prism

The surface area S of a right prism is the sum of the lateral area L and the areas of the two bases $2B$.

$$S = L + 2B$$

By replacing L with the product of the height h and the perimeter of the base of the prism P, the formula can also be written as

$$S = hP + 2B$$

The calculator screen below shows how to use the formula to find the surface area of the right rectangular prism shown.

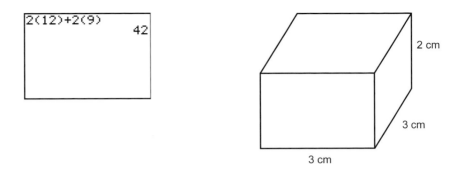

Volume of a Prism

You learned already that the volume of a rectangular prism can be found by using the formula $V = lwh$. Because lw gives the area of the base B, the formula also can be written as $V = Bh$.

The blue regions in the prisms are called **cross sections.** A cross section is the intersection of a plane and a solid. Because the bases are congruent, every cross section in a prism that is parallel to a base is congruent.

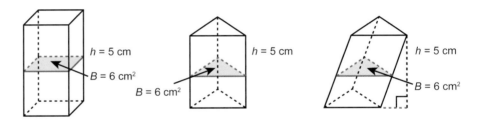

Notice that the areas of the cross sections in all three prisms are the same. The heights are also equal. It stands to reason then that the volumes of all three prisms are equal as well. This is known as Cavalieri's Principle. Cavalieri's Principle is true for any two solids, not just two prisms.

Cavalieri's Principle

If two solids have equal heights and the cross sections formed by every plane parallel to the bases of both solids have equal areas, then the two solids have equal volume.

Therefore, if the volume of the rectangular prism can be found using the formula $V = Bh$, then so can the volume of the others—even the oblique prism!

Formula for the Volume of Any Prism

The volume V of a prism where B is the base area and h is the height is
$$V = Bh$$

To find the volume of the right trapezoidal prism shown, first find the area of a base.

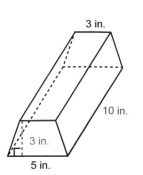

$$B = \frac{1}{2}(b_1 + b_2)h$$

$$= \frac{1}{2}(5 + 3)3$$

$$= \frac{1}{2}(24)$$

$$= 12$$

Then, use the volume formula.

$$V = Bh$$
$$= (12)(10)$$
$$= 120$$

The volume of the right trapezoidal prism is 120 in³.

The screen below shows how to find the volume using a calculator.

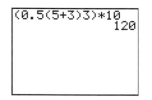

Summary

• An altitude of a prism is a perpendicular line segment that joins the planes of the bases. An altitude may lie inside, on, or outside the solid. The height of a prism is the length of an altitude.

• The surface area S of a right prism is equal to the lateral area L plus two times the area of a base: $S = L + 2B$. Because the lateral area equals the height h of the prism times the perimeter P of the base, the formula for surface area can also be written as $S = hP + 2B$.

• The volume of any prism V is the area of the base B times the height h: $V = Bh$.

Surface Area and Volume of Pyramids

This large Egyptian pyramid is called the Bent Pyramid. Structural problems during its construction caused the builders to change the angle of elevation from 55° to 43° and, in doing so, caused the pyramid to have this unique bent shape.

KEYWORDS

base edge	lateral edge
pyramid	regular pyramid
slant height	vertex of a pyramid

Pyramids

A **pyramid** is a polyhedron with a polygonal base and lateral faces. The faces are triangles, and they meet at a common vertex. The common vertex is called the **vertex of the pyramid.**

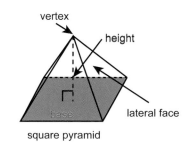

square pyramid

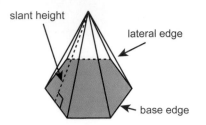

slant height

lateral edge

base edge

regular hexagonal pyramid

Pyramids are classified by the shapes of their bases. So if the base of a pyramid is a square, the pyramid is called a square pyramid. A **regular pyramid** has a base that is a regular polygon and lateral faces that are congruent isosceles triangles.

The edges that form the base of a pyramid are called **base edges.** The remaining edges are **lateral edges.**

The *altitude* of a pyramid is a perpendicular line segment that joins the vertex to the plane of the base. An altitude may lie inside, on, or outside a pyramid. The height of a pyramid is the length of the altitude. The **slant height *l*** is the length of the altitude of a lateral face. A right pyramid's altitude intersects the center of its base; an oblique pyramid's altitude does not.

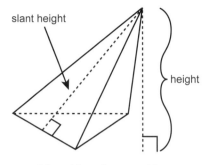

slant height

height

oblique triangular pyramid

Surface Area of a Regular Pyramid

You can study the net of a regular pyramid to determine a formula for its lateral area. Here are two possible nets for a square pyramid. The second shows the lateral faces lined up all in a row.

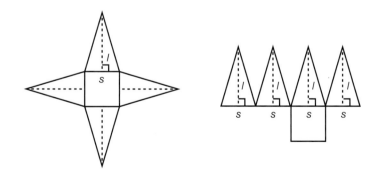

Each of the triangles has an area of $\frac{1}{2} sl$. The sum of the area of all four triangles, which is also called the lateral area L, is four times that:

$$L = 4 \left(\frac{1}{2} sl \right)$$

The expression can be rearranged:

$$L = \frac{1}{2} l(4s)$$

Finally, because $4s$ is the perimeter of the base, it can be replaced with P.

$$L = \frac{1}{2} lP$$

In the sketch below, the measurements in bold show the lateral area of the pyramid to be 4 cm². The first calculation is four times the area of one triangle; the second calculation uses the formula we derived.

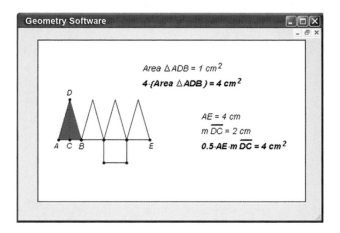

Once you know the lateral area of a pyramid, all you have to do is add on the area of the base B and you will have the total surface area.

Formula for the Surface Area of a Regular Pyramid

The surface area S of a regular pyramid with lateral area L and base area B is

$$S = L + B$$

By replacing L with one-half times the product of the slant height l and the perimeter P of the base of the prism, the formula can also be written as

$$S = \frac{1}{2}lP + B$$

Here is how you can use the formula to find the surface area of the square pyramid below.

$$S = \frac{1}{2}lP + B$$
$$= \frac{1}{2}\,7(32) + (8)^2$$
$$= 112 + 64$$
$$= 176$$

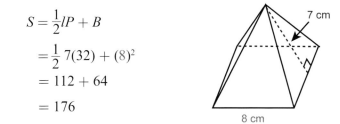

The surface area of the pyramid is 176 cm².

Volume of a Pyramid

This figure shows a square pyramid and a cube. The areas of the bases of each figure, and their heights, are equal. The ratio of the volume of the pyramid to the volume of the cube is $\frac{1}{3}$. Because the volume of the prism can be found using $V = Bh$, the volume of the pyramid can be found by taking one-third of that product.

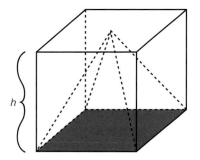

Formula for the Volume of a Pyramid

The formula for the volume of a pyramid V with base area B and height h is

$$V = \frac{1}{3}Bh$$

Cavalieri's Principle tells us that the formula for the volume of a pyramid can be used to find the volume of any pyramid, including oblique pyramids.

It is possible to use the formula to find the volume of the oblique pyramid at left. Begin by finding the area of the base.

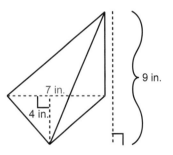

$$B = \frac{1}{2}bh$$

$$= \frac{1}{2}(7)(4)$$

$$= \frac{1}{2}(28)$$

$$= 14$$

Now, use the volume formula.

$$V = \frac{1}{3}Bh$$

$$= \frac{1}{3}(14)(9)$$

$$= 42$$

The volume of the pyramid is 42 in³.

Summary

· ·

- A pyramid is a polyhedron with a polygonal base and lateral faces. The faces are triangles, and they meet at a common vertex.

- The slant height of a pyramid is the length of the altitude of a lateral face of the pyramid.

- A regular pyramid has a base that is a regular polygon and lateral faces that are congruent isosceles triangles.

- The lateral area L of a regular pyramid is one-half of the product of the slant height l of the pyramid and the perimeter P of the base: $L = \frac{1}{2}lP$.

- The surface area S of a regular pyramid is the sum of the lateral area L and the area of the base B: $S = L + B$ or $S = \frac{1}{2}lP + B$.

- The volume V of a pyramid is one-third of the product of the area of the base B and the height h of the pyramid: $V = \frac{1}{3}Bh$.

Surface Area and Volume of Cylinders

Silos are huge cylinders that are used to store food for farm animals. Silos weren't always cylindrical. They began as rectangular containers, but the walls became bowed after a time from the pressure of the contents. Air then entered the silo, which spoiled the food and caused acids to rot the wood. Toward the end of the nineteenth century, cylindrically shaped silos were designed, which solved these problems.

Farmers need to know how to use the formula for the surface area of a cylinder to repaint a silo. They need the formula for the volume of a cylinder to determine how much storage space they have.

KEYWORDS

axis of a cylinder

lateral surface

right cylinder

cylinder

oblique cylinder

Cylinders

A **cylinder** is a solid with two parallel, congruent, circular bases joined by a curved surface. The curved surface of a cylinder is called the **lateral surface.** An *altitude* of a cylinder is a perpendicular line segment that joins the planes of the bases. An altitude may lie inside, on, or outside the cylinder. The *height* of a cylinder is the length of an altitude. The line connecting the centers of the bases is the **axis of the cylinder.** If the axis is an altitude, then the cylinder is a **right cylinder.** Otherwise it is an **oblique cylinder.**

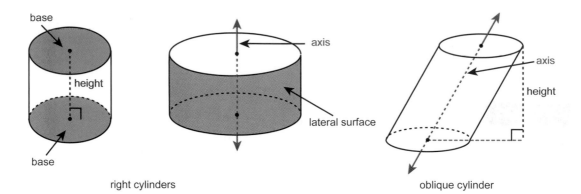

right cylinders   oblique cylinder

Surface Area of a Right Cylinder

As with other solids you have studied, the base area of a cylinder is the area of its base and the lateral area is the area of the lateral surface. The surface area of a right cylinder is the sum of the lateral area and two times the base area.

Take a closer look at the lateral surface. As shown below, the lateral surface can be unrolled to form a rectangle. The length of the rectangle is the circumference of the circle, πd, or $2\pi r$. The height of the rectangle is the height of the cylinder. Therefore the lateral area can be written as $2\pi rh$.

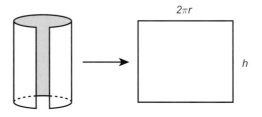

In the sketch below, the radius of the base is 1 centimeter, and the rectangle has a length of $2\pi r$, which is approximately 6.28 centimeters.

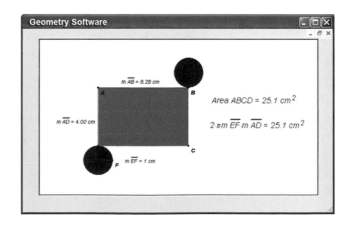

Now that you know that the area of the lateral surface is $2\pi rh$, all you have to do to find the surface area is to add the base areas. Each base is a circle, so the area of one base is πr^2 and the area of both bases is $2\pi r^2$.

Formula for the Surface Area of a Right Cylinder

The surface area S of a right cylinder with lateral area L and base area B is
$$S = L + 2B$$

By replacing L with $2\pi rh$, and B with πr^2, you can write the formula as
$$S = 2\pi rh + 2\pi r^2$$

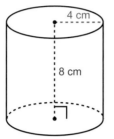

Now use the formula to find the surface area of this cylinder.

$$
\begin{aligned}
S &= 2\pi rh + 2\pi r^2 \\
&= 2\pi(4)(8) + 2\pi(4)^2 \\
&= 64\pi + 32\pi \\
&= 96\pi \approx 302
\end{aligned}
$$

The surface area of the cylinder is approximately 302 cm².

Most calculators have a key for π, although you may need to press another key first. The answer is still an estimate because it has been rounded to fit on the display, but it is a better estimate than using 3.14. Using a precise approximation for π allows us to round our answers to the tenths, hundredths, and even thousandths place with confidence. As shown in the problem above, always save rounding to the last possible step.

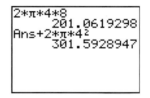

Volume of a Cylinder

You can use Cavalieri's Principle to find the volume of a cylinder because the principle refers to solids, not just to prisms. A cylinder with the same height and cross-sectional areas at every level as a prism will have the same volume as the prism, which can be found using $V = Bh$.

Formula for the Volume of a Cylinder

The formula for the volume V of a cylinder with base area B and height h is
$$V = Bh$$

By replacing B with πr^2, you can write the formula as
$$V = \pi r^2 h$$

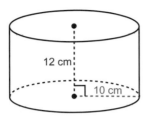

Cavalieri's Principle tells us that the formula for the volume of a cylinder can be used to find the volume of any cylinder, including oblique cylinders.

To find the volume of the cylinder shown at left, substitute 10 for r and 12 for h.

$$V = \pi r^2 h$$
$$= \pi(10)^2(12)$$
$$= 1200\pi$$
$$\approx 3770$$

The volume of the cylinder is approximately 3770 cm³.

Summary

- A cylinder is a solid with two parallel, congruent, circular bases joined by a lateral surface.

- The line connecting the centers of the bases of a cylinder is the axis. If the axis is an altitude then the cylinder is a right cylinder.

- The lateral area of a right cylinder is $2\pi rh$ where r is the radius of the bases and h is the height of the cylinder.

- The surface area of a right cylinder is $L + 2B$, where L is the lateral area and B is the area of a base. The formula for the surface area can be written then as $S = 2\pi rh + 2\pi r^2$.

- The volume of a cylinder is Bh, where B is the area of a base and h is the height of the cylinder. When B is replaced with the expression for the area of a circle, the formula for the volume of a cylinder is written as $V = \pi r^2 h$.

Surface Area and Volume of Cones

OBJECTIVES

▶ Define and identify types of cones and their parts.

▶ Develop and use the formula for the surface area of a right cone.

▶ Develop and use the formula for the volume of a cone.

Many people have claimed to have invented the ice cream cone. What is certain, however, is that after its appearance at the 1904 St. Louis World's Fair, the ice cream cone became extremely popular in the United States. Prior to that time, people ate ice cream out of a dish or a paper cone. New businesses were born, and cone production reached 245,000,000 in 1924. Today machines can produce 150,000 cones a day. Have you ever wondered how much batter it takes to make each cone? How much ice cream does each cone hold? You can answer these types of questions once you understand how to calculate surface area and volume.

KEYWORDS

cone	oblique cone
right cone	sector
slant height of a cone	vertex of a cone

Cones

A **cone** is a solid with a circular base, a **vertex,** and a curved surface. The curved surface of a cone is called the *lateral surface.* The *altitude* of a cone is a perpendicular line segment that joins the vertex to the plane of the base. An altitude may lie inside, on, or outside a cone. The *height* of a cone is the length of the altitude. The **slant height** of a cone is the distance from the vertex to a point on the edge of the base. The line connecting the vertex of a cone to the center of the base is the *axis* of the cone. If the axis is an altitude, then the cone is a **right cone.** Otherwise it is an **oblique cone.**

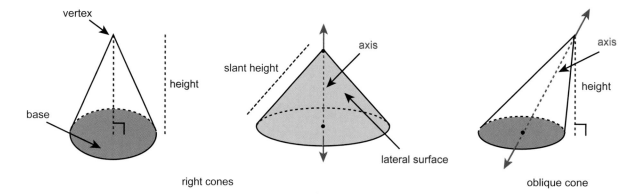

right cones   oblique cone

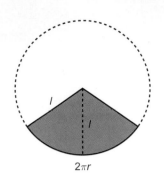

$2\pi r$

Surface Area of a Right Cone

The surface area of a right cone is the sum of the lateral area and the base area.

The lateral surface of a right cone can be unrolled to form the fanlike shape shown as a shaded area. The length of the arc is the circumference, or perimeter, of the base of the cone. The formula for circumference is $2\pi r$. The sides are the slant height l of the cone. Notice that the fanlike shape resembles a triangle. The lateral surface area of a cone is similar to the area of a triangle $\frac{1}{2}bh$, or $\frac{1}{2}(2\pi r)(l)$, which simplifies to πrl.

You can check this conjecture algebraically. The diagram shows that the lateral surface is a **sector** of a circle where the slant height is the radius. Recall that a sector is the region bounded by two radii and part of the circle. The area of a sector is proportional to the area of its circle. You can write and solve the following proportion to find the area of the sector.

$$\frac{\text{area of sector}}{\text{area of circle}} = \frac{\text{length of arc}}{\text{circumference of circle}}$$

$$\frac{x}{\pi l^2} = \frac{2\pi r}{2\pi l}$$

$$2\pi lx = 2\pi^2 rl^2$$

$$x = \frac{2\pi^2 rl^2}{2\pi l} = \pi rl$$

REMEMBER

You can solve a proportion by "cross-multiplying."

Now that you know that the lateral area of a right cone is πrl, all you need to do to find the surface area is add the area of the base. The base is a circle, so the base area is πr^2.

Formula for the Surface Area of a Right Cone

The surface area S of a right cone with lateral area L and base area B is
$$S = L + B$$

By replacing L with πrl, and B with πr^2, the formula can also be written as
$$S = \pi rl + \pi r^2$$

Use the formula to find the surface area of the right cone.

$$
\begin{aligned}
S &= \pi rl + \pi r^2 \\
&= \pi(5)(10) + \pi(5)^2 \\
&= 50\pi + 25\pi \\
&= 75\pi \approx 236
\end{aligned}
$$

The surface area of the cone is approximately 236 ft².

10 ft

5 ft

Volume of a Cone

We can use Cavalieri's Principle to find the volume of a cone. A cone with the same height and cross-sectional areas at every level as a pyramid will have the same volume as the pyramid, which is found by using $V = \frac{1}{3}Bh$.

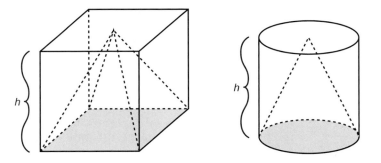

Formula for the Volume of a Cone

The formula for the volume V of a cone with base area B and height h is

$$V = \frac{1}{3}Bh$$

When B is replaced with πr^2, the formula can also be written as

$$V = \frac{1}{3}\pi r^2 h$$

Cavalieri's Principle tells you that the formula for the volume of a cone can be used to find the volume of any cone, including oblique cones.

Find the volume of the cone shown.

$$V = \frac{1}{3}\pi r^2 h$$

$$= \frac{1}{3}\pi (8)^2 (9)$$

$$= 192\pi$$

$$\approx 603$$

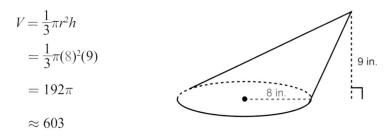

The volume of the cone is approximately 603 in³.

On a calculator, you can divide by three instead of multiplying by one-third. This can be done in one step or two.

or

Summary

- A cone is a solid with a circular base, a vertex, and a curved surface.

- The line connecting the vertex to the center of the base is the axis. If the axis is an altitude then the cone is a right cone.

- The lateral area of a right cone is πrl where r is the radius of the base and l is the slant height of the cone. The base of a cone is a circle with area πr^2.

- The surface area S of a right cone can be found by adding the base area to the lateral area, which results in the formula $S = \pi rl + \pi r^2$.

- The volume V of a cone can be found with the formula $V = \frac{1}{3}\pi r^2 h$.

Surface Area and Volume of Spheres

The surface of a modern soccer ball is made of 20 hexagonal and 12 pentagonal surfaces forming an almost perfect sphere. The formal name of this figure is *truncated icosahedron*. Its more common name is buckyball, named after architect and engineer Buckminster Fuller. He created this design and many variations of it during his long career.

Manufacturers of soccer balls calculate surface area to know how much leather they will need.

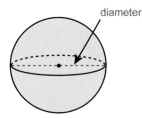

KEYWORDS
annulus
sphere

Spheres

A **sphere** is the set of all points in space that are a given distance from a point called the *center*. The *radius* of a sphere is a line segment joining the center of the sphere and a point on the surface of the sphere.

The *diameter* is a line segment passing through the center that joins two points on the sphere.

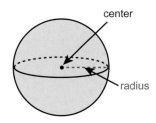

Volume of a Sphere

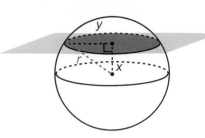

When a plane and a sphere intersect at more than one point, their intersection creates a circle. This figure shows a plane intersecting a sphere at a distance x from the center of the sphere. The radius of the sphere is r. The purple circle created by the intersection has a radius y. You know from the Pythagorean Theorem that $x^2 + y^2 = r^2$.

You can solve this equation for y^2:
$$y^2 = r^2 - x^2$$

The formula for the area of the purple circle is $A = \pi y^2$. Substitute $r^2 - x^2$ for y^2 and distribute.
$$A = \pi y^2$$
$$= \pi(r^2 - x^2)$$
$$= \pi r^2 - \pi x^2$$

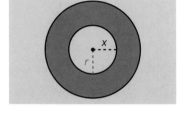

The expression $\pi r^2 - \pi x^2$ can be viewed as the difference between the areas of two circles, one with radius r and one with radius x. In the diagram, there are two concentric circles. The difference is the darker area, which is called the annulus. The **annulus** is the region between two concentric circles.

The area of the purple circle in the sphere has the same area as the annulus. To use Cavalieri's Principle, you will need to find a solid that has cross sections like the concentric circles in the diagram—and it needs to work for *every* cross section of the sphere.

You can use part of a cylinder. The cylinder in the diagram has two identical cones inside it. The bases of the cones are the bases of the cylinder, and the vertices meet in the center of the cylinder. The part of the cylinder you want is the *part that remains when the two cones are removed.*

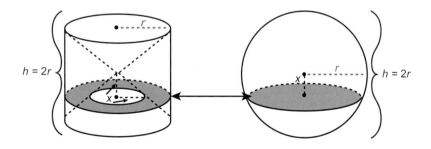

Both the cylinder and the sphere have a height of $2r$. The area of every cross section of the cylinder is equal to every area of the cross section of the sphere at that height. In the diagram above, visualize moving the cross sections up and down the figures, and match the size of the annulus on the left with the corresponding circle on the right—it's larger near the center of the sphere, and smaller near the top and bottom of the sphere.

By Cavalieri's Principle, the two solids have equal volume. To find the volume of the sphere, subtract two cones from the cylinder.

Volume of a Sphere = Volume of a Cylinder − 2(Volume of a Cone)

$$= \pi r^2 h - 2\left(\frac{1}{3}\pi r^2 h\right)$$

$$= \pi r^2 (2r) - 2\left(\frac{1}{3}\pi r^2 r\right)$$

$$= 2\pi r^3 - \frac{2}{3}\pi r^3$$

$$= \frac{4}{3}\pi r^3$$

Formula for the Volume of a Sphere

The formula for the volume V of a sphere with radius r is

$$V = \frac{4}{3}\pi r^3$$

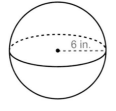

To find the volume of the sphere shown, substitute 6 for r.

$$V = \frac{4}{3}\pi r^3$$

$$= \frac{4}{3}\pi (6)^3$$

$$= 288\pi \approx 905$$

The volume of the sphere is approximately 905 in³.

You can use a calculator to find the volume of a sphere as shown above.

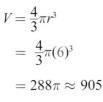

Surface Area of a Sphere

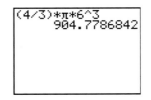

In the introduction you learned that a soccer ball closely resembled a sphere. It's not a sphere because the surface is not perfectly smooth—but what if the polygons on the surface were much, much smaller? What if they were so small you almost couldn't see them? As the polygons on the surface got smaller, the ball would more closely resemble a true sphere.

Now imagine covering the surface of a sphere with tiny congruent polygons. If a line segment were to join each polygon's vertex with the center of the sphere, the sphere could actually be viewed as a collection of tiny congruent pyramids. The height of each pyramid would be the radius of the sphere. Therefore, the volume of each pyramid would be $\frac{1}{3}Br$. You could write the volume of the sphere as the sum of the volumes of all the pyramids:

$$V = \frac{1}{3}Br + \frac{1}{3}Br + \frac{1}{3}Br + \dots$$

With *n* pyramids, you could write it more neatly like this:

$$V = n\frac{1}{3}Br$$

You could also rearrange the equation to be

$$V = \frac{1}{3}r(nB)$$

This is convenient because *nB* is the total area of the bases of the pyramids that form the surface area *S* of the sphere.

$$V = \frac{1}{3}r(S)$$

Use algebra to solve the equation for *S*.

$$S = \frac{3V}{r}$$

Now substitute the formula for the volume of a sphere for *V* and simplify.

$$S = \frac{3\left(\frac{4}{3}\pi r^3\right)}{r} = 4\pi r^2$$

Formula for the Surface Area of a Sphere

The formula for the surface area *S* of a sphere with radius *r* is
$$S = 4\pi r^2$$

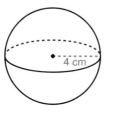

To find the surface area of the sphere shown, substitute 4 for *r*.

$$\begin{aligned} S &= 4\pi r^2 \\ &= 4\pi(4)^2 \\ &= 64\pi \approx 201 \end{aligned}$$

The surface area of the sphere is approximately 201 cm².

Summary

· ·

- A sphere is the set of all points in a space that are a given distance from a point called the center. The line segment joining the center of the sphere to any point on the edge of the sphere is called the radius.

- The annulus is the region between two concentric circles.

- The formula for the volume *V* of a sphere with radius *r* is $V = \frac{4}{3}\pi r^3$.

- The formula for the surface area *S* of a sphere with radius *r* is $S = 4\pi r^2$.

Three-Dimensional Symmetry

A torus is a doughnut-shaped figure. It is created by rotating a circle about a line. This torus was created by rotating a circle about a vertical line.

The size of the "doughnut hole" depends upon how far away the circle is placed from the line it is rotated about. When the circle is placed so that the diameter of the circle is on the line, a sphere is created instead.

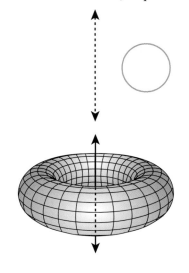

KEYWORDS

axis of revolution

plane of symmetry

solid of revolution

Transformations in Three Dimensions

RECONNECT TO THE BIG IDEA

Remember
Isometric transformations—translations, rotations, reflections—do not change distances, angles, or areas.

Recall that a transformation is a one-to-one mapping between two sets of points. In three-dimensional space, points, lines, two-dimensional figures, and three-dimensional solids can be reflected across a plane, translated along a line, or rotated about an axis. As in two-dimensional transformations, transformations in three dimensions preserve the size and shape of the original figure.

Reflections

In two dimensions, a figure can be reflected across a line. In three dimensions, a figure can be reflected across a plane. To reflect across planes formed by the intersection of the axes, use the following ordered-triple rules.

to reflect across the...	use...
xy-plane	$(x, y, z) \rightarrow (x, y, -z)$
xz-plane	$(x, y, z) \rightarrow (x, -y, z)$
yz-plane	$(x, y, z) \rightarrow (-x, y, z)$

For example, to reflect the blue line segment below across the yz-plane, use the ordered-triple rule $(x, y, z) \rightarrow (-x, y, z)$.

$$(5, 0, 6) \rightarrow (-5, 0, 6)$$
$$(4, 4, 3) \rightarrow (-4, 4, 3)$$

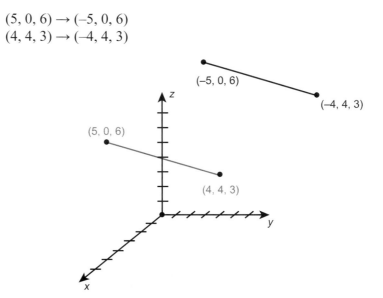

Translations

To translate a solid in space, add or subtract an amount to or from each coordinate.

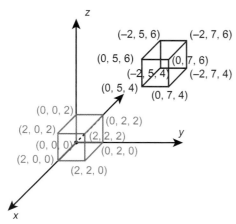

For example, you can translate the blue cube two units back, five units right, and four units up with the ordered-triple rule $(x, y, z) \rightarrow (x - 2, y + 5, z + 4)$.

$(2, 0, 0) \rightarrow (0, 5, 4)$	$(2, 2, 0) \rightarrow (0, 7, 4)$
$(0, 2, 0) \rightarrow (-2, 7, 4)$	$(0, 0, 0) \rightarrow (-2, 5, 4)$
$(2, 0, 2) \rightarrow (0, 5, 6)$	$(2, 2, 2) \rightarrow (0, 7, 6)$
$(0, 2, 2) \rightarrow (-2, 7, 6)$	$(0, 0, 2) \rightarrow (-2, 5, 6)$

Solids of Revolution

A **solid of revolution,** sometimes called a solid of rotation, is a three-dimensional solid that can be generated by rotating a plane figure about a line that lies in the same plane as the figure. The line is called the **axis of revolution.**

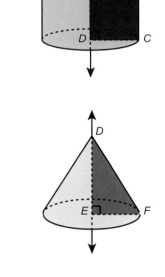

You can generate this cylinder by rotating rectangle *ABCD* about line *AD*. $\overline{AD}$ is the axis of the cylinder, and because it is a right cylinder, *AD* is the height. $\overline{BC}$ is the side of the rectangle that creates the lateral surface. $\overline{AB}$ and $\overline{DC}$ generate the bases of the cylinder.

You can generate this cone by rotating $\triangle DEF$ about line *DE*. $\overline{DE}$ is the axis of the cone, and because it is a right cone, *DE* is the height. $\overline{DF}$ is the side of the triangle that creates the lateral surface. $\overline{EF}$ generates the base of the cone.

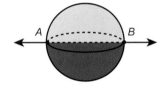

The cylinder and cone were created with polygons, but you can rotate other shapes around a line as well. If you rotated a semicircle about line *AB*, you would form a sphere.

Planes of Symmetry

Just as a line of symmetry in a two-dimensional figure divides the figure into two parts that are mirror images of each other, a **plane of symmetry** divides a three-dimensional figure into two congruent parts.

A *tetrahedron* is a solid made up of four congruent triangular faces. It has six planes of symmetry. Each plane contains one of the six edges and bisects the opposite face. One plane of symmetry is shown below.

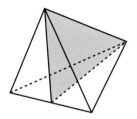

A cube has nine planes of symmetry. Three are shown below.

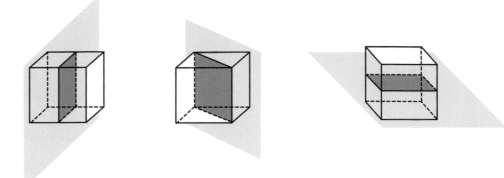

The tetrahedron and cube have a finite number of planes of symmetry. However, solids created by rotating a plane figure about a line have an infinite number of planes of symmetry that contain the axis of revolution. They may also have planes of symmetry that do not contain the axis of revolution.

Let's look back at the torus. Along with the infinite number of planes that contain the axis, it also has a plane of symmetry perpendicular to the axis of revolution, as shown in the far right illustration.

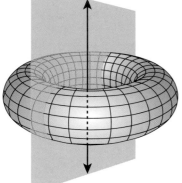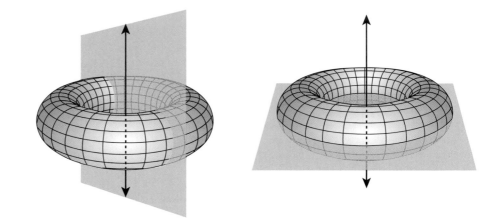

The torus has a plane of symmetry perpendicular to the axis of revolution because the plane figure that was rotated to create it, a circle, has a horizontal line of symmetry. Because a right triangle does not have a horizontal line of symmetry, a cone only has planes of symmetry that contain the axis of revolution.

line of symmetry   not a line of symmetry

Summary

· ·

- Just like two-dimensional transformations, transformations in three dimensions preserve the size and shape of the original figure.

- A solid of revolution is a three-dimensional solid that can be generated by rotating a plane figure about a line that lies in the same plane as the figure. Cylinders, cones, and spheres are solids of revolution.

- A plane of symmetry divides a three-dimensional figure into two congruent parts.

- Solids created by rotating a plane about a line have an infinite number of planes of symmetry.

UNIT 8   Similar Shapes

When a drafter creates a scale drawing of a building, he or she is creating a drawing reduced enough to fit onto a standard-size piece of paper but that still has the same proportions as the actual building. A scale drawing serves many purposes. It allows designers to simulate changes without having to change anything in the actual building. It helps the builder construct the building the way the architect envisioned and lets electricians and plumbers know where lines and pipes should go. Also, scale drawings are kept as a record of what was done, which can be used during times of renovation.

Scale drawings are also used to represent very small objects, like cells and molecules. These drawings are often used for educational purposes.

A scale drawing has a scale factor, which is a ratio that tells how much larger or smaller the drawing is when compared to the actual object. In this unit, you will use scale factors in working with similar polygons.

. . . .

UNIT OBJECTIVES

► Determine and use scale factors.

► Identify and draw contractions and expansions.

► Determine whether two polygons are similar.

► Write and solve proportions to find missing measures in similar polygons.

► Use the triangle similarity postulate and theorems to prove two triangles are similar.

► Use triangle similarity to measure distances indirectly.

► Find and use ratios for areas of similar figures.

► Find and use ratios for volumes of similar solids.

Dilations and Scale Factors

Earlier, you learned about perspective drawings such as a one-point perspective drawing, which uses a point on the horizon. Another way to construct a one-point perspective drawing is by a transformation called a dilation, which uses a center of dilation. To find out what those new words mean, read on!

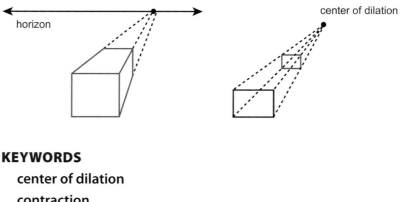

KEYWORDS
  center of dilation
  contraction
  dilation
  expansion
  scale factor

Dilations

Dilations are transformations that change the size, but not the shape, of a figure. Therefore, dilations are not isometries, which preserve both size and shape. In a dilation, the lines connecting each point on the pre-image with its corresponding point on the image intersect at a point called the **center of dilation C.** The center of dilation can lie on, inside, or outside the figure. In the illustrations of this topic, the pre-image will always be shown in red and the image in blue.

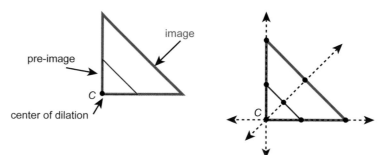

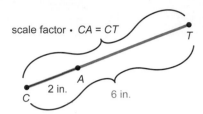

scale factor · CA = CT

C 2 in. A 6 in. T

The **scale factor** *t* of a dilation is the ratio of the length of a side on the image to the length of its corresponding side on the pre-image. In the diagram, $\overline{CA}$ is the pre-image and $\overline{CT}$ is the image. For this dilation, the scale factor is 3.

$$\frac{CT}{CA} = \frac{6}{2} = 3$$

Look at the figures showing the pre-image $\overline{AB}$ and the image $\overline{RT}$. $\overline{AB}$ is first *enlarged* by a scale factor of 2 and then by a scale factor of −2. In both cases, the length of the image $\overline{RT}$ is twice the length of $\overline{AB}$, but the images appear on opposite rays.

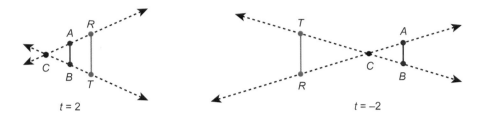

t = 2   t = −2

In the next set of illustrations, the pre-image $\overline{AB}$ is *reduced* by a scale factor of $\frac{1}{2}$ and then by a scale factor of $-\frac{1}{2}$. In both figures, the length of the image $\overline{RT}$ is one-half the length of $\overline{AB}$, but again, the image points that result from applying a positive scale factor are on rays opposite the image points that result from applying a negative scale factor.

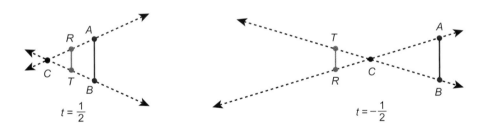

$t = \frac{1}{2}$ $t = -\frac{1}{2}$

If the image is larger than the pre-image, then the dilation is an expansion. An **expansion** is a dilation for which the absolute value of the scale factor, as related to the pre-image, is greater than 1. If the image is smaller than the pre-image, then the dilation is a contraction. A **contraction** is a dilation for which the absolute value of the scale factor, as related to the pre-image, is between 0 and 1.

You can construct dilations with geometry software. You will need to identify the center of dilation and the scale factor. The first sketch shows a dilation of $\frac{1}{4}$; the second shows a dilation of $-\frac{1}{4}$. Both dilations have their center of dilation at point *C*.

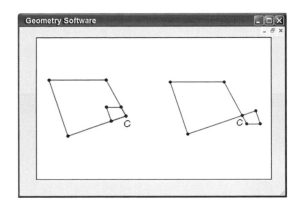

Notice that a negative scale factor dilation has the same effect as a positive scale factor dilation that is then rotated by 180°.

Dilations on the Coordinate Plane

You can perform dilations on the coordinate plane just as you can perform other transformations on the plane. To determine image points when the center of dilation is the origin, you multiply both coordinates of the pre-image points by a scale factor. That is, each point (x, y) dilated with a scale factor of t becomes (tx, ty).

To dilate trapezoid $ABCD$ with a scale factor of $-\frac{1}{2}$, you multiply the x- and y-coordinates by $-\frac{1}{2}$.

$A(2, 2) \rightarrow A'(-1, -1)$
$B(4, 6) \rightarrow B'(-2, -3)$
$C(8, 6) \rightarrow C'(-4, -3)$
$D(10, 2) \rightarrow D'(-5, -1)$

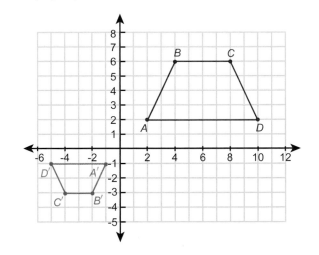

You can also perform dilations on a grid using geometry software. In the sketch below, the origin is the center of dilation.

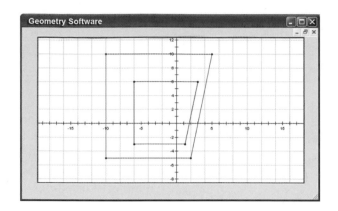

To determine the scale factor used in the dilation, find the lengths of corresponding sides. Use the lengths to form the ratio $\dfrac{\text{image length}}{\text{pre-image length}}$.

If possible, choose a pair of sides whose lengths can be determined easily. Here, we choose the left side of each figure: $\dfrac{15}{9}$.

This reduces to a scale factor of $\dfrac{5}{3}$.

Summary

· ·

- A dilation is a transformation that enlarges or reduces a figure. The shape stays the same, but the size changes.

- The scale factor of a dilation is the ratio of the length of a side on the image to the length of its corresponding side on the pre-image.

- A dilation is an expansion if the absolute value of the scale factor is greater than 1.

- A dilation is a contraction if the absolute value of the scale factor is between 0 and 1.

- If a point (x, y) is dilated with a scale factor of t and the center of dilation is at the origin, then the image of the point is (tx, ty).

Similar Polygons

OBJECTIVES

▶ Define proportion and the parts of a proportion.

▶ Describe the properties of similarity and proportions.

▶ Use properties of similar figures to solve problems.

▶ Define *similar* and similar polygons.

▶ Determine if polygons are similar and find missing lengths in similar polygons.

Ms. Stewart sees a garden in a magazine and decides she wants her garden to have the same shape. However, the dimensions given in the magazine are too large to re-create in her little backyard. Luckily for her, she knows geometry. She can use properties of similar polygons to find dimensions that will create a perfect, scaled-down version of the garden in the magazine.

KEYWORDS

extremes

proportion

similar ($\sim$)

means

proportional

Proportions

REMEMBER

Division by 0 is undefined. So, in the ratio $\frac{a}{b}$, b cannot be 0.

A ratio compares two quantities by division. That's why we often write the ratio of two quantities—for example, a and b—as the fraction $\frac{a}{b}$, although the ratio can also be written as $a : b$. An equation that states that two ratios are equal is called a **proportion.** Proportions are usually written in the form $\frac{a}{b} = \frac{c}{d}$, although they can also be written as $a : b = c : d$.

In the proportion $\frac{a}{b} = \frac{c}{d}$, b and c are called the **means** and a and d are called the **extremes.** These definitions are easier to remember when you write the proportion with colons, because the extremes are on the exterior and the means are in the middle.

$$a : b = c : d$$

When you clear the fractions of a proportion by multiplying both sides by the product of the denominators, you find that the product of the means equals the product of the extremes:

$$\frac{a}{b} = \frac{c}{d}$$

$$(bd)\frac{a}{b} = \frac{c}{d}(bd)$$

$$da = cb$$

This property is known as the Means-Extremes Product Property. It is one of the most useful of the properties of proportions.

Properties of Proportions

The Means-Extremes Product Property If $\frac{a}{b} = \frac{c}{d}$, then $ad = bc$, given that b and d are not 0.

The Reciprocal Property If $\frac{a}{b} = \frac{c}{d}$, then $\frac{b}{a} = \frac{d}{c}$, given that a, b, c, and d are not 0.

The Exchange Property If $\frac{a}{b} = \frac{c}{d}$, then $\frac{a}{c} = \frac{b}{d}$, given that b, c, and d are not 0.

The Add-One Property If $\frac{a}{b} = \frac{c}{d}$, then $\frac{a+b}{b} = \frac{c+d}{d}$, given that b and d are not 0.

You can solve proportions by using the above properties. For example, to solve the proportion

$$\frac{3}{2.25} = \frac{4}{x},$$

use the Means-Extremes Product Property.

$$\frac{3}{2.25} = \frac{4}{x}$$

$$3x = 2.25(4)$$
$$3x = 9$$
$$x = 3$$

This is sometimes called cross-multiplying.

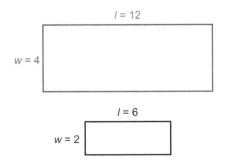

The corresponding sides of figures are said to be **proportional** if every pair of sides has the same ratio. The corresponding sides of these two rectangles are proportional because the ratio of the widths is equal to the ratio of the lengths:
$\frac{4}{2} = \frac{12}{6}$.

You can tell the ratios are equal because the product of the means equals the product of the extremes (both are 24). Also, both ratios reduce to 2.

You may have noticed that the large rectangle can be thought of as the image of the small rectangle after a dilation with a scale factor of 2. That is no coincidence. The corresponding sides of dilated figures are always proportional, and their ratios are always equal to the scale factor that was used in creating them.

Similar Polygons

When figures are **similar,** they are the same shape but they aren't necessarily the same size. The symbol $\sim$ means *is similar to*. The triangles shown here are similar. In similarity statements, we write the corresponding vertices in the same order, just as we do for congruence statements.

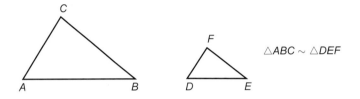

Because images created by dilations are proportional to their pre-images, we say that two polygons are similar if and only if one is congruent to the image of the other by a dilation. If the ratios of the corresponding sides of these triangles equal 2, then $\triangle ABC$ is congruent to the image of $\triangle DEF$ after a dilation with a scale factor of 2.

The following postulate gives another definition of similar polygons.

POSTULATE 8-1   Polygon Similarity Postulate

Two polygons are similar if and only if there is a correspondence between their angles and their sides so that all corresponding angles are congruent and all corresponding sides are proportional.

In this diagram showing two trapezoids, $DEFG \sim QRST$. Because it is given that the two polygons are similar, the Polygon Similarity Postulate lets you write the following statements.

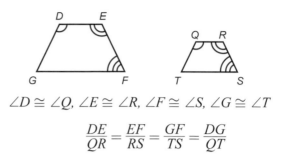

$\angle D \cong \angle Q$, $\angle E \cong \angle R$, $\angle F \cong \angle S$, $\angle G \cong \angle T$

$$\frac{DE}{QR} = \frac{EF}{RS} = \frac{GF}{TS} = \frac{DG}{QT}$$

You can use the Polygon Similarity Postulate to determine if these two triangles are similar.

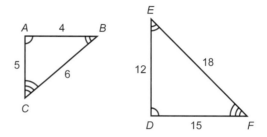

The corresponding angles are congruent, and you are given the side lengths. You can check to see if the corresponding sides are proportional.

$$\frac{AB}{DE} = \frac{4}{12} = \frac{1}{3} \qquad\qquad \frac{AC}{DF} = \frac{5}{15} = \frac{1}{3} \qquad\qquad \frac{BC}{EF} = \frac{6}{18} = \frac{1}{3}$$

The sides are proportional, therefore, $\triangle ABC \sim \triangle DEF$.

You can also use the Polygon Similarity Postulate to find unknown lengths in similar figures. In this diagram, $ABCD \sim EFGH$.

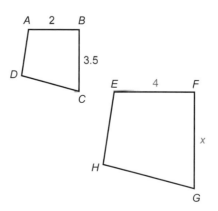

You can set up a proportion with corresponding sides and solve for x.

$$\frac{2}{4} = \frac{3.5}{x}$$

$$2x = 14$$

$$x = 7$$

Summary

- A ratio compares two quantities by division. A proportion is a statement that says two ratios are equal.

- In a proportion, the product of the means equals the product of the extremes.

- Similar figures are the same shape, but they aren't necessarily the same size.

- Two figures are similar if and only if one is congruent to the image of the other by a dilation.

- The Polygon Similarity Postulate states that two polygons are similar if and only if there is a correspondence between their angles and their sides so that all corresponding angles are congruent and all corresponding sides are proportional.

Triangle Similarity

When you look closely at this quilt block, you may wonder how many similar triangles it contains. How can you find out? You could measure every angle and side of each triangle, but that would take a lot of time. If you have the right mathematical tools, you could save some time and effort.

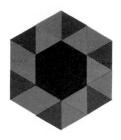

Proving Triangles Similar

You can always prove that two triangles are similar by using the Polygon Similarity Postulate, which means proving that the three pairs of corresponding angles are congruent and the three pairs of corresponding sides are proportional. But it is easier to use one of the postulates or theorems for triangle similarity, which require fewer comparisons.

Suppose you were told to draw a triangle with one angle with a measure of 60° and another angle with a measure of 70°. By the Triangle Sum Theorem, you would have no choice but to make the third angle measure 50°. Now you can make many different triangles with those angle measurements—some small, some large—but they will all have the same shape. This is the idea behind the next postulate.

RECONNECT TO THE BIG IDEA

Remember The sum of the measures of the angles of a triangle is 180°.

POSTULATE 8-2 Angle-Angle (AA) Similarity Postulate

If two angles of one triangle are congruent to two angles of another triangle, then the triangles are similar.

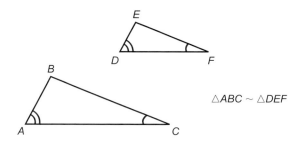

$\triangle ABC \sim \triangle DEF$

When you draw two triangles whose corresponding sides are proportional, the corresponding angles are automatically congruent. So the next theorem states that another way to prove triangles similar is to check the ratios of the sides.

THEOREM 8-1   Side-Side-Side (SSS) Similarity Theorem

If the three sides of one triangle are proportional to the three sides of another triangle, then the triangles are similar.

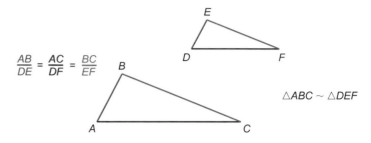

$$\frac{AB}{DE} = \frac{AC}{DF} = \frac{BC}{EF}$$

$\triangle ABC \sim \triangle DEF$

Recall that once two sides and the included angle of a triangle are drawn, there is only one way to complete the triangle. Once you know that the corresponding sides of two triangles are proportional and the included angles are congruent, the lengths of the third side cannot vary. This leads to the last combination that proves triangles similar.

THEOREM 8-2   Side-Angle-Side (SAS) Similarity Theorem

If two sides of one triangle are proportional to two sides of another triangle and if their included angles are congruent, then the triangles are similar.

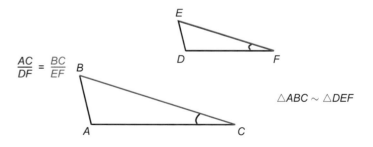

$$\frac{AC}{DF} = \frac{BC}{EF}$$

$\triangle ABC \sim \triangle DEF$

We can use the triangle similarity postulate and the two similarity theorems in two-column proofs.

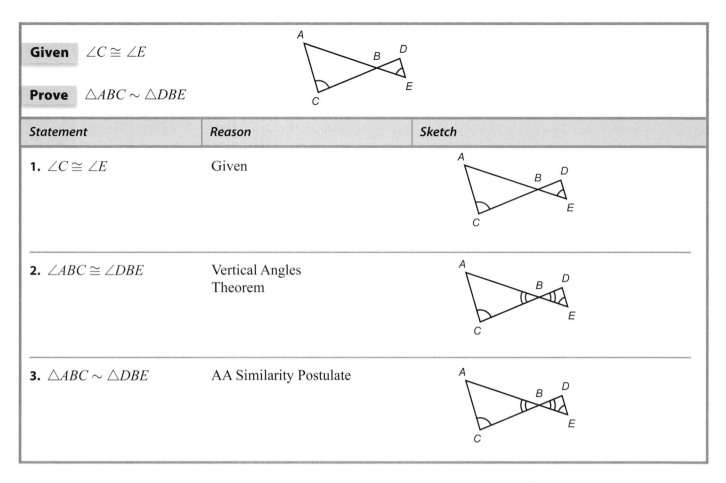

Statement	Reason	Sketch
1. $\angle C \cong \angle E$	Given	
2. $\angle ABC \cong \angle DBE$	Vertical Angles Theorem	
3. $\triangle ABC \sim \triangle DBE$	AA Similarity Postulate	

We can also use the postulate and the two theorems to determine if two triangles are similar.

Determine if $\triangle DEF \sim \triangle DYZ$.

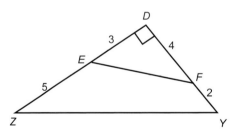

Start by separating and reflecting the triangles so they have the same orientation.

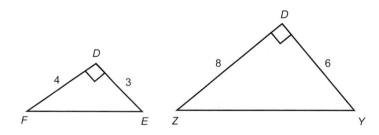

RECONNECT TO THE BIG IDEA

Remember Proportional reasoning is the key to similarity.

You have measurements for two sides and for the included angle. The included angles are congruent, so we check to see if the corresponding sides are proportional.

$$\frac{DF}{DZ} = \frac{4}{8} = \frac{1}{2} \text{ and } \frac{DE}{DY} = \frac{3}{6} = \frac{1}{2}$$

The ratios are equal. The sides are proportional. $\triangle DEF \sim \triangle DYZ$ by the SAS Similarity Theorem.

Summary

- You can prove similarity in triangles by showing that certain combinations of corresponding angles are congruent and corresponding sides are proportional.

- Two triangles are congruent if the following are true:

  - Two angles of one triangle are congruent to two angles of the other triangle (AA Similarity).

  - The three sides of one triangle are proportional to the three sides of the other triangle (SSS Similarity).

  - Two sides of one triangle are proportional to two sides of the other triangle and their included angles are congruent (SAS Similarity).

Side-Splitting Theorem

OBJECTIVES

▶ Prove and use the Side-Splitting Theorem.

▶ Describe the nature and purpose of corollaries.

▶ Use the Two-Transversal Proportionality Corollary to solve problems.

In many cities in the United States, several streets run parallel to each other, at least through the downtown part of the city. This makes it easy for out-of-towners (and local residents) to get around, especially in New York City, where numbered streets run east and west, and avenues (mostly numbered) run north and south. Yet a map of the city is not a perfect grid because some roads will run diagonal to other roads.

All these streets and avenues can be viewed as intersecting lines and transversals and, as you might suspect, geometry can help you find the missing distances between them.

KEYWORD

corollary

Proving the Side-Splitting Theorem

The Side-Splitting Theorem is an often-used theorem that tells what relationships exist when a line is drawn through a triangle such that it is parallel to one of the sides of the triangle. Before we prove the theorem, recall the Add-One Property of Proportions: If $\frac{a}{b} = \frac{c}{d}$, then $\frac{a+b}{b} = \frac{c+d}{d}$, given that b and d are not 0. The converse is: If $\frac{a+b}{b} = \frac{c+d}{d}$, and b and d are not 0, then $\frac{a}{b} = \frac{c}{d}$.

We can show algebraically why the converse is true:

$$\frac{a+b}{b} = \frac{c+d}{d}$$

$$\frac{a}{b} + \frac{b}{b} = \frac{c}{d} + \frac{d}{d}$$

$$\frac{a}{b} + 1 = \frac{c}{d} + 1$$

$$\frac{a}{b} = \frac{c}{d}$$

This property can help us prove the Side-Splitting Theorem.

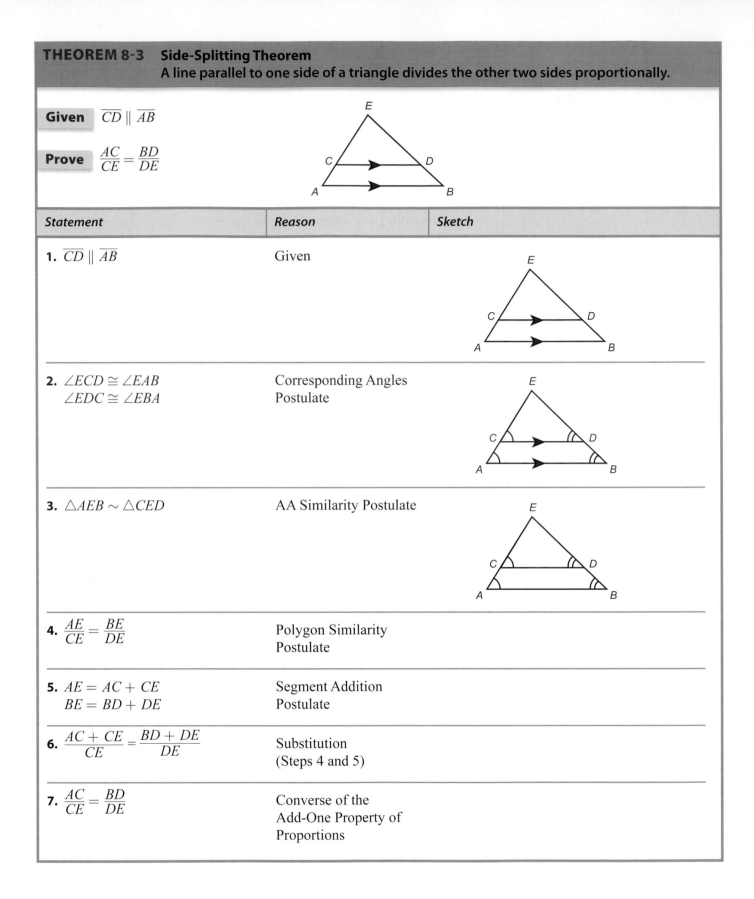

THEOREM 8-3 Side-Splitting Theorem
A line parallel to one side of a triangle divides the other two sides proportionally.

Given $\overline{CD} \parallel \overline{AB}$

Prove $\dfrac{AC}{CE} = \dfrac{BD}{DE}$

Statement	Reason	Sketch
1. $\overline{CD} \parallel \overline{AB}$	Given	
2. $\angle ECD \cong \angle EAB$ $\angle EDC \cong \angle EBA$	Corresponding Angles Postulate	
3. $\triangle AEB \sim \triangle CED$	AA Similarity Postulate	
4. $\dfrac{AE}{CE} = \dfrac{BE}{DE}$	Polygon Similarity Postulate	
5. $AE = AC + CE$ $BE = BD + DE$	Segment Addition Postulate	
6. $\dfrac{AC + CE}{CE} = \dfrac{BD + DE}{DE}$	Substitution (Steps 4 and 5)	
7. $\dfrac{AC}{CE} = \dfrac{BD}{DE}$	Converse of the Add-One Property of Proportions	

Use the Side-Splitting Theorem to find the value of x.

$$\frac{5}{7} = \frac{4}{x}$$

$$5x = 28$$

$$x = 5.6$$

A **corollary** is a proposition that follows directly from a postulate or theorem and can be easily proven. The Two-Transversal Proportionality Corollary follows from the Side-Splitting Theorem.

COROLLARY 8-1   Two-Transversal Proportionality Corollary

Three or more parallel lines divide two intersecting transversals proportionally.

Corollary 8-1 follows directly from the Side-Splitting Theorem because intersecting transversals across several lines form several triangles. In this diagram we have $\triangle CXD$, $\triangle BXE$, and $\triangle AXF$.

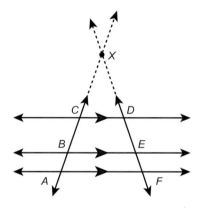

Two of the proportions you can write are $\frac{CB}{CA} = \frac{DE}{DF}$ and $\frac{AC}{FD} = \frac{AB}{FE}$.

Summary

The Side-Splitting Theorem and the Two-Transversal Proportionality Corollary help you find lengths when parallel lines are intersected by transversals.

- Side-Splitting Theorem: A line parallel to one side of a triangle divides the other two sides proportionally.

- Two-Transversal Proportionality Corollary: Three or more parallel lines divide two intersecting transversals proportionally.

Indirect Measurement and Additional Similarity Theorems

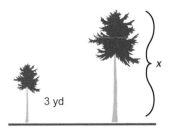

3 yd

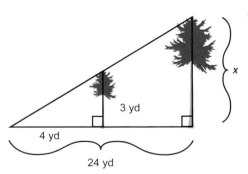

3 yd

4 yd

24 yd

Mount Kilimanjaro is a mountain in Africa whose highest point reaches an amazing 19,340 feet. Measuring a mountain, or even a tall tree, is no easy feat. You can't just line up a ruler next to it and make a reading. And climbing trees is very dangerous. Therefore, very tall objects must be measured *indirectly*. One way to measure a mountain is by measuring barometric pressure and using mathematical formulas. Trees can be measured by forming similar triangles with the ground and another nearby vertical object—such as a smaller tree or a person.

KEYWORD

indirect measurement

Indirect Measurement

Long distances and tall heights are sometimes difficult to measure directly. For example, measuring a tall tree with a tape measure is just about impossible. But there are other ways to measure tall objects, and these use a technique called **indirect measurement.** Indirect measurement is used to measure quantities that cannot be measured by comparing to a standard ruler or scale.

Suppose there are two trees in a yard. The shorter one is 3 yards tall and can be measured with a tape measure. The other cannot be measured directly.

Although the taller tree can't be measured directly, its shadow can. You can make similar triangles by measuring each tree's shadow at the same time of day. The shadow of the taller tree is 24 yards long and the shadow of the shorter tree is 4 yards long. Using the AA Similarity Postulate, you can view the measures as corresponding sides of two similar, overlapping triangles.

You can find the height of the taller tree by writing and solving a proportion:

$$\frac{3}{x} = \frac{4}{24}$$

$$4x = 72$$

$$x = 18$$

The taller tree is 18 yards tall.

More Triangle Similarity Theorems

Similar triangles have proportional parts. The following theorems state these relationships.

THEOREM 8-4	Proportional Altitudes Theorem
	If two triangles are similar, then their corresponding altitudes have the same ratio as their corresponding sides.

Given $\triangle ABC \sim \triangle EFG$
$\overline{BD}$ and $\overline{FH}$ are altitudes.

Prove $\dfrac{BD}{FH} = \dfrac{AB}{EF}$

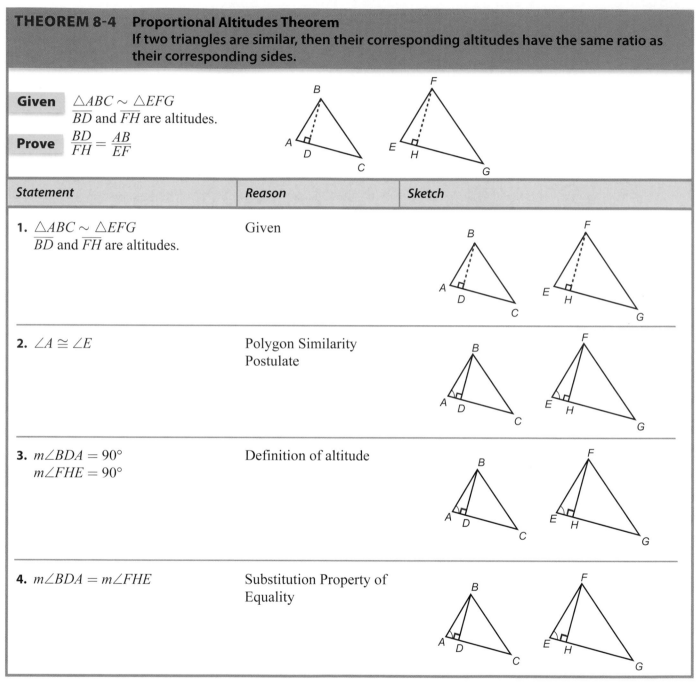

Statement	Reason	Sketch
1. $\triangle ABC \sim \triangle EFG$ $\overline{BD}$ and $\overline{FH}$ are altitudes.	Given	
2. $\angle A \cong \angle E$	Polygon Similarity Postulate	
3. $m\angle BDA = 90°$ $m\angle FHE = 90°$	Definition of altitude	
4. $m\angle BDA = m\angle FHE$	Substitution Property of Equality	

proof continued on next page

Statement	Reason	Sketch
5. $\angle BDA \cong \angle FHE$	Angle Congruence Postulate	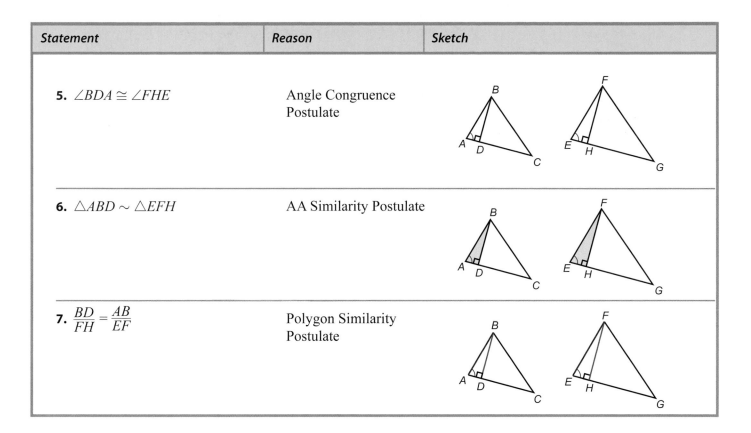
6. $\triangle ABD \sim \triangle EFH$	AA Similarity Postulate	
7. $\dfrac{BD}{FH} = \dfrac{AB}{EF}$	Polygon Similarity Postulate	

THEOREM 8-5 Proportional Angle Bisectors Theorem

If two triangles are similar, then their corresponding angle bisectors have the same ratio as their corresponding sides.

$\triangle JKL \sim \triangle MNP$

$\dfrac{JH}{MQ} = \dfrac{JK}{MN}$

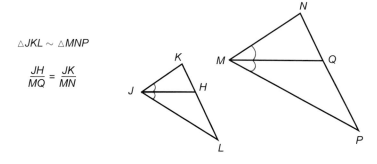

THEOREM 8-6 Proportional Medians Theorem

If two triangles are similar, then their corresponding medians have the same ratio as their corresponding sides.

$\triangle ABC \sim \triangle DEF$

$\dfrac{BG}{EH} = \dfrac{AB}{DE}$

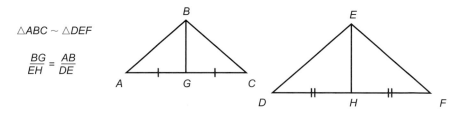

THEOREM 8-7 Proportional Segments Theorem

An angle bisector of a triangle divides the opposite side into two segments that have the same ratio as the other two sides.

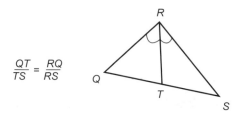

$$\frac{QT}{TS} = \frac{RQ}{RS}$$

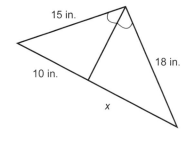

To find the value of x in this diagram, set up and solve a proportion.

$$\frac{10}{x} = \frac{15}{18}$$

$$15x = 180$$

$$x = 12$$

The length of the missing side is 12 inches.

Summary

- Indirect measurement measures a quantity that is difficult to measure by comparing it to a standard ruler or scale. It is possible to use triangle similarity to measure distances indirectly.

- If two triangles are similar, then the following is true:

  - Their corresponding altitudes have the same ratio as their corresponding sides.

  - Their corresponding medians have the same ratio as their corresponding sides.

  - Their corresponding angle bisectors have the same ratio as their corresponding sides.

- If a ray bisects an angle of a triangle, then it divides the opposite side into two segments that have the same ratio as the other two sides.

Area and Volume Ratios

OBJECTIVES

- ► Find and use ratios between areas of similar polygons.
- ► Find and use ratios between volumes of similar solids.
- ► Use ratios for areas, volumes, and weights to find missing dimensions and measures.

Suppose you want to make a large banner similar to this flag to hang in your room. You will need to know how much fabric to buy for the banner. First, you need to know how many times larger than the flag the banner will be. Then you can use what you will learn here about the ratios of the areas of similar figures to find out exactly how much fabric to buy.

KEYWORD

similar solids

Areas of Similar Polygons

The rectangles shown here are similar. The ratio of the corresponding sides is $\frac{6}{2} = \frac{12}{4} = 3$. The area of each rectangle is shown.

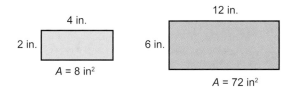

4 in.

2 in.

$A = 8 \text{ in}^2$

12 in.

6 in.

$A = 72 \text{ in}^2$

Find the ratio of the areas: $\frac{72}{8} = 9$. The ratio of the areas, 9, is the square of the ratio of the corresponding sides, 3. This is true for the areas of all similar figures.

REMEMBER

The ratio of the corresponding sides is the scale factor t.

Ratios of Areas of Similar Polygons

If two similar polygons have the lengths of their corresponding sides in the ratio of t, then the ratio of their areas is t^2.

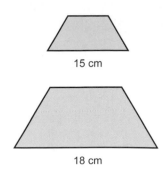

15 cm

18 cm

These two trapezoids are similar. The area of the larger trapezoid is 144 cm². To find the area of the smaller trapezoid, first find the ratio of the lengths of the corresponding sides: $\frac{15}{18} = \frac{5}{6}$. Square it to get the ratio of the areas: $\frac{25}{36}$. Finally, write and solve a proportion.

$$\frac{25}{36} = \frac{x}{144} \quad \longrightarrow \text{smaller trapezoid} \\ \longrightarrow \text{larger trapezoid}$$

$$36x = 3600$$

$$x = 100$$

The area of the smaller trapezoid is 100 cm².

Suppose that the area of a triangle is 20 m² and the area of a similar triangle is 320 m². To find the ratio of the corresponding sides:

Divide to find the ratio of the areas: $\frac{320}{20} = 16$.

Then take the square root: $\sqrt{16} = 4$.

The ratio of the corresponding sides is 4.

Volumes of Similar Solids

Like similar figures, **similar solids** have the same shape, and all the corresponding dimensions are proportional.

These rectangular prisms are similar. The ratio of the corresponding dimensions is $\frac{6}{2} = \frac{6}{2} = \frac{9}{3} = 3$. The volume of each prism is shown.

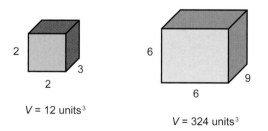

2   2   3
V = 12 units³

6   6   9
V = 324 units³

Find the ratio of the volumes: $\frac{324}{12} = 27$. The ratio of the volumes, 27, is the cube of the ratio of the corresponding dimensions, 3. This principle is true for the volumes of all similar solids.

Ratios of Volumes of Similar Solids

If two similar solids have corresponding dimensions
in the ratio of t, then the ratio of their volumes is t^3.

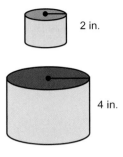

2 in.

4 in.

These two cylinders are similar. The volume of the smaller cylinder is
4.5π in^3. To find the volume of the larger cylinder, first find the ratio of the
heights: $\frac{2}{4} = \frac{1}{2}$. Cube it to get the ratio of the volumes: $\frac{1}{8}$. Finally, write and
solve a proportion.

$$\frac{1}{8} = \frac{4.5\pi}{x} \quad \longrightarrow \text{smaller cylinder}$$
$$\longrightarrow \text{larger cylinder}$$

$$x = 36\pi$$

The volume of the larger cylinder is 36π in^3.

Suppose that the volume of a cone is 200π m^3 and the volume of a similar
cone is $25,000\pi$ m^3. To find the ratio of the corresponding dimensions:

Divide to find the ratio of the volumes: $\frac{25,000}{200} = 125$.

Then take the cube root: $\sqrt[3]{125} = 5$.

The ratio of the corresponding dimensions is 5.

Relationships also exist between the height of a solid and its volume, area,
and cross-sectional area; between the height of a solid and its volume; and
between the volume of a solid and the pressure inside the solid. These relationships play critical roles in the sciences.

Suppose a block weighs 20 pounds. A second block, made of the same material, is similar to the first block, and its length is 3 times the length of the first
block. How much does the second block weigh?

Similar to volume, the ratio of the weights is t^3. Because the second block
is three times as long as the first, the ratio of the lengths is $\frac{1}{3}$. Cube it to get
the ratio of the weights: $\frac{1}{27}$. Then set up and solve a proportion.

$$\frac{1}{27} = \frac{20}{x} \quad \longrightarrow \text{smaller block}$$
$$\longrightarrow \text{larger block}$$

$$x = 540$$

The weight of the larger block is 540 pounds.

Summary

- The ratio of the areas of similar figures is the square of the ratio of their corresponding sides.

- Similar solids have the same shape, and all of their corresponding dimensions are proportional.

- The ratio of the volumes of similar solids is the cube of the ratio of their corresponding dimensions.

- The ratio of the weights of similar solids is the cube of the ratio of their corresponding dimensions.

UNIT 9   Circles

Look around whatever room you are in and notice all the circular shapes. Perhaps you see a clock with a circular face, the rim of a cup or glass, or the top of a fishbowl. Circles have perfect symmetry, and their beauty can be seen in the design of many everyday objects. Ralph Waldo Emerson, in his essay called *Circles,* described them wonderfully:

> "The eye is the first circle; the horizon which it forms is the second; and throughout nature this primary figure is repeated without end."

But circles are not used just for beauty; they are used for function as well. Imagine the problems we would have with square Ferris wheels or rectangular bicycle wheels.

In this unit, you will study the parts of a circle and the relationships that exist among lines, angles, and arcs in circles.

. . . .

UNIT OBJECTIVES

► Identify parts of a circle.

► Find the degree measure of an arc and the length of an arc.

► Solve problems involving inscribed angles, central angles, and intercepted arcs.

► Use theorems involving secants, tangents, chords, and arcs to solve problems.

► Use theorems involving secant segments, tangent segments, and chord segments to find missing measures.

► Write the equation of a circle and sketch a circle from its equation.

Chords and Arcs

OBJECTIVES

▶ Define and name a circle and the parts of a circle.

▶ Identify and define major arcs, minor arcs, and semicircles.

▶ Find the degree measure and length of an arc.

▶ Use the Chords and Arcs Theorem and its converse.

A Ferris wheel can help you understand the parts of a circle. Think of each car as a point on a circle. All the cars are the same distance away from the center of the Ferris wheel. A support beam that connects a car to the center is a radius. The car that is at the very bottom and the car that is at the very top are endpoints of a diameter. You will soon learn more circle terms that can be associated with the Ferris wheel.

KEYWORDS

arc	arc length	center
central angle	chord	circle
diameter	inscribed angle	major arc
minor arc	radius	semicircle

Parts of Circles

A **circle** is the set of all points in a plane that are equidistant from a given point in the plane called the **center.** Circles are named by their center. The circle shown is circle M.

A **radius** of a circle is a segment that connects the center to a point on the circle. In circle M, $\overline{MN}$, $\overline{MQ}$, and $\overline{MP}$ are radii. A **diameter** of a circle is a segment that connects two points on the circle and passes through the center. In circle M, $\overline{NP}$ is a diameter.

A **chord** connects any two points on the circle. In circle M, $\overline{ST}$ and $\overline{NP}$ are chords. Notice that $\overline{NP}$ is also a diameter. Diameters are chords that pass through the center of a circle.

An **arc** is an unbroken part of a circle. It is formed by two points on the circle and the continuous part of the circle that lies between the two points. If the endpoints of an arc are also the endpoints of a diameter, the arc is a **semicircle.**

REMEMBER

All radii of a circle have equal length.

All diameters of a circle have equal length.

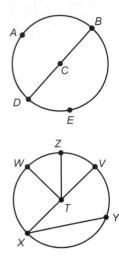

Arcs smaller than a semicircle are called **minor arcs** and are named by only their endpoints. To avoid confusion, semicircles and **major arcs,** arcs larger than a semicircle, include another point between the endpoints. In circle C, $\overset{\frown}{AB}$ is a minor arc. We could also name it $\overset{\frown}{BA}$. If we want the arc that has endpoints A and B but is not shaded red, we could write $\overset{\frown}{ADB}$ or $\overset{\frown}{BEA}$. Two semicircles in circle C are $\overset{\frown}{DAB}$ and $\overset{\frown}{DEB}$.

When we place chords and radii on a circle, we create angles. The type of angle formed depends on the location of the vertex. If the vertex is the center of the circle, we call the angle a **central angle**. If the vertex is on the circle, we call it an **inscribed angle.** In circle T, $\angle XTW$, $\angle WTZ$, and $\angle ZTV$ are central angles and $\angle VXY$ is an inscribed angle.

Angle and Arc Measures

The degree measure of an arc is the same as the degree measure of its corresponding central angle. In circle C,

$$m\angle ACB = 90° \text{ so } m\overset{\frown}{AB} = 90°$$

Since a complete rotation measures $360°$,
$$\begin{aligned} m\overset{\frown}{AXB} &= 360° - m\overset{\frown}{AB} \\ &= 360° - 90° \\ &= 270° \end{aligned}$$

Arc Measures

- The degree measure of a minor arc is the measure of its central angle.

- The degree measure of a major arc is $360°$ minus the degree measure of its central angle.

- The degree measure of a semicircle is $180°$.

Two circles are congruent if they have the same radius. Two arcs are said to be congruent if they are on congruent circles and have the same angle measure.

The circumference of a complete circle is $2\pi r$. Because an arc is part of a circle, **arc length** is a part of the circumference of a circle. It can be found by writing the part as a fraction over $360°$ and multiplying by the circumference.

Formula for Arc Length

The length L of an arc, where m is the degree measure of the arc and r is the radius, is

$$L = \left(\frac{m}{360°}\right) 2\pi r$$

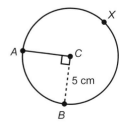

To find the length of $\overset{\frown}{AB}$:

$$\begin{aligned} L &= \left(\frac{90°}{360°}\right) 2\pi(5) \\ &= \left(\frac{1}{4}\right) 10\pi \\ &= 2.5\pi \approx 7.85 \end{aligned}$$

The arc length of $\overset{\frown}{AB}$ is about 7.85 cm.

Chords and Arcs

Chords and arcs have the following relationship.

THEOREM 9-1	**Chords and Arcs Theorem**
	In a circle or in congruent circles, the arcs of congruent chords are congruent.

Given   Circle C with $\overline{RS} \cong \overline{DF}$

Prove $\overset{\frown}{RS} \cong \overset{\frown}{DF}$

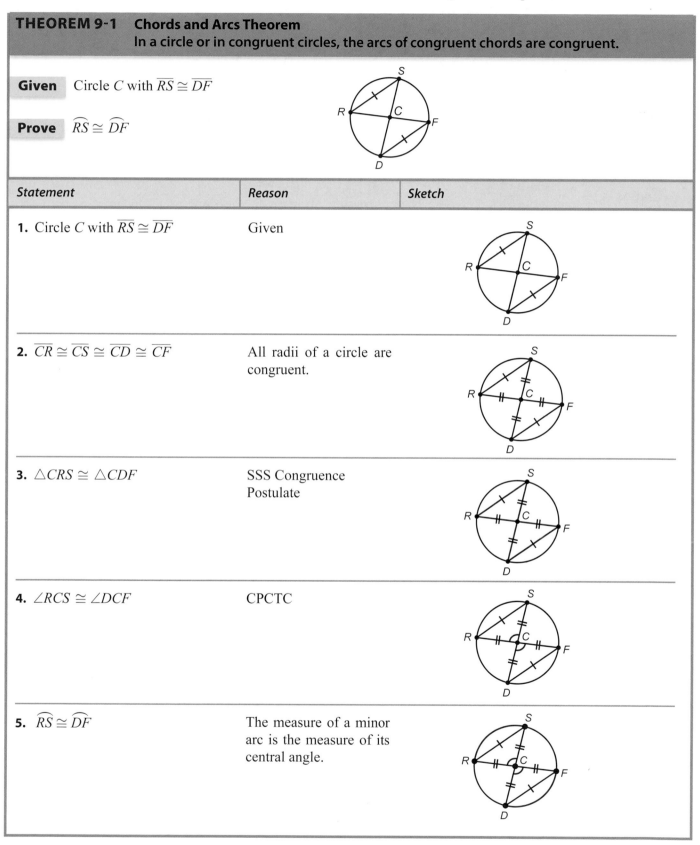

Statement	Reason	Sketch
1. Circle C with $\overline{RS} \cong \overline{DF}$	Given	
2. $\overline{CR} \cong \overline{CS} \cong \overline{CD} \cong \overline{CF}$	All radii of a circle are congruent.	
3. $\triangle CRS \cong \triangle CDF$	SSS Congruence Postulate	
4. $\angle RCS \cong \angle DCF$	CPCTC	
5. $\overset{\frown}{RS} \cong \overset{\frown}{DF}$	The measure of a minor arc is the measure of its central angle.	

The converse of the Chords and Arcs Theorem is also true.

THEOREM 9-2   **Converse of the Chords and Arcs Theorem**

In a circle or in congruent circles, the chords of congruent arcs are congruent.

Summary

- A circle is the set of all points in a plane that are a given distance from a center point.

- A segment that connects the center to the circle is a radius. A segment that connects two points on the circle is a chord. If the chord passes through the center, the chord is also a diameter.

- An arc is part of a circle. A minor arc is less than half the circle, a major arc is more than half the circle, and a semicircle is half the circle.

- A central angle of a circle is an angle whose vertex is the center of the circle. An inscribed angle of a circle has its vertex on the circle.

- The degree measure of a minor arc is the measure of its central angle. The degree measure of a major arc is the difference between the measure of the minor arc and 360°. All semicircles measure 180°.

- The length L of an arc is a fraction of the circle's circumference, or $L = \left(\dfrac{m}{360°}\right) 2\pi r$, where r is the radius of the circle and m is the measure of the central angle.

- In a circle or in congruent circles, the arcs of congruent chords are congruent. Also, the chords of congruent arcs are congruent.

Tangents to Circles

OBJECTIVES

▶ Define and identify tangents and secants.

▶ Use the Tangent Theorem and its converse.

▶ Develop and use the Radius and Chord Theorem.

▶ Show that the perpendicular bisector of a chord passes through the center of a circle.

Look at the train wheel on the track below. If you consider the wheel to be a circle and the track it rolls on to be a line, then you can say that the track is *tangent* to the train wheel. The wheel always touches the track at just one point.

KEYWORDS

point of tangency

secant

tangent

Tangents and Secants

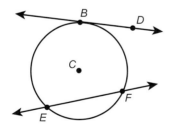

A **tangent** to a circle is a line in the plane of the circle that intersects the circle in exactly one point. In the diagram at left, $\overleftrightarrow{BD}$ is tangent to circle C. You can also say $\overleftrightarrow{BD}$ is a tangent of circle C. The point where the circle and the tangent intersect is called the **point of tangency.** Point B is the point of tangency in this figure.

A **secant** is a line that intersects a circle in two points. $\overleftrightarrow{EF}$ is a secant of circle C. Notice that secant $\overleftrightarrow{EF}$ contains chord $\overline{EF}$.

Tangent Theorems

THEOREM 9-3   The Tangent Theorem

A line that is tangent to a circle is perpendicular to a radius of the circle at the point of tangency.

The sketch below shows that tangent $\overleftrightarrow{BC}$ is perpendicular to radius $\overline{AB}$ at the point of tangency, B.

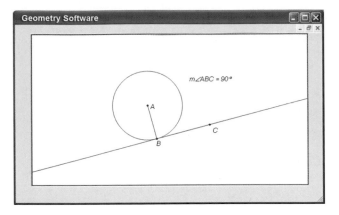

You can use the Tangent Theorem to find angle measures.

In the diagram, $\overleftrightarrow{AB}$ is tangent to circle C and $m\angle ABD = 55°$.

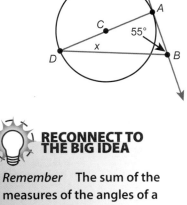

The Tangent Theorem tells us that $m\angle DAB = 90°$. The sum of the measures of the angles of a triangle is $180°$ so,

$$m\angle DAB + m\angle ABD + m\angle BDA = 180°$$
$$90° + 55° + x = 180°$$
$$145° + x = 180°$$
$$x = 35°$$

The Converse of the Tangent Theorem is also true.

THEOREM 9-4   The Converse of the Tangent Theorem

A line that is perpendicular to a radius of a circle at its endpoint on the circle is tangent to the circle.

You can use the Converse of the Tangent Theorem to determine if a line is tangent to a circle.

To determine if $\overleftrightarrow{RS}$ is a tangent to circle C, you use the Converse of the Pythagorean Theorem to see if $\triangle CRS$ is a right triangle.

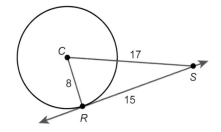

$$c^2 = a^2 + b^2$$
$$17^2 = 8^2 + 15^2$$
$$289 = 64 + 225$$
$$289 = 289$$

$\triangle CRS$ is a right triangle with right angle CRS. So, $\overline{CR} \perp \overleftrightarrow{RS}$ and $\overleftrightarrow{RS}$ is tangent to circle C.

Radii and Chords

There is a relationship between the radius of a circle and a chord of that circle.

THEOREM 9-5	The Radius and Chord Theorem
	A radius that is perpendicular to a chord of a circle bisects the chord.

Given Circle A with radius $\overline{AR} \perp \overline{PQ}$

Prove $\overline{AR}$ bisects $\overline{PQ}$.

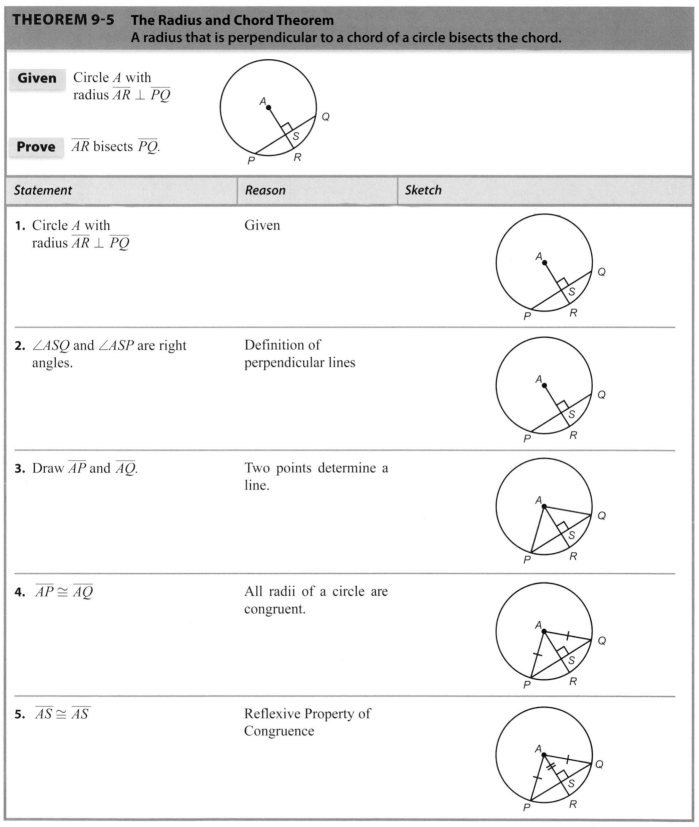

Statement	Reason	Sketch
1. Circle A with radius $\overline{AR} \perp \overline{PQ}$	Given	
2. $\angle ASQ$ and $\angle ASP$ are right angles.	Definition of perpendicular lines	
3. Draw $\overline{AP}$ and $\overline{AQ}$.	Two points determine a line.	
4. $\overline{AP} \cong \overline{AQ}$	All radii of a circle are congruent.	
5. $\overline{AS} \cong \overline{AS}$	Reflexive Property of Congruence	

proof continued on next page

Statement	Reason	Sketch
6. $\triangle ASP \cong \triangle ASQ$	HL Congruence Theorem	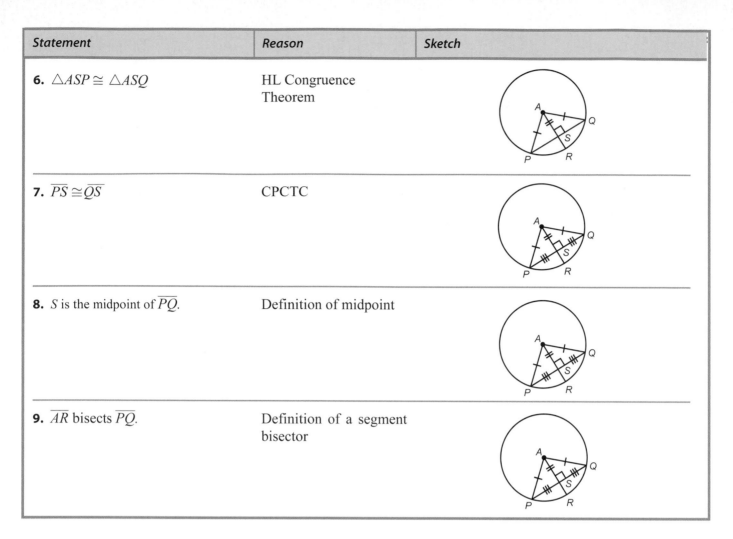
7. $\overline{PS} \cong \overline{QS}$	CPCTC	
8. S is the midpoint of $\overline{PQ}$.	Definition of midpoint	
9. $\overline{AR}$ bisects $\overline{PQ}$.	Definition of a segment bisector	

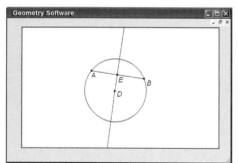

The perpendicular bisector of any chord is a diameter of the circle and therefore will pass through the center of the circle. In the sketch shown, the perpendicular bisector $\overleftrightarrow{DE}$ of chord $\overline{AB}$ was constructed. $\overleftrightarrow{DE}$ passes through the center of the circle.

Summary

- A tangent to a circle is a line in the plane of the circle that intersects the circle in exactly one point. The point where the circle and the tangent intersect is called the point of tangency.

- A secant is a line that intersects a circle in two points. Every secant contains a chord.

- The Tangent Theorem states that a line that is tangent to a circle is perpendicular to a radius of a circle at the point of tangency. The Converse of the Tangent Theorem is also true.

- A radius that is perpendicular to a chord of a circle bisects the chord.

- The perpendicular bisector of a chord passes through the center of the circle because it is always a diameter of the circle.

Inscribed Angles and Arcs

OBJECTIVES

► Define and identify inscribed angles and their intercepted arcs.

► Use the Inscribed Angle Theorem and its corollaries to find measures of inscribed angles and intercepted arcs.

String art is created by hammering nails into a board in a geometric shape and wrapping and arranging string around the nails to create a symmetrical design. Though the string forms a series of line segments, our eyes see circular shapes. You begin creating the design that is shown by constructing sets of inscribed angles. These form the points around the circumference of the design.

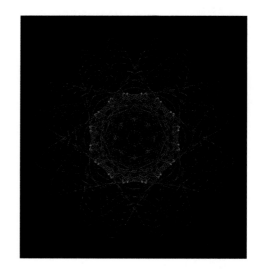

KEYWORDS

inscribed angle

intercepted arc

Inscribed Angles and Intercepted Arcs

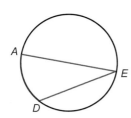

An **inscribed angle** of a circle has its vertex on the circle and its sides are chords of the circle. $\angle AED$ is an inscribed angle of the circle at left.

We call $\overarc{AD}$ the **intercepted arc** of $\angle AED$. We can also say that $\angle AED$ *intercepts* $\overarc{AD}$. The endpoints of an intercepted arc are the points where the sides of the inscribed angle meet the circle.

The next theorem describes how the measure of the inscribed angle relates to the measure of its intercepted arc.

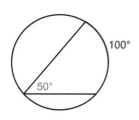

THEOREM 9-6 Inscribed Angle Theorem

An angle inscribed in a circle has a measure that equals one-half the measure of its intercepted arc.

There are three cases to consider when proving the theorem.

Case 1: The center of the circle lies on a side of the inscribed angle.

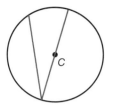

Case 2: The center of the circle lies inside the inscribed angle.

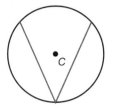

Case 3: The center of the circle lies outside the inscribed angle.

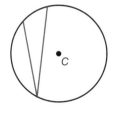

Here is the proof of Case 1.

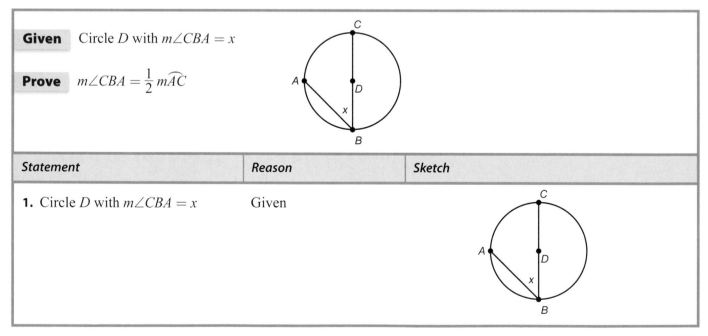

Given   Circle D with $m\angle CBA = x$

Prove $m\angle CBA = \frac{1}{2} m\widehat{AC}$

Statement	Reason	Sketch
1. Circle D with $m\angle CBA = x$	Given	

proof continued on next page

Statement	Reason	Sketch
2. Draw $\overline{AD}$.	Two points determine a line.	
3. $\overline{AD} \cong \overline{BD}$	All radii of a circle are congruent.	
4. $\triangle ADB$ is isosceles.	Definition of isosceles triangle	
5. $\angle ABD \cong \angle BAD$	Isosceles Triangle Theorem	
6. $m\angle ADC = 2x$	Exterior Angle Theorem	
7. $m\widehat{AC} = 2x$	The degree measure of a minor arc is the measure of its central angle.	
8. $m\angle CBA = \frac{1}{2} m\widehat{AC}$	Substitution Property of Equality	

Recall that a semicircle measures 180°. An inscribed angle that intercepts a semicircle also measures 90°. This is the next corollary.

COROLLARY 9-1   Right-Angle Corollary

An angle that is inscribed in a semicircle is a right angle.

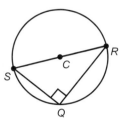

Every arc has many inscribed angles.

COROLLARY 9-2   Arc-Intercept Corollary

Two inscribed angles that intercept the same arc have the same measure.

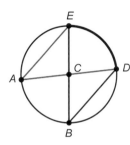

$\angle EAD$ and $\angle EBD$ both intercept $\overarc{ED}$.
So, $m\angle EAD = m\angle EBD$.

Summary

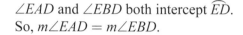

- An inscribed angle of a circle has its vertex on the circle and its sides are chords of the circle.

- The arc opposite the angle is the intercepted arc. The endpoints of the intercepted arc are the points where the sides of the inscribed angle meet the circle.

- The measure of an inscribed angle equals one-half the measure of its intercepted arc. An angle that is inscribed in a semicircle is a right angle.

- Two inscribed angles that intercept the same arc have the same measure.

Angles Formed by Secants and Tangents

A solar eclipse occurs when the moon is between the earth and the sun at a position that causes the moon's shadow to fall on the earth's surface. Though it may seem like this would happen frequently, it is a rather rare occurrence. The moon's orbit around the earth is tilted by 5° to the earth's orbit around the sun. The tilting causes the moon's shadow to almost always miss the earth's surface. The lines in the diagram show what happens when the moon completely blocks the rays of the sun from reaching a particular spot on the earth. The lines are tangent to the circles representing the sun and moon.

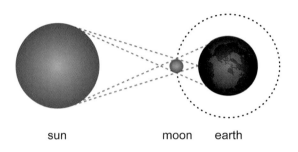

sun   moon   earth

More Angle and Arc Relationships

So far you have learned the relationships between angles and arcs for both central and inscribed angles. Now you will learn even more angle and arc relationships. They fall into three basic categories.

1. The vertex is *on* the circle.

2. The vertex is *outside* the circle.

3. The vertex is *inside* the circle.

Vertex on the Circle

The Inscribed Angle Theorem states that the measure of an inscribed angle is half the measure of its intercepted arc. It turns out that this theorem can be extended to include angles other than inscribed angles whose vertex is on a circle. This happens when a tangent and secant intersect.

THEOREM 9-7

If a tangent and a secant or chord intersect on a circle at the point of tangency, then the measure of the angle formed equals one-half the measure of the intercepted arc.

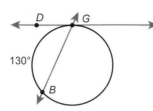

$$m\angle DGB = \frac{1}{2} m\widehat{GB}$$
$$= \frac{1}{2}(130°)$$
$$= 65°$$

Vertex Outside the Circle

There are three ways for two lines to intersect so that the vertex is outside the circle. In each of these cases, there are two intercepted arcs. Also, in each, the measure of the angle is half the difference of the intercepted arcs. These are our next three theorems.

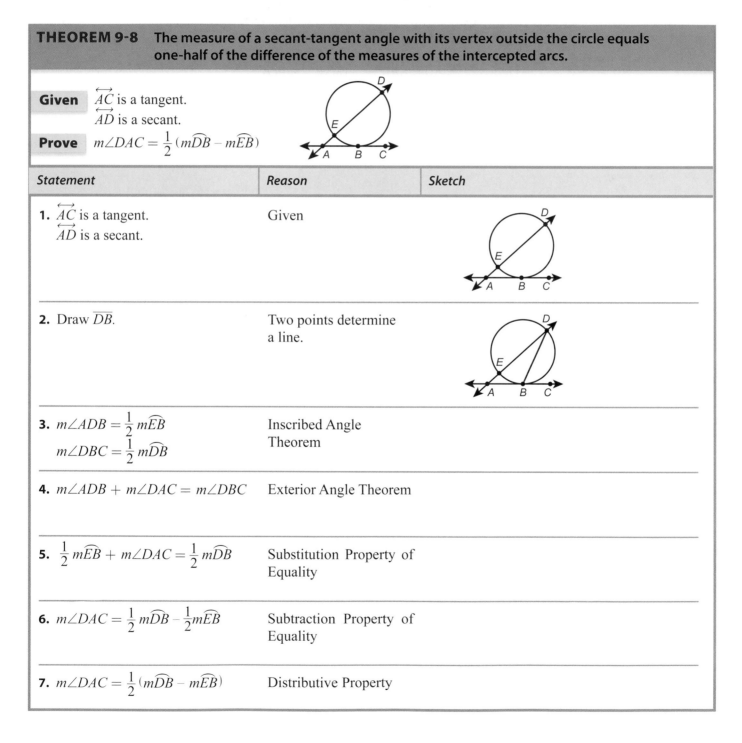

THEOREM 9-8	The measure of a secant-tangent angle with its vertex outside the circle equals one-half of the difference of the measures of the intercepted arcs.

Given $\overleftrightarrow{AC}$ is a tangent.
$\overleftrightarrow{AD}$ is a secant.

Prove $m\angle DAC = \frac{1}{2}(m\widehat{DB} - m\widehat{EB})$

Statement	Reason	Sketch
1. $\overleftrightarrow{AC}$ is a tangent. $\overleftrightarrow{AD}$ is a secant.	Given	
2. Draw $\overline{DB}$.	Two points determine a line.	
3. $m\angle ADB = \frac{1}{2} m\widehat{EB}$ $m\angle DBC = \frac{1}{2} m\widehat{DB}$	Inscribed Angle Theorem	
4. $m\angle ADB + m\angle DAC = m\angle DBC$	Exterior Angle Theorem	
5. $\frac{1}{2} m\widehat{EB} + m\angle DAC = \frac{1}{2} m\widehat{DB}$	Substitution Property of Equality	
6. $m\angle DAC = \frac{1}{2} m\widehat{DB} - \frac{1}{2} m\widehat{EB}$	Subtraction Property of Equality	
7. $m\angle DAC = \frac{1}{2}(m\widehat{DB} - m\widehat{EB})$	Distributive Property	

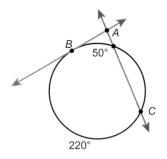

We will use the theorem to find $m\angle BAC$.

$$m\angle BAC = \frac{1}{2}(220° - 50°)$$
$$= \frac{1}{2}(170°)$$
$$= 85°$$

THEOREM 9-9

The measure of an angle that is formed by two secants that intersect in the exterior of a circle equals one-half of the difference of the measures of the intercepted arcs.

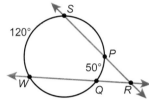

$$m\angle SRW = \frac{1}{2}(m\overset{\frown}{SW} - m\overset{\frown}{PQ})$$
$$= \frac{1}{2}(120° - 50°)$$
$$= \frac{1}{2}(70°)$$
$$= 35°$$

THEOREM 9-10

The measure of a tangent-tangent angle with its vertex outside the circle equals one-half of the difference of the measures of the intercepted arcs, or the measure of the major arc minus 180°.

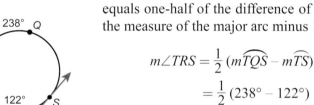

$$m\angle TRS = \frac{1}{2}(m\overset{\frown}{TQS} - m\overset{\frown}{TS})$$
$$= \frac{1}{2}(238° - 122°)$$
$$= \frac{1}{2}(116°)$$
$$= 58°$$

Vertex Inside the Circle

The only way for two lines to intersect inside a circle is if both lines are secants.

THEOREM 9-11

The measure of an angle that is formed by two secants or chords that intersect in the interior of a circle equals one-half the sum of the measures of the arcs intercepted by the angle and its vertical angle.

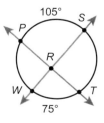

$$m\angle PRS = \frac{1}{2}(m\overset{\frown}{PS} + m\overset{\frown}{WT})$$
$$= \frac{1}{2}(105° + 75°)$$
$$= \frac{1}{2}(180°)$$
$$= 90°$$

These theorems can be used to find missing arcs as well as missing angles. It just takes a little algebra.

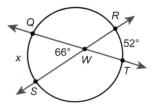

$$m\angle QWS = \tfrac{1}{2}\,(m\overarc{QS} + m\overarc{RT})$$

$$66° = \tfrac{1}{2}\,(x + 52°)$$

$$132° = x + 52°$$

$$80° = x$$

Summary

- Secants and tangent lines of circles form angles that intercept arcs. The vertex can lie on, outside, or inside the circle.

- When the vertex lies on the circle, there is one intercepted arc, and the measure of the angle is half the measure of the intercepted arc.

- When the vertex lies outside the circle, there are two intercepted arcs, and the measure of the angle is half the difference of the measures of the intercepted arcs.

- When the vertex lies inside the circle, there are two intercepted arcs, and the measure of the angle is half the sum of the measures of the intercepted arcs.

Segments of Tangents, Secants, and Chords

One of the oldest types of bridges in the world is the arch bridge. Roman builders were among the first to build arch bridges. Whereas modern builders use other types of arcs, the Romans used semicircles. You can find the diameter of the circle that contains the arc with what you will learn in this lesson.

KEYWORDS

external secant segment

secant segment

tangent segment

Tangent Segments

A **tangent segment** is a segment of a tangent line with one of its endpoints at the point of tangency. In the diagram, $\overline{AC}$ and $\overline{AB}$ are tangent segments.

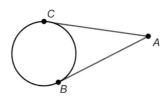

Two segments that are tangent to a circle from the same external point are of equal length.

Given $\overline{YX}$ and $\overline{YZ}$ are tangent segments of circle W.

Prove $\overline{YX} \cong \overline{YZ}$

Statement	Reason	Sketch
1. $\overline{YX}$ and $\overline{YZ}$ are tangent segments.	Given	
2. Draw $\overline{XW}$, $\overline{YW}$, and $\overline{ZW}$.	Two points determine a line.	
3. $\angle YXW$ and $\angle YZW$ are right angles.	A tangent is perpendicular to a radius at the point of tangency.	
4. $\overline{WX} \cong \overline{WZ}$	All radii of a circle are congruent.	
5. $\overline{YW} \cong \overline{YW}$	Reflexive Property of Congruence	
6. $\triangle YXW$ and $\triangle YZW$ are right triangles. See Step 3.	Definition of right triangles	
7. $\triangle YXW \cong \triangle YZW$	HL Congruence Theorem	

proof continued on next page

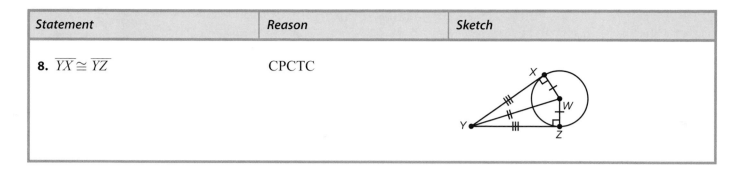
Secant Segments

A **secant segment** is a segment of a secant with at least one of its endpoints on the circle. Below, $\overline{RN}$, $\overline{JN}$, $\overline{TN}$, and $\overline{MN}$ are secant segments.

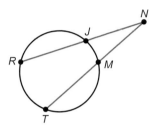

An **external secant segment** is a secant segment that lies in the exterior of the circle with one of its endpoints on the circle. $\overline{JN}$ and $\overline{MN}$ are external secant segments.

The next theorem gives the relationship among these segments.

THEOREM 9-13

If two secants intersect outside a circle, then the product of the lengths of one secant segment and its external segment equals the product of the lengths of the other secant segment and its external segment.
(Whole × Outside = Whole × Outside)

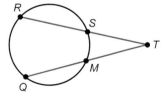

$$RT \times ST = QT \times MT$$

You can use this theorem to find missing segment lengths like *MK* at left.

$$GJ \times HJ = MJ \times KJ$$
$$(8 + 6)(6) = (x + 7)(7)$$
$$(14)(6) = (x + 7)(7)$$
$$84 = 7x + 49$$
$$35 = 7x$$
$$5 = x$$

$$MK = 5$$

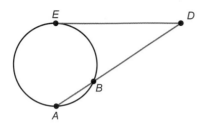

Secant-Tangent Segments

THEOREM 9-14

If a secant and a tangent intersect outside a circle, then the product of the lengths of the secant segment and its external segment equals the length of the tangent segment squared. (Whole × Outside = Tangent²)

$$AD \times BD = ED^2$$

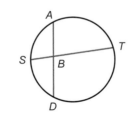

Use Theorem 9-14 to find GR.

$$AR \times BR = GR^2$$
$$(5 + 4)(4) = x^2$$
$$9(4) = x^2$$
$$36 = x^2$$
$$6 = x$$

$GR = 6$ cm

Chord-Chord Segments

THEOREM 9-15

If two chords intersect inside a circle, then the product of the lengths of the segments of one chord equals the product of the lengths of the segments of the other chord.

$$AB \times BD = SB \times BT$$

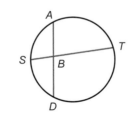

Find BE.
$$AE \times ED = BE \times EC$$
$$(5)(6) = x(10)$$
$$30 = 10x$$
$$3 = x$$

$BE = 3$ m

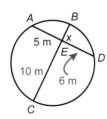

An arch of a bridge that passes over a river is the arc of a circle. As shown at left, the height from the center of the arc to the water below the bridge is 35 feet. The distance from one side of the bridge to the other, at the water line, is 120 feet. Find the diameter of the circle that includes the arc.

The situation can be viewed as a 120-ft chord being bisected by a perpendicular segment from the midpoint of the arc. First find the missing distance, x.

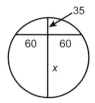

$$35x = 3600$$
$$x \approx 102.9$$

To find the diameter, add 35: $102.9 + 35 = 137.9$.

The diameter is about 138 feet.

Summary

- A tangent segment is a segment of a tangent line with one of its endpoints at the point of tangency.

- A secant segment is a segment of a secant with at least one of its endpoints on the circle. An external secant segment is a secant segment that lies in the exterior of the circle with one of its endpoints on the circle.

- Segments that are tangents to a circle from the same external point are equal in length.

- If two secants intersect outside the circle, the length of a secant segment (whole) times the length of its external segment (outside) equals the length of the other secant segment (whole) times its external segment (outside).

- If a secant and tangent intersect outside the circle, the length of the secant segment (whole) times the length of the external secant segment (outside) equals the length of the tangent segment squared.

- If two chords intersect, the product of the lengths of the segments of one chord equals the product of the lengths of the segments of the other chord.

Circles in the Coordinate Plane

OBJECTIVES

▶ Write the equation of a circle given its center and radius, or its center and another point on the circle.

▶ Sketch a circle given its equation.

▶ Find the intercepts of a circle.

▶ Translate a circle on the coordinate plane.

Seismologists use intersecting circles to determine the epicenter of an earthquake. The point underground where the earthquake releases energy is called the focus of the earthquake. The point directly above the focus on the earth's surface is called the epicenter.

During an earthquake, seismologists use a seismograph to measure vibrations in three different locations. Then they draw a circle around each location on a map. The radius of each circle is the distance of the earthquake from the seismograph. The intersection of the three circles is the epicenter.

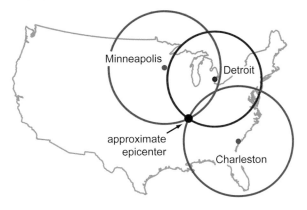

Minneapolis
Detroit
approximate epicenter
Charleston

The Equation of a Circle

REMEMBER

The distance between two points (x_1, y_1) and (x_2, y_2) is

$$d = \sqrt{(x_2 - x_1)^2 + (y_2 - y_1)^2}.$$

You can use the Distance Formula to understand the formula for the equation of a circle. The diagram shows a circle with center (h, k) and radius r.

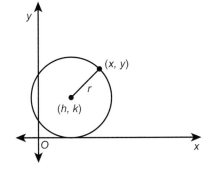

For any point (x, y) on the circle, you represent the distance r from the fixed point (h, k) by using the Distance Formula:

$$r = \sqrt{(x - h)^2 + (y - k)^2}$$

When we square each side, we get:

$$r^2 = (x - h)^2 + (y - k)^2$$

The Equation of a Circle

The equation of a circle with center (h, k) and radius r is
$$(x - h)^2 + (y - k)^2 = r^2$$

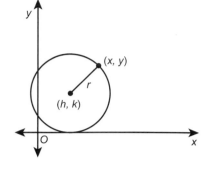

If you know the center and the radius of a circle you can write the equation of the circle.

For example, to find the equation of a circle with center $(3, 5)$ and radius 4, substitute those values into the formula:

$$(x - h)^2 + (y - k)^2 = r^2$$
$$(x - 3)^2 + (y - 5)^2 = 4^2$$
$$(x - 3)^2 + (y - 5)^2 = 16$$

Notice that the operation in each set of parentheses in the formula is subtraction. Remember that subtracting a negative is the same as adding a positive. For example, the equation of a circle with center $(-1, 0)$ and radius 3 is:

$$(x - (-1))^2 + (y - 0)^2 = 3^2$$
$$(x + 1)^2 + y^2 = 9$$

If you know the center of the circle and a point on the circle, you can find the radius and then write the equation of the circle.

To find the equation of a circle with center $(3, -2)$ that passes through the point $(7, -5)$ you first find the radius by using the Distance Formula.

$$r = \sqrt{(3 - 7)^2 + (-2 - (-5))^2}$$

$$= \sqrt{(-4)^2 + (-2 + 5)^2}$$

$$= \sqrt{(-4)^2 + (3)^2}$$

$$= \sqrt{25}$$

$$= 5$$

Now substitute 5 for r, 3 for h, and -2 for k in the equation and simplify.

$$(x - 3)^2 + (y - (-2))^2 = 5^2$$
$$(x - 3)^2 + (y + 2)^2 = 25$$

Sketching a Circle

If you know the equation of a circle, you know its radius and its center. You can use this information to sketch the circle. Let's sketch the circle described by the equation:

$$(x - 2)^2 + (y)^2 = 16$$

The equation can be rewritten as $(x - 2)^2 + (y - 0)^2 = 4^2$, where $(2, 0)$ is the center of the circle and 4 is the radius.

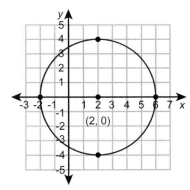

Step 1: Plot the center point $(2, 0)$.

Step 2: From the center point, count the number of units of the radius, 4, up, down, left, and right and place a point at each location.

Step 3: Sketch the circle that passes through these four points. A compass would help with this sketch.

You can see from the sketch that the x-intercepts are -2 and 6 and that the y-intercepts are approximately 3.5 and -3.5. To find the intercepts algebraically, substitute 0 for y to find the x-intercepts and 0 for x to find the y-intercepts.

x-intercepts	y-intercepts
$(x - 2)^2 + (y)^2 = 16$	$(x - 2)^2 + (y)^2 = 16$
$(x - 2)^2 + (0)^2 = 16$	$(0 - 2)^2 + (y)^2 = 16$
$(x - 2)^2 = 16$	$4 + y^2 = 16$
$x - 2 = \pm 4$	$y^2 = 12$
$x = 6$ and $x = -2$	$y = \pm\sqrt{12}$
	$y \approx 3.46$ and $y \approx -3.46$

The x-intercepts are $(6, 0)$ and $(-2, 0)$.

The y-intercepts are approximately $(0, 3.46)$ and $(0, -3.46)$.

You can also use geometry software to sketch a circle on the coordinate plane. The sketch below is a graph of the circle $(x - 4)^2 + (y - 2)^2 = 9$.

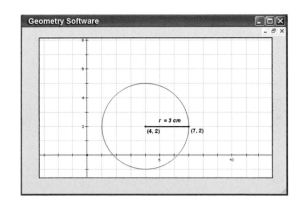

You can translate a circle by moving its center. To move the previous circle 2 units to the right and 3 units up, add 2 to h and 3 to k. The image circle will have the equation $(x - (4 + 2))^2 + (y - (2 + 3))^2 = 9$, which simplifies to $(x - 6)^2 + (y - 5)^2 = 9$. You can also translate a circle with geometry software. Draw a vector from the center of the circle to a point that is 2 units to the right and 3 units up. Then translate the circle by the vector.

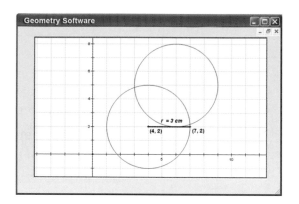

Summary

- The equation of a circle with center (h, k) and radius r is $(x - h)^2 + (y - k)^2 = r^2$.

- If you know the center and the radius of a circle, you can write the equation of the circle.

- If you know the center of the circle and a point on the circle, you can find the equation of the circle by first using the Distance Formula to find the radius.

- To sketch a circle in the coordinate plane, plot the center point, and then count the number of units of the radius in each direction to plot four other points to guide you in sketching the circle.

- To find the x- and y-intercepts algebraically, substitute 0 for y and solve for x, then substitute 0 for x and solve for y.

- You can translate a circle by adding and subtracting units from the coordinates of the center point.

UNIT 10   Trigonometry

Literally translated, the word *trigonometry* means "triangle measurement." Right triangle trigonometry is the study of the relationships between the side lengths and angle measures of right triangles. Trigonometry is one of the most useful subjects in all of geometry because of its many real-world applications. Astronomy, medical imaging, meteorology, cartography, and computer graphics are just a few of the fields in which it is used.

Trigonometry is also very useful in finding indirect measurements. During "The Great Trigonometric Survey" of the 1800s, trigonometry was used to find land measurements necessary for mapmaking. Indirect measurement was used to find the heights of these Himalayan mountains: K2, Kanchenjunga, and Mount Everest.

In this unit, you will study the three basic trigonometric ratios—sine, cosine, and tangent—and use them to solve problems involving both right triangles and all other triangles.

. . . .

UNIT OBJECTIVES

▶ Define the sine, cosine, and tangent ratios.

▶ Use the sine, cosine, and tangent ratios to find missing angle measures and missing side lengths in right triangles.

▶ Identify trigonometric identities.

▶ Use the relationships in 45°-45°-90° and 30°-60°-90° triangles to find trigonometric ratios and use those ratios to solve problems.

▶ Use the Laws of Sines and Cosines to find missing angle or side measures in triangles.

Tangents

OBJECTIVES

▶ Define the tangent ratio and express tangent ratios as fractions or decimals.

▶ Use a calculator to find the value of the tangent of an angle.

▶ Find the measure of an angle, given its tangent value.

Sometimes guidebooks give the grade of a hiking trail. What does it mean when a hill has a grade of 15%? It means the slope is 15%, so it rises 15 feet over a horizontal distance of 100 feet. But that can be hard to comprehend. Knowing the angle of elevation might give you a better idea of how steep and difficult you can expect your climb to be. The first trigonometric ratio you will learn about, *tangent,* will show you how you can find the angle of elevation of a hill with a given grade.

KEYWORDS

adjacent side   inverse tangent

opposite side   tangent

trigonometric ratio

Trigonometric Ratios

When you find the ratio of the lengths of two sides of a right triangle, you are finding a **trigonometric ratio.** These ratios relate the sides of the triangle to either of the acute angles. Specific to one of the acute angles, the sides are referred to as **adjacent, opposite,** and hypotenuse.

The hypotenuse is the side opposite the right angle. The opposite side is across from the given angle, and the adjacent side is next to the given angle, but is not the hypotenuse.

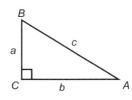

For $\triangle ABC$:

With respect to $\angle A$, a is the opposite side, and b is the adjacent side.

With respect to $\angle B$, b is the opposite side, and a is the adjacent side.

c is always the hypotenuse.

The Tangent Ratio

One of the most commonly used ratios is the **tangent** ratio. It is abbreviated *tan*. The tangent of an angle is the ratio of the length of the leg opposite that angle to the length of the leg adjacent to that angle.

$$\tan A = \frac{\text{opposite}}{\text{adjacent}} = \frac{a}{b}$$

$$\tan B = \frac{\text{opposite}}{\text{adjacent}} = \frac{b}{a}$$

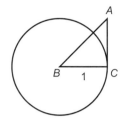

The tangent ratio in trigonometry is related to tangents to circles. Look at circle B. It has a radius of 1. $\overline{AC}$ is tangent to circle B at point C. The tangent of B is the ratio of the length of the tangent segment to the radius.

$$\tan B = \frac{\text{opposite}}{\text{adjacent}} = \frac{AC}{BC} = \frac{AC}{1} = AC$$

That is, the tangent of the angle is the length of the tangent segment.

Trigonometric ratios can be expressed as either a fraction or decimal.

$$\tan D = \frac{12}{5} = 2.4$$

$$\tan E = \frac{5}{12} \approx 0.4167$$

You can use a calculator to find a decimal approximation for a tangent ratio. To do so, set your calculator in degree mode and use the *tan* key. The screen below shows that the tangent of a 55° angle is approximately 1.4281.

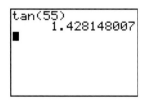

To find the value of x in the diagram below, we set up the tangent ratio and solve for x.

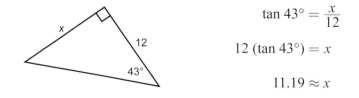

$$\tan 43° = \frac{x}{12}$$

$$12\,(\tan 43°) = x$$

$$11.19 \approx x$$

The Inverse Tangent

Sometimes you know the lengths of the legs of a right triangle and you want to find the measure of an acute angle. For this, you use the **inverse tangent,** abbreviated *tan*⁻¹. Your calculator may have *tan*⁻¹, or you may have to use an INV key.

As shown below, if the tangent of an angle is $\frac{3}{5}$, or 0.6, the angle measure is approximately 31°.

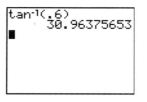

The grade of a hill is given to be 15%. To find the angle of elevation, draw a right triangle with a slope of $\frac{15}{100}$. Then find the inverse tangent.

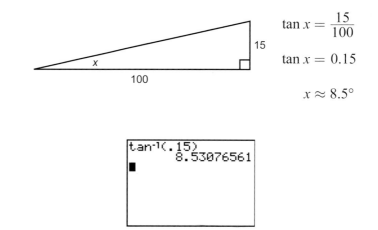

$$\tan x = \frac{15}{100}$$

$$\tan x = 0.15$$

$$x \approx 8.5°$$

The angle of elevation is about 8.5°.

Summary

• •

- The tangent of an acute angle of a right triangle is the ratio of the length of the side opposite the angle to the length of the side adjacent to the angle:
  $$\tan x = \frac{\text{opposite}}{\text{adjacent}}.$$

- You use the tangent of an angle to find the length of a missing leg in a right triangle. To find a missing angle, use the inverse tangent: tan⁻¹.

Sines and Cosines

OBJECTIVES

▶ Express the sine and cosine ratios of given angles as fractions or decimals.

▶ Use a calculator to find the value of the sine or cosine of an angle.

▶ Use the inverse sine and cosine to find the measure of an angle.

Trigonometric ratios can be used to make indirect measurements. For instance, suppose you are flying a kite and let it out to its full length. By knowing the length of the string and by estimating the angle the string is making with the ground, you can estimate how far directly above the ground the kite is flying.

KEYWORDS
cosine
identity
sine

The Sine and Cosine Ratios

The tangent ratio only involves the legs of a right triangle, because opposite and adjacent (the two legs) are never the hypotenuse. Now you will learn about two more trigonometric ratios, both of which involve the hypotenuse. They are **sine** and **cosine,** abbreviated *sin* and *cos*.

The sine of an angle is the ratio of the length of the leg that is opposite the angle to the length of the hypotenuse.

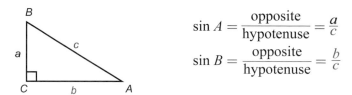

$$\sin A = \frac{\text{opposite}}{\text{hypotenuse}} = \frac{a}{c}$$

$$\sin B = \frac{\text{opposite}}{\text{hypotenuse}} = \frac{b}{c}$$

The cosine of an angle is the ratio of the length of the leg adjacent to that angle to the length of the hypotenuse.

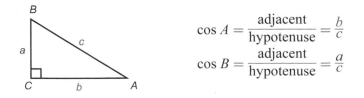

$$\cos A = \frac{\text{adjacent}}{\text{hypotenuse}} = \frac{b}{c}$$

$$\cos B = \frac{\text{adjacent}}{\text{hypotenuse}} = \frac{a}{c}$$

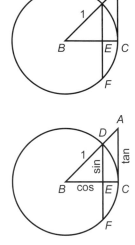

As with tangent, both sine and cosine can be defined as lengths of segments on a circle with a radius of 1. Return to circle B where $\overline{AC}$ is a tangent segment, B, D, and A are collinear, and B, E, and C are also collinear. $\overline{DE}$ is a half-chord because $\overline{BC}$ is a perpendicular bisector of chord $\overline{DF}$. The original word for half-chord in Sanskrit was translated to Arabic, and then mistranslated to the Latin word *sinus*, which we now call *sine*.

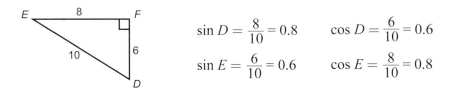

$$\sin B = \frac{\text{opposite}}{\text{hypotenuse}} = \frac{DE}{BD} = \frac{DE}{1} = DE$$

$$\cos B = \frac{\text{adjacent}}{\text{hypotenuse}} = \frac{BE}{BD} = \frac{BE}{1} = BE$$

The illustration at left summarizes how the ratios of sine, cosine, and tangent relate to the circle.

Also like the tangent ratio, the sine and cosine ratios can be expressed as either fractions or decimals.

$$\sin D = \frac{8}{10} = 0.8 \qquad \cos D = \frac{6}{10} = 0.6$$

$$\sin E = \frac{6}{10} = 0.6 \qquad \cos E = \frac{8}{10} = 0.8$$

Notice that the sine of one acute angle is the same as the cosine of the other acute angle from the same triangle.

As you did for the tangent ratio, you can use your calculator to find decimal approximations for the sine and cosine of an angle. Use the *sin* and *cos* keys on your calculator. The screen below shows that the sine of a 35° angle is approximately 0.5736 and the cosine is approximately 0.8192. Remember that your calculator must be set in degree mode.

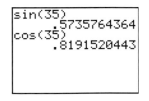

Here is an example of how to use sine to find a missing side length.

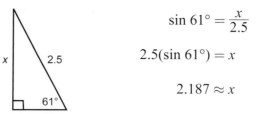

$$\sin 61° = \frac{x}{2.5}$$

$$2.5(\sin 61°) = x$$

$$2.187 \approx x$$

And here is an example that uses cosine.

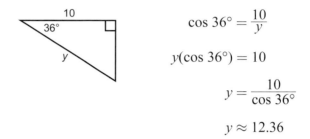

$$\cos 36° = \frac{10}{y}$$

$$y(\cos 36°) = 10$$

$$y = \frac{10}{\cos 36°}$$

$$y \approx 12.36$$

You can use trigonometry to make indirect measurements. Suppose a kite is at the end of a 250 ft string. If the string makes an angle of about 50° with the ground, we can approximate the height of the kite above the ground by setting up and solving the following equation.

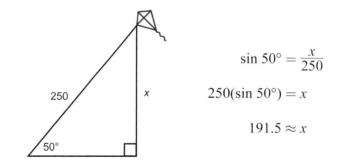

$$\sin 50° = \frac{x}{250}$$

$$250(\sin 50°) = x$$

$$191.5 \approx x$$

The kite is about 192 feet high.

The Inverse Sine and Cosine

To find the measure of an acute angle, given the length of a leg and the length of the hypotenuse, you use the inverse sine and cosine: $\sin^{-1}$ and $\cos^{-1}$.

As shown below, if the sine of an angle is $\frac{1}{2}$, or 0.5, the angle measure is 30°. If the cosine of an angle is 0.5, the angle measure is 60°.

```
sin-1(.5)
             30
cos-1(.5)
             60
```

A 16-foot ladder is leaning against a house. The top of the ladder reaches 10 feet above the ground. To find the angle the base of the ladder makes with the ground, we set up an equation and find the inverse sine.

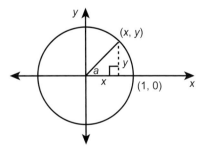

$$\sin x = \frac{10}{16}$$

$$\sin x = 0.625$$

$$x \approx 38.7°$$

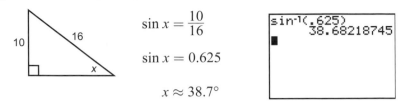

Trigonometric Identities

A trigonometric **identity** is an equation containing a trigonometric ratio that is true for all values of the variable. There are many trigonometric identities. We will examine two of them and show they are true.

Identity 1 $\tan x = \dfrac{\sin x}{\cos x}$

To show that this is true, we substitute the ratios for sine and cosine into the equation.

$$\tan x = \frac{\dfrac{\text{opposite}}{\text{hypotenuse}}}{\dfrac{\text{adjacent}}{\text{hypotenuse}}}$$

$$\tan x = \frac{\text{opposite}}{\cancel{\text{hypotenuse}}} \bullet \frac{\cancel{\text{hypotenuse}}}{\text{adjacent}}$$

$$\tan x = \frac{\text{opposite}}{\text{adjacent}}$$

The last equation is the definition of the tangent ratio, so the original equation is true.

Identity 2 $\sin^2 x + \cos^2 x = 1$

We can use a circle on the coordinate plane to show that this identity is true. Its center is located at (0, 0) and it has a radius of 1.
Since all radii of a circle are congruent, the hypotenuse of the triangle has a radius of 1, and we can write the sine and cosine of angle a as follows:

$$\sin a = \frac{y}{1} = y \quad \text{and} \quad \cos a = \frac{x}{1} = x$$

The equation of a circle with its center at the origin and a radius 1 is:

$$(x - 0)^2 + (y - 0)^2 = 1^2$$
$$x^2 + y^2 = 1$$

Now we use the Commutative Property of Addition and substitute sin a and cos a into the equation for x and y.

$$(\sin a)^2 + (\cos a)^2 = 1$$

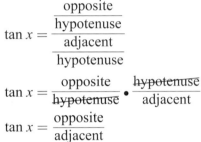

> **MEMORYTIP**
>
> To remember that **s**ine is **o**pposite over **h**ypotenuse, **c**osine is **a**djacent over **h**ypotenuse, and **t**angent is **o**pposite over **a**djacent, use each first letter to make the word "sohcahtoa," pronounced "soak-a-toe-ah."

To make things a bit easier to read, mathematicians usually replace $(\sin a)^2$ with $\sin^2 a$, so the identity can be written in the form

$$\sin^2 a + \cos^2 a = 1$$

Summary

- The sine of an angle is the ratio of the length of the side opposite the angle to the length of the hypotenuse: $\sin x = \dfrac{\text{opposite}}{\text{hypotenuse}}$.

- The cosine of an angle is the ratio of the length of the side adjacent the angle to the length of the hypotenuse: $\cos x = \dfrac{\text{adjacent}}{\text{hypotenuse}}$.

- You can use the sine and cosine of an angle to find a missing side of a right triangle. To find a missing angle, you can use the inverses: $\sin^{-1}$ and $\cos^{-1}$.

- A trigonometric identity is an equation containing a trigonometric ratio that is true for all values of the variable. Two trigonometric identities are: $\tan x = \dfrac{\sin x}{\cos x}$ and $\sin^2 x + \cos^2 x = 1$.

Special Right Triangles

In life, there are often many ways to solve a problem. It's the same with mathematics. For some triangles, you can find a missing side by applying the Pythagorean Theorem, by using a formula, or by writing a proportion. They all give the same answer. So, how do you know which way to go? The choice is yours. The decision may depend on whether or not you have a calculator. Or you can solve a problem one way, and use another way to check your answer.

The 45°-45°-90° Triangle

Because of the measures of its angles, the 45°-45°-90° triangle is commonly used, so knowing the trigonometric ratios for a 45° angle can come in handy. Let us first review the relationship between the legs and hypotenuse of a 45°-45°-90° triangle.

When you construct the diagonal of a square, you create two 45°-45°-90° triangles with a side length of s. You can then use the Pythagorean Theorem to see that the length of the diagonal is $\sqrt{2}$ times the length of a side.

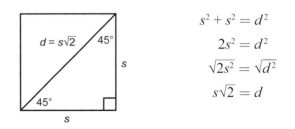

$$s^2 + s^2 = d^2$$
$$2s^2 = d^2$$
$$\sqrt{2s^2} = \sqrt{d^2}$$
$$s\sqrt{2} = d$$

Now use s and $s\sqrt{2}$ to find the sine, cosine, and tangent of a 45° angle. You can use either of the 45° angles.

$$\sin 45° = \frac{\text{opposite}}{\text{hypotenuse}} = \frac{s}{s\sqrt{2}} = \frac{1}{\sqrt{2}} = \frac{\sqrt{2}}{2}$$

$$\cos 45° = \frac{\text{adjacent}}{\text{hypotenuse}} = \frac{s}{s\sqrt{2}} = \frac{1}{\sqrt{2}} = \frac{\sqrt{2}}{2}$$

$$\tan 45° = \frac{\text{opposite}}{\text{adjacent}} = \frac{s}{s} = 1$$

The 30°-60°-90° Triangle

The 30°-60°-90° triangle is also a commonly used triangle, so it is a good idea to know the trigonometric ratios for 30° and 60°.

When you construct the altitude of an equilateral triangle, you create two 30°-60°-90° triangles with a hypotenuse of s and a base (the shorter side) of $\frac{s}{2}$. Again, you can use the Pythagorean Theorem to see that the height is $\sqrt{3}$ times the length of the shorter side.

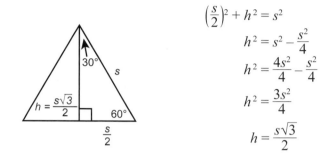

$$\left(\frac{s}{2}\right)^2 + h^2 = s^2$$

$$h^2 = s^2 - \frac{s^2}{4}$$

$$h^2 = \frac{4s^2}{4} - \frac{s^2}{4}$$

$$h^2 = \frac{3s^2}{4}$$

$$h = \frac{s\sqrt{3}}{2}$$

Now use s, $\frac{s}{2}$, and $\frac{s\sqrt{3}}{2}$ to find the sine, cosine, and tangent of a 30° and 60° angle.

$$\sin 30° = \frac{\text{opposite}}{\text{hypotenuse}} = \frac{\frac{s}{2}}{s} = \frac{s}{2s} = \frac{1}{2}$$

$$\sin 60° = \frac{\text{opposite}}{\text{hypotenuse}} = \frac{\frac{s\sqrt{3}}{2}}{s} = \frac{s\sqrt{3}}{2s} = \frac{\sqrt{3}}{2}$$

$$\cos 30° = \frac{\text{adjacent}}{\text{hypotenuse}} = \frac{\frac{s\sqrt{3}}{2}}{s} = \frac{s\sqrt{3}}{2s} = \frac{\sqrt{3}}{2}$$

$$\cos 60° = \frac{\text{adjacent}}{\text{hypotenuse}} = \frac{\frac{s}{2}}{s} = \frac{s}{2s} = \frac{1}{2}$$

$$\tan 30° = \frac{\text{opposite}}{\text{adjacent}} = \frac{\frac{s}{2}}{\frac{s\sqrt{3}}{2}} = \frac{2s}{2s\sqrt{3}} = \frac{1}{\sqrt{3}} = \frac{\sqrt{3}}{3}$$

$$\tan 60° = \frac{\text{opposite}}{\text{adjacent}} = \frac{\frac{s\sqrt{3}}{2}}{\frac{s}{2}} = \frac{2s\sqrt{3}}{2s} = \sqrt{3}$$

Using the Trigonometric Ratios to Solve Problems

A construction worker stands on a rooftop 65 feet above the ground. She throws down a rope, which another worker should anchor to the ground at a 30° angle. To the nearest foot, how far away from the base of the building should the rope be anchored to make the correct angle?

Use the tangent of a 30° angle to set up and solve a proportion.

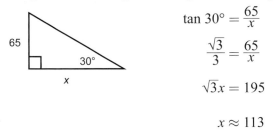

$$\tan 30° = \frac{65}{x}$$

$$\frac{\sqrt{3}}{3} = \frac{65}{x}$$

$$\sqrt{3}x = 195$$

$$x \approx 113$$

The rope should be anchored 113 feet from the base of the building.

A display screen is shaped like a square with a diagonal length of 14 centimeters. To the nearest tenth of a centimeter, find the length and width of the screen.

Use the sine (or cosine) of a 45° angle to set up and solve a proportion.

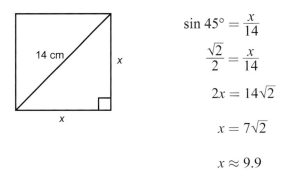

$$\sin 45° = \frac{x}{14}$$

$$\frac{\sqrt{2}}{2} = \frac{x}{14}$$

$$2x = 14\sqrt{2}$$

$$x = 7\sqrt{2}$$

$$x \approx 9.9$$

The screen has a length and width of about 9.9 centimeters.

Summary

. . . .

- You can find the sine, cosine, and tangent of a 45° angle by applying the trigonometric definitions to the sides of a 45°-45°-90° triangle.

- You can find the sine, cosine, and tangent of a 30° angle and a 60° angle by applying the trigonometric definitions to the sides of a 30°-60°-90° triangle.

- The trigonometric ratios that can be derived from special right triangles are summarized in the table.

Angle Measure	sine	cosine	tangent
30°	$\frac{1}{2}$	$\frac{\sqrt{3}}{2}$	$\frac{\sqrt{3}}{3}$
45°	$\frac{\sqrt{2}}{2}$	$\frac{\sqrt{2}}{2}$	1
60°	$\frac{\sqrt{3}}{2}$	$\frac{1}{2}$	$\sqrt{3}$

- You can find the lengths of missing sides in special right triangles by using trigonometric ratios.

The Laws of Sines and Cosines

The Pythagorean Theorem is an invaluable tool, but it has its limitations. It is only true for right triangles, and there are many situations that involve triangles that are not right triangles. For example, imagine that two boats leave a dock at the same time and head in different directions. At any point in time, the two boats and dock make up the vertices of a triangle. The new formulas you will learn will allow you to find side and angle measures for any type of triangle, not just a right triangle.

KEYWORD

solve a triangle

The Law of Sines

So far we have used trigonometric ratios only to solve right triangles. We can also use trigonometry to solve triangles that are not right. One way is to use the Law of Sines. We will prove it before we state it.

Consider $\triangle ABC$ below. It is not a right triangle, but by drawing the altitude $\overline{CD}$, we have created two right triangles: $\triangle ADC$ and $\triangle BDC$.

First we find the sine of $\angle A$:
$$\sin A = \frac{h}{b}$$

and solve for h:
$$h = b \sin A$$

Then we find the sine of $\angle B$:
$$\sin B = \frac{h}{a}$$

and solve for h:
$$h = a \sin B$$

Now we have two expressions equal to h. By substitution:
$$b \sin A = a \sin B$$

Finally, we divide both sides by ab:
$$\frac{\sin A}{a} = \frac{\sin B}{b}$$

By drawing different altitudes, we can show that $\frac{\sin A}{a} = \frac{\sin B}{b} = \frac{\sin C}{c}$. This is the Law of Sines.

The Law of Sines

For any $\triangle ABC$, where a, b, and c are the measures of the opposite sides of A, B, and C, respectively,
$$\frac{\sin A}{a} = \frac{\sin B}{b} = \frac{\sin C}{c}$$

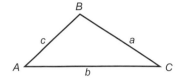

Using the Law of Sines, you can find a missing triangle measure in the following two cases.

- You are given two angles and any side (ASA or AAS).
- You are given two sides and the nonincluded angle (SSA).

When you use the Law of Sines, you set up and solve a proportion using two of the three ratios. To find the length of side a below, we set up a proportion using the ratios with A and B.

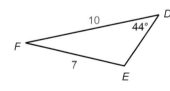

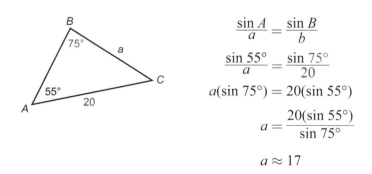

$$\frac{\sin A}{a} = \frac{\sin B}{b}$$

$$\frac{\sin 55°}{a} = \frac{\sin 75°}{20}$$

$$a(\sin 75°) = 20(\sin 55°)$$

$$a = \frac{20(\sin 55°)}{\sin 75°}$$

$$a \approx 17$$

You can also use the Law of Sines to find angle measures of triangles. To find the measure of $\angle E$ below, we set up a proportion and use the inverse sine.

$$\frac{\sin E}{e} = \frac{\sin D}{d}$$

$$\frac{\sin E}{10} = \frac{\sin 44°}{7}$$

$$7(\sin E) = 10(\sin 44°)$$

$$\sin E = \frac{10(\sin 44°)}{7}$$

$$m\angle E = \sin^{-1}\left(\frac{10(\sin 44°)}{7}\right) \approx 83°$$

The Law of Cosines

The Law of Sines can only be used for certain angle and side combinations. When you cannot use the Law of Sines, you may be able to use the Law of Cosines. We will prove the law before we state it.

Again, we have $\triangle ABC$ with altitude $\overline{CD}$ creating two right triangles: $\triangle ADC$ and $\triangle BDC$. Let $AD = x$ and $BD = c - x$.

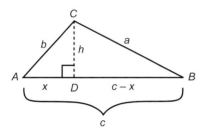

First we find the cosine of angle A: $\quad\quad \cos A = \dfrac{x}{b}$
and we solve for x: $\quad\quad\quad\quad\quad\quad\quad\quad\quad x = b \cos A$

We use the Pythagorean Theorem for $\triangle ADC$: $\quad b^2 = h^2 + x^2$
and solve for h^2: $\quad\quad\quad\quad\quad\quad\quad\quad\quad\quad h^2 = b^2 - x^2$

Then we use the
Pythagorean Theorem in $\triangle BDC$: $\quad\quad\quad a^2 = h^2 + (c - x)^2$

and square the binomial: $\quad\quad\quad\quad\quad\quad a^2 = h^2 + c^2 - 2cx + x^2$

Now we substitute for h^2: $\quad\quad\quad\quad\quad a^2 = b^2 - x^2 + c^2 - 2cx + x^2$

combine like terms: $\quad\quad\quad\quad\quad\quad\quad a^2 = b^2 + c^2 - 2cx$

substitute for x: $\quad\quad\quad\quad\quad\quad\quad\quad a^2 = b^2 + c^2 - 2c(b \cos A)$

and rearrange factors: $\quad\quad\quad\quad\quad\quad a^2 = b^2 + c^2 - 2bc \cos A$

We can draw different altitudes and follow similar reasoning for each.

The Law of Cosines

For any $\triangle ABC$, where a, b, and c are the measures of the opposite sides of A, B, and C, respectively,
$$a^2 = b^2 + c^2 - 2bc \cos A$$
$$b^2 = a^2 + c^2 - 2ac \cos B$$
$$c^2 = a^2 + b^2 - 2ab \cos C$$

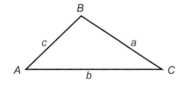

Use the Law of Cosines to find a missing triangle measure in the following two cases.

• You are given two sides and the included angle (SAS).

• You are given three sides (SSS).

When you use the Law of Cosines to find a missing side, choose the formula that has that side on the left side of the equation. To find the length of side b below, we choose the formula with b^2 on the left side.

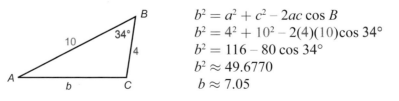

$$b^2 = a^2 + c^2 - 2ac \cos B$$
$$b^2 = 4^2 + 10^2 - 2(4)(10)\cos 34°$$
$$b^2 = 116 - 80 \cos 34°$$
$$b^2 \approx 49.6770$$
$$b \approx 7.05$$

If you know the lengths of three sides of a triangle, you can use the Law of Cosines to find the measure of any angle of the triangle.

Two ships leave a dock at the same time and head in different directions without changing course. After a few hours, one ship is 200 miles from the dock and the other is 325 miles from the dock. They are 410 miles from each other. What angle is formed by the paths of the two ships at the dock?

In the diagram, $\angle A$ is the missing angle, so we use the formula that has A on the right side. Notice below that we isolate $\cos A$ and then use the inverse cosine.

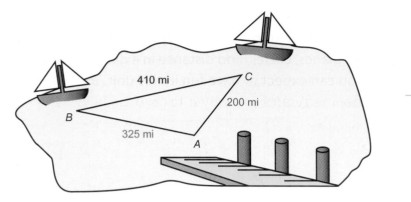

$$a^2 = b^2 + c^2 - 2bc \cos A$$
$$410^2 = 200^2 + 325^2 - 2(200)(325)\cos A$$
$$168{,}100 = 145{,}625 - 130{,}000 \cos A$$
$$22{,}475 = -130{,}000 \cos A$$
$$-\frac{22{,}475}{130{,}000} = \cos A$$
$$m\angle A \approx 100°$$

If you want to **solve the triangle,** which means to find all missing measures, you can now use the Law of Sines to find another angle, and then subtract the sum of the two known measures from 180° to find the last angle measure.

Summary

···

- The Laws of Sines and Cosines can be used to solve triangles other than right triangles.

- The Law of Sines states that for any $\triangle ABC$,
  $$\frac{\sin A}{a} = \frac{\sin B}{b} = \frac{\sin C}{c}.$$

- Use the Law of Sines when you are given two angles and any side, or two sides and a nonincluded angle.

- The Law of Cosines states that for any $\triangle ABC$,

  $$a^2 = b^2 + c^2 - 2bc \cos A$$
  $$b^2 = a^2 + c^2 - 2ac \cos B$$
  $$c^2 = a^2 + b^2 - 2ab \cos C$$

- Use the Law of Cosines when you are given two sides and the included angle, or all three sides.

UNIT 11 Beyond Euclidean Geometry

Up to this point, you have studied the geometry of Euclid. In this unit, you will learn about other kinds of geometry and be challenged to think about lines, planes, circles, and distance in a different way.

Most of all, you can expect to have fun in this unit. You will learn about taxicab geometry and see why a taxicab circle looks like a square. You'll see when a circle is the same as an oval, and the same as a triangle, and the same as a square. You'll learn characteristics about mazes and be introduced to the intriguing Möbius strip. Then you'll enjoy the beauty of fractals, see how a triangle can have three right angles, project figures onto other planes, and create input-output tables for logic gates.

Turn the page and enjoy.

. . . .

UNIT OBJECTIVES

▶ Use the golden ratio to find a missing measure in a golden rectangle.

▶ Calculate the taxidistance between two points, and sketch a taxicab circle.

▶ Identify topologically equivalent shapes.

▶ Calculate the Euler characteristic for a polyhedron.

▶ Use the Jordan Curve Theorem to determine if a point is inside or outside a closed curve.

▶ Explain how spherical geometry differs from Euclidean geometry.

▶ Build and describe the properties of fractals.

▶ Describe the implications of Pappus's Theorem and Desargues' Theorem.

▶ Convert a base 2 number to base 10.

▶ Complete and interpret input-output tables for logic gates or networks of logic gates.

The Golden Rectangle

OBJECTIVES

- ▶ Define golden rectangle and golden ratio.
- ▶ Use the golden ratio to find missing side lengths of golden rectangles.
- ▶ Use straightedge and compass or technology to construct a golden rectangle.

Believe it or not, some rectangles are considered more aesthetically pleasing than others. Some people think that the golden rectangle is the most appealing. It's not too narrow, it's not too wide—it is just right. Golden rectangles are used often in art and architecture. For example, there are many instances of it in the Parthenon, an ancient building whose remains still stand today in Athens, Greece.

KEYWORDS

golden ratio   golden rectangle

The Golden Rectangle

A **golden rectangle** is one whose length to width ratio is about 8 to 5, or 1.6, such as those below. This ratio is called the **golden ratio.** Generally speaking, the width is slightly more than half the length. The exact ratio is $\frac{1 + \sqrt{5}}{2}$, or approximately 1.618. Mathematicians use the Greek letter ϕ (*phi*, pronounced "fee") to stand for the golden ratio.

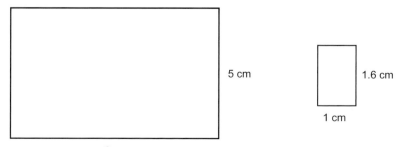

5 cm

8 cm

1.6 cm

1 cm

Of all length to width proportions in rectangles, this is considered the most pleasing to the human eye.

Because all golden rectangles have the same ratio, they are all similar. To find the approximate value of x in the golden rectangle below, set up and solve a proportion.

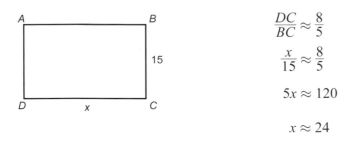

$$\frac{DC}{BC} \approx \frac{8}{5}$$

$$\frac{x}{15} \approx \frac{8}{5}$$

$$5x \approx 120$$

$$x \approx 24$$

Constructing a Golden Rectangle

It's easy to construct a golden rectangle. Start with a square. Construct the midpoint of the base and then construct a circle such that the radius is the length of the segment from the midpoint to the upper right corner of the square. The intersection of the base (extended) and the circle is the bottom right corner of a golden rectangle. Complete the rectangle by constructing parallel and perpendicular lines.

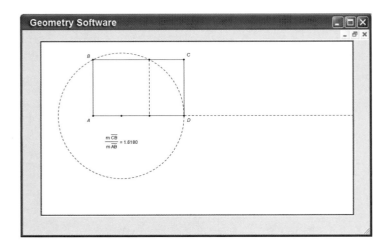

More About the Golden Rectangle and Ratio

- When a square is removed from a golden rectangle, the remaining rectangle is also a golden rectangle. This can be done repeatedly to make smaller and smaller golden rectangles (shown in blue below).

 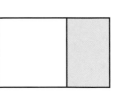 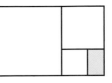

- The Fibonacci sequence (where a term is derived by adding the previous two terms) is related to the golden ratio. The first several terms of the Fibonacci sequence are $1, 1, 2, 3, 5, 8, 13, 21, 34....$ The ratio of consecutive terms gets closer to the golden ratio as the pattern progresses:

$$\frac{1}{1} = 1, \frac{2}{1} = 2, \frac{3}{2} = 1.5, \frac{5}{3} \approx 1.67, \frac{13}{8} = 1.625, \frac{21}{13} \approx 1.615, \frac{34}{21} \approx 1.619...$$

- You always get close to the golden ratio when following this procedure repeatedly: Take the square root of any number, add 1, take the square root of that number.

- Adding 1 to the golden ratio is the same as squaring the golden ratio.

- Many parts of the human body have lengths with the golden ratio. One example is the ratio of a person's height to the distance from the top of their head to their fingertips (when their arms are at their side). The ratio of the latter distance to the distance from their head to their elbow is also the golden ratio. Dolphins and ants also have body parts that form the golden ratio.

- When a regular decagon (10-sided polygon) is inscribed in a circle, the ratio of the radius and a side of the decagon is the golden ratio.

Summary

- A golden rectangle has a length to width ratio of about 1.6. This ratio for rectangles is considered the most pleasing to the eye.

- All golden rectangles are similar, which means their corresponding sides are proportional.

- The golden rectangle and the golden ratio appear in nature and in some ratios of animal and human body parts.

- The golden ratio has interesting mathematical characteristics.

Taxicab Geometry

OBJECTIVES

▶ Define taxicab geometry.

▶ Develop and use the taxidistance formula.

▶ Draw a taxicab circle.

You may have heard the expression, "The shortest distance between two points is a straight line." That may be true in Euclidean geometry but it's not true in taxicab geometry. Taxicab geometry is so named because movement and distance are similar to the way a taxicab driver must drive a person to a destination in a city that is laid out in a grid. A driver cannot drive a diagonal distance through a building but must travel in horizontal and vertical distances along city streets.

KEYWORDS

block	taxicab circle
taxidistance	taxicab geometry
taxicab perpendicular bisector	taxicab radius

What Is Taxicab Geometry?

Taxicab geometry is a non-Euclidean geometry where distance is measured along paths made of horizontal and vertical segments—the way you would have to travel from one place to another if you took a taxicab on city streets. In taxicab geometry a diagonal distance between two points is not allowed. Suppose you want to move from point A to point B below. To travel that distance in taxicab geometry, you must move horizontally and vertically along the grid. The side of each square is one city **block.**

There are many paths you can choose to get from A to B. Three of them are shown in the diagram below. The distance of each path is the number of blocks traveled to get from A to B. In the diagram, the red path has a distance of 11 blocks, the blue path has a distance of 17 blocks, and the green path has a distance of 13 blocks.

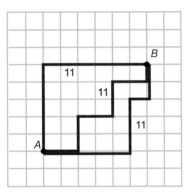

The shortest path between two points in taxicab geometry is called the **taxidistance.** In the diagram, the shortest distance between A and B is 11. The red path is not the only path with a taxidistance of 11. The diagram below shows some of the other paths.

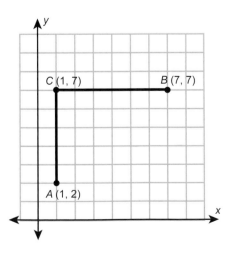

If we move taxicab geometry onto the coordinate plane, we can develop a formula for the taxidistance between two points.

Using the Distance Formula, you can find the distance from A to C and the distance from C to B.

$$AC = \sqrt{(1-1)^2 + (7-2)^2} = \sqrt{25} = 5$$

$$CB = \sqrt{(7-1)^2 + (7-7)^2} = \sqrt{36} = 6$$

The taxidistance from A to B is:

$$AC + CB = 5 + 6 = 11$$

Notice when you found AC, the x-coordinates were equal, and when you found CB, the y-coordinates were equal. That is the case because the segments are horizontal and vertical. So,

$$AC = \sqrt{(y_2 - y_1)^2} = |y_2 - y_1|$$

$$CD = \sqrt{(x_2 - x_1)^2} = |x_2 - x_1|$$

This allows us to write the following general formula.

Taxidistance Formula

The taxidistance t between two points (x_1, y_1) and (x_2, y_2) is
$$t = |y_2 - y_1| + |x_2 - x_1|$$

Taxicab Circles

In Euclidean geometry, a circle was defined as the set of all points on a plane that are the same distance from a given point in the plane. The same idea can be extended to taxicab geometry. To draw a **taxicab circle,** you find all the points, or intersections, that are a given taxidistance from a given intersection. You can think of a **taxicab radius** as any path you can take from a place in a city if you could walk only a certain number of blocks.

Compare the two circles below. They are alike in that they both have a radius of 3. In circle C, all the points on the circle are 3 units from point C. In circle O, all the points are 3 blocks from point O. There are two obvious ways the circles are different. First, their shapes are different. Second, circle C is made up of an infinite number of points, whereas circle O has a finite number of points—12 to be precise. A taxicab circle with a greater radius would have a greater number of points.

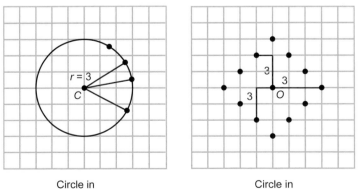

Circle in
Euclidean Geometry

Circle in
Taxicab Geometry

Taxicab Perpendicular Bisectors

A **taxicab perpendicular bisector** is the set of all points that are the same taxidistance from two given points. Not every pair of two points will have a perpendicular bisector. In fact, only points whose taxidistance between them is an even number of blocks have a perpendicular bisector.

In the figures below, the points in red form the perpendicular bisector for each pair of points.

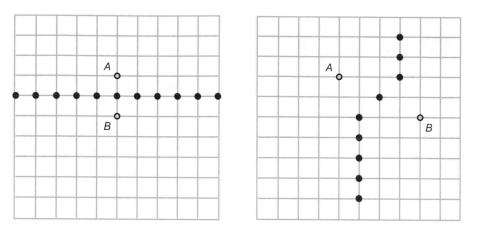

Summary

• •

- Taxicab geometry is a non-Euclidean geometry where distance is measured along paths made of horizontal and vertical segments.

- The shortest path between two points in taxicab geometry is called the taxidistance.

- The taxidistance t between two points (x_1, y_1) and (x_2, y_2) can be found using the formula $t = |y_2 - y_1| + |x_2 - x_1|$.

- Points on a taxicab circle must lie on the intersection of two streets.

- A taxicab circle is made up of a finite number of points.

- A taxicab perpendicular bisector is the set of all points that are the same distance from two given points. Two points have a perpendicular bisector only when the distance between them is an even number of blocks.

Graph Theory

OBJECTIVES

▶ Define and identify the parts of a graph.

▶ Determine when a graph has an Euler walk and an Euler circuit.

▶ Find Euler walks and circuits in graphs.

▶ Find Hamiltonian circuits in graphs.

Graph theory has its roots in the city of Königsberg (now Kaliningrad). The Pregel River ran through the city, and seven bridges were constructed to connect the land on either side of the river by way of the two islands in the river, as shown below. The citizens wanted to know if they could travel over all seven bridges without crossing the same bridge twice. In the eighteenth century, mathematician Leonhard Euler proved that it cannot be done. In 1736, he published a paper with his proof, which is considered to be the first paper on graph theory.

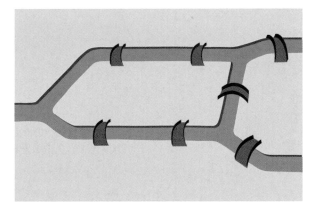

KEYWORDS

bridge	circuit
degree of a vertex	edge of a graph
Euler circuit	Euler path
even vertex	graph
Hamiltonian circuit	odd vertex
vertex of a graph	

What Is a Graph?

You have seen graphs of lines and planes earlier in this course and have probably graphed functions in an algebra course. In the branch of mathematics know as graph theory, a graph is something different. A **graph** is a set of points connected by line segments or curves. The points are called **vertices** and the line segments or curves are called **edges.**

Two graphs are shown below. The graph on the left has 5 vertices and 6 edges. The graph on the right has 7 vertices and 9 edges, where edge $\overline{JH}$ is a bridge. An edge is a **bridge** if its removal disconnects the graph.

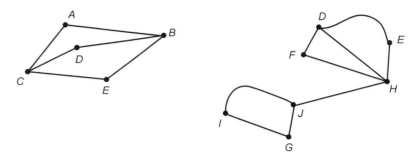

Graphs are used to represent real-life scenarios. For instance, each vertex can represent a person, and each edge could mean that they are friends. In that case, the graph below means Ann is friends with Bob and Cal. Bob is friends with Ann, Dan, and Eve. Bob is not friends with Cal because no edge directly connects the two of them.

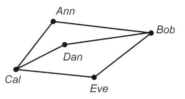

The shape of a graph and whether or not the edges are straight or curved are irrelevant. The purpose of the graph is to show what relationships exist. The friendship graph can also be drawn like this because the same people are connected.

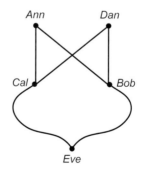

Euler Paths and Circuits

A *path* is a connected sequence of edges. For the graph below, the path that you would travel to move from point A to E, through B, can be written as *A-B-E*.

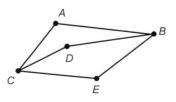

A **circuit** is a path that begins and ends at the same vertex. The path *A-B-E-C-A* is a circuit. *C-D-B-E-C* is another circuit.

If a path uses every edge once, and only once, it is an **Euler path.** You can determine if a graph has an Euler path by studying the **degree** of each vertex. The degree of a vertex is the number of edges connected to it. In the previous graph, vertices *A, D,* and *E* each have a degree of two, so they are **even vertices.** Vertices *B* and *C* have a degree of three, so they are **odd vertices.**

THEOREM 11-1 Euler Path Theorem

A graph has an Euler path if and only if one of the following is true:

- Exactly two vertices have an odd degree.

- Every vertex has an even degree.

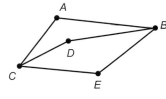

When a graph has exactly two odd vertices, the Euler path must begin at one of those vertices and end at the other. In the graph at left, *C-A-B-D-C-E-B* is an Euler path. *B-E-C-A-B-D-C* is another.

An Euler path that begins and ends at the same vertex is called an **Euler circuit.** This only happens when each vertex has an even degree. The graph below has the Euler circuit: *A-B-F-C-A-D-F-E-A.* This is not the only Euler circuit in the graph.

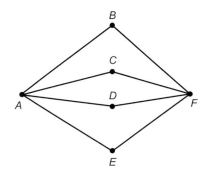

Let's look back at why the citizens of Königsberg could not travel over every bridge once and only once. In the graph below, the vertices represent the land and the edges represent the bridges.

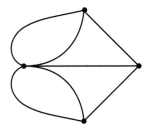

All four vertices have an odd degree. It does not meet either condition of the Euler Path Theorem.

A hiker wants to hike all the trails in a park. She doesn't care where she starts and where she ends because someone can drop her off and pick her up. Determine two routes she can take.

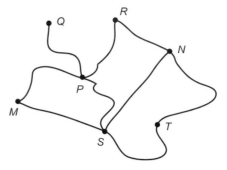

First, determine the degree of each vertex. There are two odd vertices (*Q* and *N*), so she must begin at one of these vertices and end at the other. Two possible routes are: *Q-P-M-S-T-N-S-P-R-N* and *N-T-S-M-P-R-N-S-P-Q*.

Hamiltonian Circuits

Notice that in an Euler path, vertices can be used more than once. The important thing is that the edges are all used and not repeated. In some real-life situations, such as when salespeople make travel plans, it is more important to visit every vertex once and only once.

Recall that a circuit begins and ends at the same vertex. A circuit is a **Hamiltonian circuit** if it uses every vertex once and only once. Not every edge needs to be used.

For instance, consider a salesman who has to visit each of the six cities below. The edges in the graph show the existing airline routes he can use.

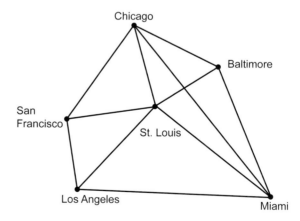

One Hamiltonian circuit is: Los Angeles-San Francisco-Chicago-St. Louis-Baltimore-Miami-Los Angeles. It allows the salesman to visit each city and return to the starting city without visiting any city more than once. It is not the only Hamiltonian circuit in the graph.

Summary

- In graph theory, a graph is a set of points connected by line segments or curves. The points are called vertices and the line segments or curves are called edges. If the removal of an edge makes the graph disconnected, the edge is a bridge.

- A path is a connected sequence of edges. If it starts and ends at the same vertex then it is a circuit.

- An Euler path uses every edge once and only once, and an Euler circuit is an Euler path that begins and ends at the same vertex.

- A graph has an Euler path if and only if all the vertices are even, or if exactly two vertices are odd. If all the vertices are even, the path is a circuit. If exactly two vertices are odd, they are the starting and ending points of the path.

- A circuit is a Hamiltonian circuit if it uses every vertex once and only once.

Topology

There is an old math joke that goes, "A topologist is a person who doesn't know the difference between a coffee mug and a doughnut." To a topologist, any two objects with exactly one hole are equivalent, such as a coffee mug and a doughnut—hence the joke. The figure below shows a coffee mug being transformed into a torus, or doughnut.

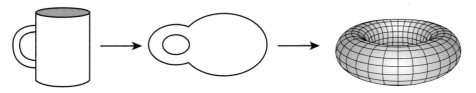

KEYWORDS

Euler characteristic

Möbius strip

topology

torus

invariant

simple closed curve

topologically equivalent

What Is Topology?

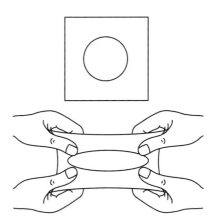

Topology is the study of the properties of a figure that remain unchanged, or **invariant,** when the size and shape of the figure are deformed through continuous bending, twisting, or stretching. As shown at left, a circle can be stretched into an ellipse, or oval shape. For this reason, topology is sometimes called *rubber sheet geometry.* Size and proportion are *not* topological invariants.

Two figures are **topologically equivalent** if one can be transformed into the same shape as the other without tearing or breaking it. The diagram below shows that a circle is topologically equivalent to both an ellipse and a square, but not to three circles fused together.

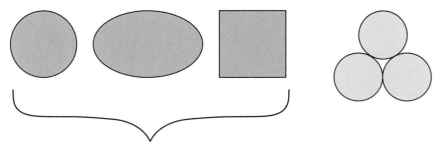

topologically equivalent

The Jordan Curve Theorem

A **simple closed curve** is a curve that does not intersect itself and can be traced by starting at one point and ending at the same point without passing over any part twice. Circles and ellipses are examples of simple closed curves.

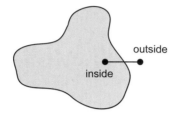

THEOREM 11-2   The Jordan Curve Theorem

Every simple closed curve divides the plane into two distinct regions, the inside and the outside, and every curve that connects a point on the inside to a point on the outside must intersect the curve.

This theorem can be used to answer the classic Three Utilities Problem. Can you connect each of three utilities—water, gas, and electric—to three houses without crossing any of the connections?

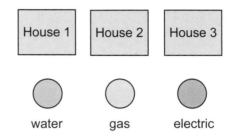

The diagram below shows part of a design. Houses 1 and 2 are connected to all three utilities without any intersections. At this point, House 3 is inside a closed curve as shown in the figure. Because House 3 is on the inside of this curve, and the gas is on the outside, the Jordan Curve Theorem tells us that House 3 cannot be connected to the gas without intersecting the curve.

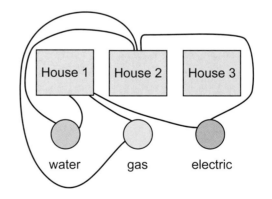

The Jordan Curve Theorem is also used to solve certain maze problems. If the border of a maze consists of a simple closed curve, then you can use the theorem to decide whether a given point is inside or outside the maze.

Two copies of a simple closed curve maze are shown below. On the left, notice that any two points inside the maze can be connected by a segment that crosses the maze border an *even* number of times. The same is true for any two points outside the maze. On the right, you can see that any point inside the maze can be connected to any point outside the maze by a segment that crosses the maze border an *odd* number of times.

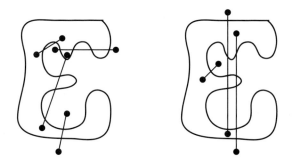

Therefore, if you are asked whether a given point is inside or outside the maze, draw a segment connecting the given point to a point outside the maze. Then count the number of times the segment crosses the maze border. If it crosses an even number of times, then the given point is *outside* the maze. If it crosses an odd number of times, then the given point is *inside* the maze. A simple example is shown below. Is the dot inside or outside the maze?

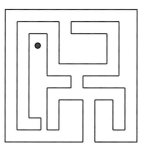

The dot is inside the maze because the segment that joins it to a point outside the maze crosses the curve three times. The maze is shaded to show this.

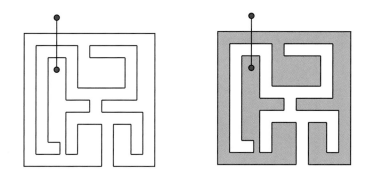

Euler's Formula and the Euler Characteristic

Euler's formula describes the relationship between the vertices, edges, and faces of a polyhedron. Euler's formula is named for the noted Swiss mathematician Leonhard Euler.

Euler's Formula

For any convex polyhedron with V vertices, E edges, and F faces,
$$V - E + F = 2$$

Let's look at a cube as an example. A cube has 8 vertices, 12 edges, and 6 faces.

$$V - E + F = 8 - 12 + 6$$
$$= 2$$

For any polyhedron, the value of the expression $V - E + F$ is called its **Euler characteristic.** Convex polyhedra have an Euler characteristic of 2.

A convex polyhedron has 5 vertices and 8 edges. Use Euler's formula to find the number of faces.

$$V - E + F = 2$$
$$5 - 8 + F = 2$$
$$-3 + F = 2$$
$$F = 5$$

The polyhedron has 5 faces.

Notice that the above definition of the Euler characteristic, in terms of vertices, faces, and edges, only makes sense for polyhedra. In topology, however, figures are considered equivalent when they can be deformed continuously so that they have the same shape. This idea can be used to define the Euler characteristic of a shape that is not a polyhedron, but is topologically equivalent to one. For example, a sphere is topologically equivalent to a cube, and a cube has an Euler characteristic of 2, so a sphere also has an Euler characteristic of 2. It can be shown that when the Euler characteristic is defined in this way, it is a topological invariant.

Notice also that Euler's formula only applies to polyhedra that are convex. Non-convex figures do not always have an Euler characteristic of 2.

For example, the figure below is a non-convex polyhedron called a *tetrahemihexahedron*. It has 6 vertices, 12 edges, and 7 faces, so it has an Euler characteristic of 1.

$$V - E + F = 6 - 12 + 7$$
$$= 1$$

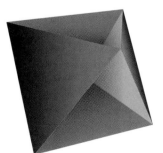

A **Möbius strip** is a surface with only one side (face). Many people who see it think it has two sides, but if you draw a line down the center of one side of it until you reach the starting point again, you will find that there is no side without a line. You can create a Möbius strip by cutting out a long rectangular piece of paper. Hold one end of the rectangle in each hand, give the strip a half-twist, and tape the two ends of the rectangle together. A Möbius strip has 0 vertices, 1 face, and 1 edge, so its Euler characteristic is $0 - 1 + 1 = 0$.

A **torus** is a non-convex figure formed when a circle is rotated about a line that does not intersect the circle. A torus resembles a doughnut or a life preserver. It can be shown that adding a handle to a sphere decreases its Euler characteristic by 2. A torus is topologically equivalent to a sphere with a handle, and a sphere has an Euler characteristic of 2, so a torus has an Euler characteristic of 0.

In topology, you frequently hear of "gluing" parts of a figure together. This process can be used to create models of different figures using rectangles and directed line segments. For example, consider the rectangle below.

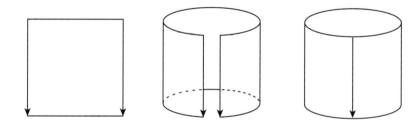

The left and right edges of the rectangle are both *directed* line segments, as indicated by the arrows. Imagine continuously deforming the rectangle to bring the two edges together so that their directions coincide, as shown in the middle. When the edges are joined, the result will be topologically equivalent to a cylindrical band, as shown at the right. This process is called *identifying* the two edges.

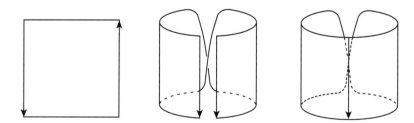

A similar process can model the Möbius strip. Start with a rectangle as before, but reverse the orientations of the left and the right edges.

In order to bring the two edges together so that their directions coincide, you will have to twist the rectangle in space. This represents the half-twist necessary to make a Möbius strip from a rectangular band of paper.

A torus can be modeled by identifying *both* pairs of edges in a rectangle. Consider the rectangle below. All four of its edges are directed line segments, as shown by the arrows.

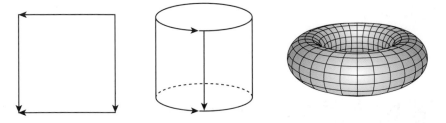

First, identify the left and right edges of the rectangle to form a cylinder. Then identify the circular rings at the top and bottom of the cylinder, so that the arrowheads coincide. The result is topologically equivalent to a torus.

Summary

- Topology studies the properties of a figure that remain unchanged when the size and shape of the figure are changed through continuous distortion, twisting, and stretching. Tearing or breaking of an object is not allowed.

- Two figures are topologically equivalent if one figure can be transformed into the same shape as the other without tearing or breaking it.

- A simple closed curve is a curve that does not intersect itself and can be traced starting at one point and ending at the same point without tracing over any part twice.

- The Jordan Curve Theorem states that every simple closed curve divides the plane into two distinct regions, the inside and the outside, and every curve that connects a point on the inside to a point on the outside must intersect the curve.

- A point is inside a closed curved maze if the segment joining it to a point outside the maze crosses the curve an odd number of times.

- Euler's formula states that for any convex polyhedron with V vertices, E edges, and F faces, $V - E + F = 2$.

- An invariant is a property that does not change when the figure is transformed. The Euler characteristic is a topological invariant.

Spherical Geometry

OBJECTIVES

- ▶ Explain differences between Euclidean and non-Euclidean geometries.
- ▶ Identify and draw lines, segments, planes, and angles in spherical geometry.
- ▶ Identify and draw triangles in spherical geometry.

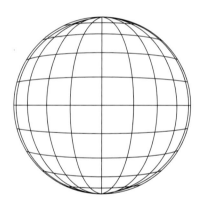

Hundreds of years ago, many people believed that the earth was flat, like a plane. If this were true, then navigation would be much easier because traveling along the earth's surface could be understood in terms of Euclidean geometry. For example, the shortest distance between any two points on the earth's surface would lie along a straight line. Because the earth is not flat, however, Euclidean geometry does not apply, and the problems of navigation are much more difficult. These problems are best understood by using *non-Euclidean geometry*.

KEYWORDS

antipodal   great circle

logically equivalent   non-Euclidean geometry

spherical geometry

Euclidean vs. Non-Euclidean Geometries

The geometry in Euclid's *Elements* begins with five postulates. The fifth postulate, known as the Parallel Postulate, states:

> If two straight lines lying in a plane are met by another line and if the sum of the interior angles on one side is less than two right angles, then the straight lines, if extended sufficiently, will meet on the side on which the sum of the angles is less than two right angles.

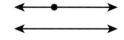

You may think you've never heard of it, but you have, in a sense. You saw a *logically equivalent* form of the parallel postulate in Unit 3. Two statements are **logically equivalent** if each can be proven by using the other. The diagram you are familiar with is shown at left. The wording you are familiar with is:

> Given a line and a point not on the line, there is one and only one line that contains the given point and is parallel to the given line.

After Euclid, many mathematicians thought that the method of indirect proof could be used to derive the Parallel Postulate from the first four postulates. Recall that an indirect proof begins by assuming the negation of the statement to be proven, and then uses deductive reasoning to obtain a contradiction. There are two different ways to negate the Parallel Postulate.

1. Given a line and a point not on the line, there is *no* line that contains the given point and is parallel to the given line.

2. Given a line and a point not on the line, there is *more than one line* that contains the given point and is parallel to the given line.

Mathematicians eventually discovered that neither of these statements leads to a contradiction. Instead, each one leads to a logically consistent form of geometry that is different from the geometry in Euclid's *Elements*. Such a geometry is called a **non-Euclidean geometry**.

Spherical Geometry

The geometry that results from assuming that there is no line containing a given point and parallel to a given line can be modeled in terms of points and circles on the surface of a sphere. For this reason it is called **spherical geometry**.

To understand spherical geometry, first recall that the most basic objects in Euclidean geometry are points and lines. Also recall the following basic relationships between points and lines.

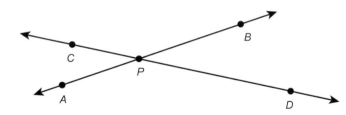

- Any two points determine exactly one line. In the figure above, points *A* and *B* determine a line, and points *C* and *D* determine a different line.

- Any two nonparallel lines determine exactly one point. In the figure above, point *P* is determined by the two lines.

- The shortest distance between any two points lies along the line that they determine.

In spherical geometry, on the other hand, the most basic objects are points and **great circles**. A great circle is a circle on the surface of a sphere whose center coincides with the center of the sphere. Such a circle has the greatest possible diameter of any circle drawn on the surface of the sphere. Two points that have the greatest possible distance between them along the surface of the sphere are called **antipodal**. Antipodal points lie on opposite sides of a great circle, and they can be joined by a segment passing through the center of the sphere.

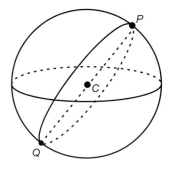

The figure at left shows two great circles on the surface of a sphere with center C. The points P and Q are antipodal.

The basic relationships between points and great circles in spherical geometry are comparable to the basic relationships for points and lines in Euclidean geometry. In particular:

- Any two non-antipodal points on the surface of the sphere determine exactly one great circle. In the figure below, points A and B determine one great circle, and points C and D determine another.

- Any two great circles determine exactly two antipodal points on the surface of the sphere. In the figure below, points P and Q are antipodal points determined by the two great circles.

- The shortest distance between any two points on the surface of a sphere lies along the great circle that these points define.

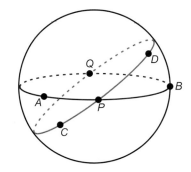

In Euclidean geometry, two lines are parallel if they never intersect. On the surface of a sphere, it is impossible to draw two great circles that do not intersect. So, there is no great circle parallel to a given great circle and passing through a given point on the sphere. This statement coincides with the first negation of the Parallel Postulate.

One application of spherical geometry is in aviation. Because earth has the shape of a sphere, the shortest distance between any two points on its surface lies along a great circle. For this reason, flight paths between many cities lie along great circles. To fly from New York to Tokyo, the shortest path goes along a great circle that goes through northern Canada.

Spherical Triangles

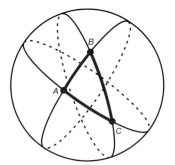

In Euclidean geometry, any three noncollinear points can be joined by segments of lines to form a triangle. In a similar way, three points on the surface of a sphere can be joined by arcs along great circles. The resulting figure is called a spherical triangle. The figure to the left shows a spherical triangle defined by points A, B, and C.

Spherical triangles have different properties than the familiar triangles from Euclidean geometry. For example, the sum of the angle measures in a triangle in Euclidean geometry is always equal to 180°. Also, a triangle in Euclidean geometry cannot have more than one right angle.

On the other hand, the sum of the angle measures in a spherical triangle can be anywhere between 180° and 540°. This means that a spherical triangle can have more than one right angle. The figure below shows a spherical triangle with three right angles.

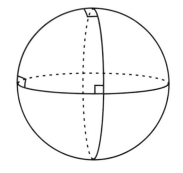

Summary

· ·

- Spherical geometry is one kind of non-Euclidean geometry. Non-Euclidean geometry developed from attempts to prove that Euclid's fifth postulate could be deduced from his first four postulates.

- In spherical geometry, a plane is considered to be a spherical surface, and a line is a great circle of the sphere.

- There are no parallel lines in spherical geometry because all great circles intersect other great circles.

- The sum of the angle measures in a spherical triangle can be anywhere between 180° and 540°.

Fractal Geometry

OBJECTIVES

► Define fractal.

► Build fractals.

► Recognize and explain how to build the Sierpinski Gasket, Koch Snowflake, Cantor Dust, and Menger Sponge fractals.

Though figures that are now called fractals have been around for centuries, the term *fractal* was first used by Benoit Mandelbrot in 1975. He was the first person to use the speed and recursive power of a computer to generate a now-famous fractal called the Mandelbrot set.

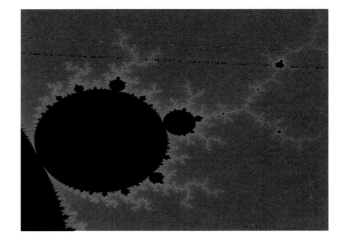

KEYWORDS

Cantor Dust	Cantor Set
fractal	Koch Snowflake
Menger Sponge	recursion
self-similarity	Sierpinski Gasket

What Are Fractals?

A **fractal** is a geometric figure having the property of self-similarity. A figure has **self-similarity** if it is similar to a part or parts of itself. Fractals are constructed by using a repetitive process called **recursion**. In recursion the same sequence of steps is repeated over and over again. There are many different kinds and classifications of fractals. We will look at how a few different fractals are generated.

The Sierpinski Gasket

The **Sierpinski Gasket** is a fractal named after Polish mathematician Waclaw Sierpinski.

Step 0	Step 1	Step 2	Step 3	Step 4

To construct the Sierpinski Gasket:

- Start with an equilateral triangle.

- Join the midpoints of each side to form four equilateral triangles. Remove the middle triangle.

- For each of the remaining equilateral triangles, join the midpoints of each side to form four equilateral triangles and remove the middle triangle.

- Repeat for each successively smaller triangle.

The Koch Snowflake

The **Koch Snowflake** is named after Swedish mathematician Helge von Koch.

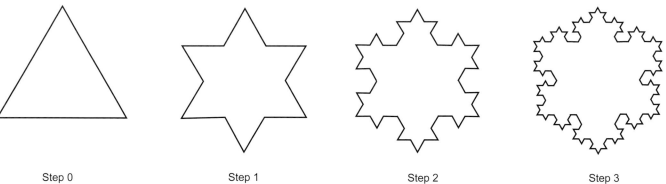

Step 0	Step 1	Step 2	Step 3

To construct the Koch Snowflake:

- Start with an equilateral triangle.
- Divide each side into thirds. On each side, form a new equilateral triangle with the middle third as its base. Then remove the middle third.
- Repeat for each remaining segment.

The Cantor Set and Cantor Dust

The Cantor Set and Cantor Dust were first constructed by German mathematician Georg Cantor.

In the **Cantor Set**, you begin with a segment and remove the middle third, leaving two congruent segments behind. Then you remove the middle third of each of those segments, and continue indefinitely. Each segment represents a set of points. The coordinates of these points are the numbers that make up the Cantor Set.

For example, if you begin with the interval from 0 to 1, you have:

Once the middle third is removed, you have:

And once the middle third of each of those segments is removed, you have:

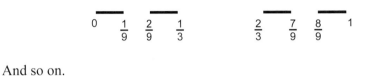

And so on.

Here is **Cantor Dust**:

Step 0   Step 1   Step 2   Step 3   Step 4

To construct the Cantor Dust:

- Start with a square.

- Divide the square into nine congruent squares, and remove the center square as well as the center square from each side.

- For each of the remaining four squares, divide each into nine congruent squares and remove the center square and the center square from each side.

- Repeat for each successively smaller square.

The Menger Sponge

The **Menger Sponge** was first described by Austrian mathematician Karl Menger. It is a three-dimensional fractal.

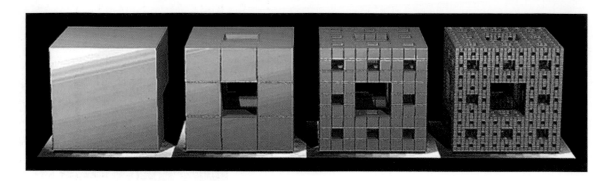

To construct the Menger Sponge:

- Start with a cube.

- Divide the cube into 27 congruent cubes and remove the center cube as well as the center cube from each face.

- For each of the remaining 20 cubes, divide each into 27 congruent cubes and remove the center cube and the center cube of each face.

- Repeat for each successively smaller cube.

On paper, you can only build fractals through a finite number of steps because the shapes become too small to break down further. But in actuality, fractals have an infinite number of steps. Computers have allowed mathematicians the ability to see more steps than they could have ever constructed by hand. Once color is added, some are so beautiful they can be viewed as works of art.

Fractals can be used to model natural phenomena such as fern leaves, crystal growth, tree branches, coastlines, and other features.

Summary

- A fractal is a geometric figure having the property of self-similarity and is constructed by using an iterative process called recursion.

- The Sierpinski Gasket, Koch Snowflake, Cantor Dust, and Menger Sponge are examples of fractals.

- Fractals have an infinite number of iterations. Computer technology has allowed mathematicians to take fractals to a level not possible with paper and pencil.

Projective Geometry

Projective geometry began with the study of perspective drawing during the Renaissance. Before that time artists were concerned more with what a painting or drawing was depicting than they were with it looking realistic to the eye. That all changed when the Renaissance artists were able to master the mathematics required to create the illusion of depth.

KEYWORDS

affine transformation   center of projection

central projection   projective rays

What Is Projective Geometry?

A projection is the directing, or transmitting, of something onto a surface, as a film is said to be projected onto a screen. A projection can also be defined as a representation of a figure as it would look from a particular direction. For instance, a square viewed from an angle can appear to be a different-shaped quadrilateral.

Projective geometry deals with the properties of plane figures that do not change when they are projected. In projective geometry, a projection is defined as a transformation of points and lines from one plane to another. This is why projective geometry formerly was called the geometry of position. In the figure below, the triangle in red is projected onto another plane to create the triangle colored in blue.

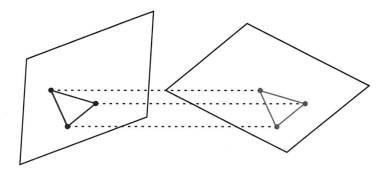

This projection is an **affine transformation.** An affine transformation preserves straight lines (the pre-image points that were collinear were projected into image points that were also collinear), ratios of distances (a midpoint of a segment in the pre-image will project onto a midpoint of a segment in the image), and parallel lines (any parallel lines in a pre-image are also parallel in the image). All of the transformations you have studied so far—reflections, rotations, translations, and dilations—have been affine transformations.

Central projection can be viewed as a transformation that transforms points of a figure along lines, or **projective rays**, that meet at a single point called the **center of projection.** In the figure below, P is the center of projection. The plane the pre-image lies on is not parallel to the plane the image lies on, which creates a distorted view of the figure. Notice that while $\overline{AB}$ is parallel to $\overline{CD}$ in the pre-image, $\overline{A'B'}$ is not parallel to $\overline{C'D'}$ in the image because they lie on lines that meet at point Q. Because the parallel lines did not remain parallel, this central projection is not an affine transformation.

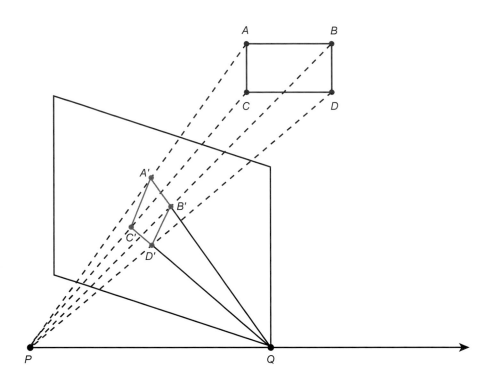

A central projection through parallel planes, such as in one-point perspective, is an affine transformation. The result in that case is a dilation.

Pappus's Theorem and Desargues' Theorem

There are two theorems in projective geometry that seem to get the most attention: Pappus's Theorem and Desargues' Theorem. First we look at Pappus's Theorem, which was discovered by Pappus of Alexandria in the third century.

THEOREM 11–3 Pappus's Theorem

If A_1, B_1, and C_1 are three distinct points on a line, and A_2, B_2, and C_2 are three distinct points on another, and if $\overline{A_1 B_2}$ and $\overline{A_2 B_1}$ intersect at point X, $\overline{A_1 C_2}$ and $\overline{A_2 C_1}$ intersect at point Y, and $\overline{B_1 C_2}$ and $\overline{B_2 C_1}$ intersect at point Z, then points X, Y, and Z are collinear.

You can explore this theorem with geometry software. Study the following sketch. The point where the red lines intersect, the point where the green lines intersect, and the point where the blue lines intersect all lie on the yellow line. This remains true even as points and lines are dragged around.

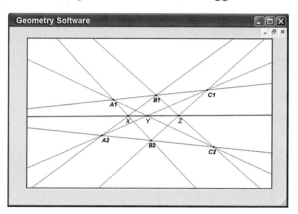

Gérard Desargues, born in the sixteenth century, is considered to be one of the founders of projective geometry and discovered the following.

THEOREM 11–4 Desargues' Theorem

If one triangle is a projection of another triangle, then the intersections of the lines containing the corresponding sides of the two triangles are collinear.

In the diagram below, $\triangle A'B'C'$ is a projection of $\triangle ABC$. The dashed lines are the projective rays from point P. The intersection of $\overleftrightarrow{AB}$ with $\overleftrightarrow{A'B'}$, the intersection of $\overleftrightarrow{AC}$ with $\overleftrightarrow{A'C'}$, and the intersection of $\overleftrightarrow{BC}$ with $\overleftrightarrow{B'C'}$ all lie on the same line.

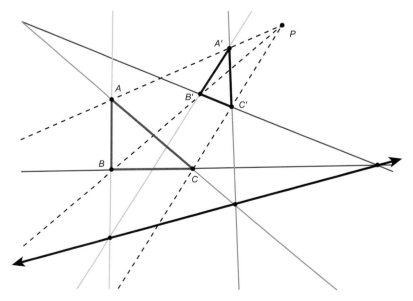

Summary

· ·

- Projective geometry deals with the properties of plane figures that do not change when they are transformed from one plane to another.

- Affine transformations preserve straight lines, ratios of distances, and parallel lines.

- Pappus's Theorem states if A_1, B_1, and C_1 are three distinct points on a line, and A_2, B_2, C_2 are three distinct points on another, and if $\overleftrightarrow{A_1 B_2}$ and $\overleftrightarrow{A_2 B_1}$ intersect at point X, $\overleftrightarrow{A_1 C_2}$ and $\overleftrightarrow{A_2 C_1}$ intersect at point Y, and $\overleftrightarrow{B_1 C_2}$ and $\overleftrightarrow{B_2 C_1}$ intersect at point Z, then points X, Y, and Z are collinear.

- Desargues' Theorem states if one triangle is a projection of another triangle, then the intersections of the lines containing the corresponding sides of the two triangles are collinear.

Computer Logic

OBJECTIVES

► Define the binary number system and switch from base 2 to base 10.

► Create input-output tables for logic gates.

► Write logical expressions for networks of gates.

► Create input-output tables for networks of gates.

How does a computer know what to do? Everything a computer can do is based on instructions someone gave it in a computer program. Computers today are capable of making millions of decisions in an incredibly short amount of time. But no matter how fast the processing speed, the decisions are still made one at a time using Boolean logic. In Unit 2, you learned about truth tables. Boolean logic is an extension of truth tables. Both computer hardware circuitry and computer software use Boolean logic in their design.

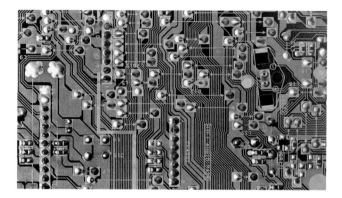

KEYWORDS

binary number system

input-output table

logic gate

The Binary Number System

Computers use digital technology. When you make a request to a computer, for example, to go to a website or to print a document, that request is translated into binary digits or bits to be understood and processed by the computer. When you store data on a computer, both numbers and characters are stored in a binary format. The **binary number system**, or base 2 number system, uses two digits—0 and 1—to represent numbers. In the base 10 number system, each place value is a power of 10. In the binary number system, each place value is a power of 2.

The number $10011_{\text{base 2}}$ is shown below along with each place value.

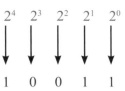

$$2^4 \quad 2^3 \quad 2^2 \quad 2^1 \quad 2^0$$

$$1 \quad 0 \quad 0 \quad 1 \quad 1$$

What is the number $10011_{\text{base 2}}$ equal to in our base 10 system?

REMEMBER

A nonzero number raised to a power of 0 is equal to 1.

$$(1 \times 2^4) + (0 \times 2^3) + (0 \times 2^2) + (1 \times 2^1) + (1 \times 2^0)$$

$$16 \quad + \quad 0 \quad + \quad 0 \quad + \quad 2 \quad + \quad 1 \quad = 19$$

$$10011_{\text{base 2}} = 19_{\text{base 10}}$$

Many decisions must be made by a computer. Some of those decisions are logical decisions. For example, a computer program may want to test the compound condition "Is $x > 8$ and $y > 7$?" This compound condition is a logical statement connected by the word AND. Digital circuits are used to correctly evaluate logical instructions. The computer uses circuitry called a **logic gate** to determine if the compound condition is true or false. Let's examine the logic gates for NOT, AND, and OR and the **input-output table** associated with each.

Logic Gates

Logic gates work by receiving electronic pulses. In a digital model an electronic pulse is either on or off. Think of turning on a light switch. When you flip it on, the light turns on, and when you flip it off, the light goes out. In a logic gate, 1 represents ON or TRUE, and 0 represents OFF or FALSE. If you substitute true for 1 and false for 0 in the input-output tables, they become identical to truth tables, which you should be familiar with.

AND gates use the logical operation *and* to evaluate two conditions, A and B. The symbol for an AND gate and its input-output table are shown below.

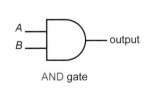

AND gate

Input		Output
A	*B*	*A* AND *B*
1	1	1
1	0	0
0	1	0
0	0	0

OR gates use the logical operation *inclusive or* to evaluate two conditions, *A* and *B*. The symbol for an OR gate and its input-output table are shown below.

OR gate

Input		Output
A	*B*	*A* OR *B*
1	1	1
1	0	1
0	1	1
0	0	0

NOT gates negate a single condition, *A*. The symbol for a NOT gate and its input-output table are shown below.

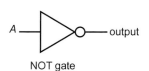

NOT gate

Input	Output
A	NOT *A*
1	0
0	1

Networks of Logic Gates

Since the output of a logic gate is a 1 or 0, it can be used as input to another logic gate. This creates a network of logic gates for more complex compound conditions. Look at the network below. *A* and *B* enter an OR gate, then the result and *B* enter an AND gate, and that result enters a NOT gate.

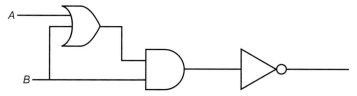

To complete the input-output table, use each possible value for *A* and *B* and evaluate the expression NOT((*A* OR *B*) AND *B*). Just as in algebraic expressions, parentheses are worked from the inside out in logical expressions. One example is shown below.

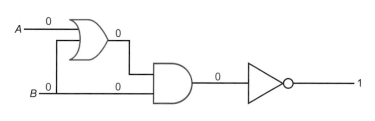

Input		Output
A	*B*	NOT ((*A* OR *B*) AND *B*)
1	1	0
1	0	1
0	1	0
0	0	1

Summary

- The binary number system uses two digits—0 and 1—to represent numbers. A computer's data and instructions are stored in binary numbers.

- In the binary, or base 2, system, each place value is a power of 2.

- Logic gates are used in the design of computer hardware and are used to evaluate logical expressions. Similar to truth tables, they use AND, OR, and NOT.

Postulates and Theorems

POSTULATE 1-1 Two points determine a line.

POSTULATE 1-2 Three noncollinear points determine a plane.

POSTULATE 1-3 Ruler Postulate
The points on a line can be numbered so that positive number differences measure distances.

POSTULATE 1-4 Segment Addition Postulate
If B is between A and C, then $AB + BC = AC$. Also, if $AB + BC = AC$ and A, B, and C are collinear, then B is between A and C.

POSTULATE 1-5 Segment Congruence Postulate If two segments have the same length as measured by a fair ruler, then the segments are congruent ($\cong$). Also, if two segments are congruent, then they have the same length as measured by a fair ruler.

POSTULATE 1-6 Angle Addition Postulate
If point D lies in the interior of $\angle ABC$, then $m\angle ABD + m\angle DBC = m\angle ABC$.

POSTULATE 1-7 Angle Congruence Postulate
If two angles have the same measure as measured by a protractor, then the angles are congruent. Also, if two angles are congruent, then they have the same measure as measured by a protractor.

POSTULATE 1-8 Linear Pair Postulate
If two angles form a linear pair, then they are supplementary angles.

THEOREM 2-1 Theorem of Overlapping Segments If point B is between A and C and point C is between B and D, then $AB = CD$ iff $AC = BD$.

THEOREM 2-2 Theorem of Overlapping Angles If point B lies in the interior of $\angle AWC$ and point C lies in the interior of $\angle BWD$, then $m\angle AWB = m\angle CWD$ iff $m\angle AWC = m\angle BWD$.

THEOREM 2-3 Vertical Angles Theorem
If two angles form a pair of vertical angles, then they are congruent.

POSTULATE 3-1 Corresponding Angles Postulate If two parallel lines are intersected by a transversal, then corresponding angles are congruent.

THEOREM 3-1 Alternate Interior Angles Theorem If two parallel lines are intersected by a transversal, then the alternate interior angles are congruent.

THEOREM 3-2 Alternate Exterior Angles Theorem If two parallel lines are intersected by a transversal, then the alternate exterior angles are congruent.

THEOREM 3-3 Same-Side Interior Angles Theorem If two parallel lines are intersected by a transversal, then the same-side interior angles are supplementary.

POSTULATE 3-2 Converse of the Corresponding Angles Postulate If two coplanar lines are intersected by a transversal and the corresponding angles are congruent, then the lines are parallel.

THEOREM 3-4 Converse of the Alternate Interior Angles Theorem If two coplanar lines are intersected by a transversal and the alternate interior angles are congruent, then the lines are parallel.

THEOREM 3-5 Converse of the Alternate Exterior Angles Theorem If two coplanar lines are intersected by a transversal and the alternate exterior angles are congruent, then the lines are parallel.

THEOREM 3-6 Converse of the Same-Side Interior Angles Theorem If two coplanar lines are intersected by a transversal and the same-side interior angles are supplementary, then the lines are parallel.

THEOREM 3-7 If two coplanar lines are perpendicular to the same line, then the two lines are parallel.

THEOREM 3-8 If two coplanar lines are parallel to the same line, then the two lines are parallel.

POSTULATE 3-3 Parallel Postulate Given a line and a point not on the line, there is one and only one line that contains the given point and is parallel to the given line.

THEOREM 3-9 Triangle Sum Theorem The sum of the measures of the interior angles of a triangle is 180°.

THEOREM 3-10 Exterior Angle Theorem The measure of an exterior angle of a triangle is equal to the sum of the measures of the remote interior angles.

THEOREM 3-11 Parallel Lines Theorem Two coplanar nonvertical lines are parallel if and only if they have the same slope. Any two vertical lines are parallel.

THEOREM 3-12 Perpendicular Lines Theorem Two coplanar nonvertical lines are perpendicular if and only if the product of their slopes equals –1. Any vertical line is perpendicular to any horizontal line.

POSTULATE 4-1 Polygon Congruence Postulate Two polygons are congruent if and only if there is a correspondence between their sides and angles so that all pairs of corresponding angles are congruent and all pairs of corresponding sides are congruent.

POSTULATE 4-2 SSS (Side-Side-Side) Congruence Postulate If the three sides of one triangle are congruent to the three sides of another triangle, then the two triangles are congruent.

POSTULATE 4-3 SAS (Side-Angle-Side) Congruence Postulate If two sides and the included angle in one triangle are congruent to two sides and the included angle in another triangle, then the two triangles are congruent.

POSTULATE 4-4 ASA (Angle-Side-Angle) Congruence Postulate If two angles and the included side in one triangle are congruent to two angles and the included side in another triangle, then the two triangles are congruent.

THEOREM 4-1 Isosceles Triangle Theorem If two sides of a triangle are congruent, then the angles opposite those sides are congruent.

THEOREM 4-2 Converse of the Isosceles Triangle Theorem If two angles of a triangle are congruent, then the sides opposite those angles are congruent.

THEOREM 4-3 AAS (Angle-Angle-Side) Congruence Theorem If two angles and a non-included side of one triangle are congruent to the corresponding angles and non-included side of another triangle, then the two triangles are congruent.

THEOREM 4-4   Hypotenuse-Leg (HL) Congruence Theorem If the hypotenuse and a leg of one right triangle are congruent to the hypotenuse and corresponding leg of another right triangle, then the two triangles are congruent.

THEOREM 4-5   If two pairs of opposite sides of a quadrilateral are congruent, then the quadrilateral is a parallelogram.

THEOREM 4-6   If two opposite sides of a quadrilateral are parallel and congruent, then the quadrilateral is a parallelogram.

THEOREM 4-7   If the diagonals of a quadrilateral bisect each other, then the quadrilateral is a parallelogram.

THEOREM 4-8   If one angle of a parallelogram is a right angle, then the parallelogram is a rectangle.

THEOREM 4-9   If the diagonals of a parallelogram are congruent, then the parallelogram is a rectangle.

THEOREM 4-10   If the diagonals of a parallelogram are perpendicular, then the parallelogram is a rhombus.

THEOREM 4-11   If two adjacent sides of a parallelogram are congruent, then the parallelogram is a rhombus.

THEOREM 4-12   If the diagonals of a parallelogram bisect the angles of the parallelogram, then the parallelogram is a rhombus.

THEOREM 4-13   In a triangle, the angle opposite the longer side is greater than the angle opposite the shorter side.

THEOREM 4-14   In a triangle, the side opposite the greater angle is longer than the side opposite the lesser angle.

THEOREM 4-15   Triangle Inequality Theorem The sum of the lengths of any two sides of a triangle is greater than the length of the third side.

POSTULATE 5-1   Area Sum Postulate If a figure is made up of nonoverlapping regions, then the area of the figure is the sum of the areas of the regions.

THEOREM 5-1   The Pythagorean Theorem For all right triangles, the square of the length of the hypotenuse c equals the sum of the squares of the lengths of the legs a and b: $c^2 = a^2 + b^2$.

THEOREM 5-2   The Converse of the Pythagorean Theorem If the square of the length of the longest side of a triangle equals the sum of the squares of the lengths of the other two sides, then the triangle is a right triangle.

THEOREM 5-3   45°-45°-90° Triangle Theorem In any 45°-45°-90° triangle, the length of the hypotenuse is $\sqrt{2}$ times the length of a leg.

THEOREM 5-4   30°-60°-90° Triangle Theorem In any 30°-60°-90° triangle, the length of the hypotenuse is 2 times the length of the shorter leg, and the length of the longer leg is $\sqrt{3}$ times the length of the shorter leg.

THEOREM 5-5   Area of a Regular Polygon Theorem The area A of a regular polygon with apothem a and perimeter P is $A = \frac{1}{2}aP$.

POSTULATE 8-1   Polygon Similarity Postulate
Two polygons are similar if and only if there is a correspondence between their angles and their sides so that all corresponding angles are congruent and all corresponding sides are proportional.

POSTULATE 8-2   Angle-Angle (AA) Similarity Postulate If two angles of one triangle are congruent to two angles of another triangle, then the triangles are similar.

THEOREM 8-1   Side-Side-Side (SSS) Similarity Theorem If the three sides of one triangle are proportional to the three sides of another triangle, then the triangles are similar.

THEOREM 8-2   Side-Angle-Side (SAS) Similarity Theorem If two sides of one triangle are proportional to two sides of another triangle and if their included angles are congruent, then the triangles are similar.

THEOREM 8-3   Side-Splitting Theorem A line parallel to one side of a triangle divides the other two sides proportionally.

COROLLARY 8-1   Two-Transversal Proportionality Corollary Three or more parallel lines divide two intersecting transversals proportionally.

THEOREM 8-4   Proportional Altitudes Theorem
If two triangles are similar, then their corresponding altitudes have the same ratio as their corresponding sides.

THEOREM 8-5   Proportional Angle Bisectors Theorem If two triangles are similar, then their corresponding angle bisectors have the same ratio as their corresponding sides.

THEOREM 8-6   Proportional Medians Theorem
If two triangles are similar, then their corresponding medians have the same ratio as their corresponding sides.

THEOREM 8-7   Proportional Segments Theorem An angle bisector of a triangle divides the opposite side into two segments that have the same ratio as the other two sides.

THEOREM 9-1 Chords and Arcs Theorem
In a circle or in congruent circles, the arcs of congruent chords are congruent.

THEOREM 9-2   Converse of the Chords and Arcs Theorem In a circle or in congruent circles, the chords of congruent arcs are congruent.

THEOREM 9-3   The Tangent Theorem
A line that is tangent to a circle is perpendicular to a radius of the circle at the point of tangency.

THEOREM 9-4   The Converse of the Tangent Theorem A line that is perpendicular to a radius of a circle at its endpoint on the circle is tangent to the circle.

THEOREM 9-5   The Radius and Chord Theorem
A radius that is perpendicular to a chord of a circle bisects the chord.

THEOREM 9-6   Inscribed Angle Theorem
An angle inscribed in a circle has a measure that equals one-half the measure of its intercepted arc.

COROLLARY 9-1   Right-Angle Corollary
An angle that is inscribed in a semicircle is a right angle.

COROLLARY 9-2 Arc-Intercept Corollary
Two inscribed angles that intercept the same arc have the same measure.

THEOREM 9-7 If a tangent and a secant or chord intersect on a circle at the point of tangency, then the measure of the angle formed equals one-half the measure of the intercepted arc.

THEOREM 9-8 The measure of a secant-tangent angle with its vertex outside the circle equals one-half of the difference of the measures of the intercepted arcs.

THEOREM 9-9 The measure of an angle that is formed by two secants that intersect in the exterior of a circle equals one-half of the difference of the measures of the intercepted arcs.

THEOREM 9-10 The measure of a tangent-tangent angle with its vertex outside the circle equals one-half of the difference of the measures of the intercepted arcs, or the measure of the major arc minus $180°$.

THEOREM 9-11 The measure of an angle that is formed by two secants or chords that intersect in the interior of a circle equals one-half the sum of the measures of the arcs intercepted by the angle and its vertical angle.

THEOREM 9-12 Two segments that are tangent to a circle from the same external point are of equal length.

THEOREM 9-13 If two secants intersect outside a circle, then the product of the lengths of one secant segment and its external segment equals the product of the lengths of the other secant segment and its external segment.
(Whole × Outside = Whole × Outside)

THEOREM 9-14 If a secant and a tangent intersect outside a circle, then the product of the lengths of the secant segment and its external segment equals the length of the tangent segment squared.
(Whole × Outside = Tangent²)

THEOREM 9-15 If two chords intersect inside a circle, then the product of the lengths of the segments of one chord equals the product of the lengths of the segments of the other chord.

THEOREM 11-1 Euler Path Theorem A graph has an Euler path if and only if one of the following is true:
• Exactly two vertices have an odd degree.
• Every vertex has an even degree.

THEOREM 11-2 The Jordan Curve Theorem
Every simple closed curve divides the plane into two distinct regions, the inside and the outside, and every curve that connects a point on the inside to a point on the outside must intersect the curve.

THEOREM 11-3 Pappus's Theorem
If A_1, B_1, and C_1 are three distinct points on a line, and A_2, B_2, and C_2 are three distinct points on another, and if $\overline{A_1 B_2}$ and $\overline{A_2 B_1}$ intersect at point X, $\overline{A_1 C_2}$ and $\overline{A_2 C_1}$ intersect at point Y, and $\overline{B_1 C_2}$ and $\overline{B_2 C_1}$ intersect at point Z, then points X, Y, and Z are collinear.

THEOREM 11-4 Desargues' Theorem
If one triangle is a projection of another triangle, then the intersections of the lines containing the corresponding sides of the two triangles are collinear.

Pronunciation Guide

The table below provides sample words to explain the sounds associated with specific letters and letter combinations used in the respellings in this book. For example, *a* represents the short "a" sound in *cat*, while *ay* represents the long "a" sound in *day*.

Letter combinations are used to approximate certain more complex sounds. For example, in the respelling of *trapezoid*—TRA-puh-zoyd—the letters *uh* represent the vowel sound you hear in *shut* and *other*.

Vowels

a	short a: apple, cat
ay	long a: cane, day
e, eh	short e: hen, bed
ee	long e: feed, team
i, ih	short i: lip, active
iy	long i: try, might
ah	short o: hot, father
oh	long o: home, throw
uh	short u: shut, other
yoo	long u: union, cute

Letter Combinations

ch	chin, ancient
sh	show, mission
zh	vision, azure
th	thin, health
th	then, heather
ur	bird, further, word
us	bus, crust
or	court, formal
ehr	error, care
oo	cool, true, rule
ow	now, out
ou	look, pull, would
oy	coin, toy
aw	saw, maul, fall
ng	song, finger
air	Aristotle, barrister
ahr	cart, martyr

Consonants

b	butter, baby
d	dog, cradle
f	fun, phone
g	grade, angle
h	hat, ahead
j	judge, gorge
k	kite, car, black
l	lily, mile
m	mom, camel
n	next, candid
p	price, copper
r	rubber, free
s	small, circle, hassle
t	ton, pottery
v	vase, vivid
w	wall, away
y	yellow, kayak
z	zebra, haze

Glossary

30°-60°-90° triangle a triangle with angle measures of 30°, 60°, and 90°

45°-45°-90° triangle a triangle with angle measures of 45°, 45°, and 90°

acute angle an angle that measures less than 90°

acute triangle a triangle with three acute angles

adjacent angles two angles with a common side and a common vertex but with no common points in their interiors

adjacent side in a right triangle, the side that is adjacent to the acute angle being discussed but is not the hypotenuse

affine (a-FIYN) transformation a transformation that preserves straight lines, ratios of distances, and parallel lines

alternate exterior angles the outside angles on opposite diagonal sides of a transversal crossing two lines

alternate interior angles the inside angles on opposite diagonal sides of a transversal crossing two lines

altitude a perpendicular line segment that measures the height of a geometric figure

altitude of a parallelogram a perpendicular segment that extends from a line containing the base of the parallelogram to the line containing the side opposite the base

altitude of a trapezoid a perpendicular segment that extends from the line containing one base of the trapezoid to a line containing the other base

altitude of a triangle a perpendicular segment from a vertex of the triangle to a line containing the base opposite the vertex

angle the figure formed by two rays, called sides, that share the same endpoint

angle bisector a line, line segment, or ray that divides an angle into two congruent angles

annulus (AN-yuh-luhs) the region between two concentric circles

antipodal (an-TIH-puh-duhl) lying on opposite sides of a great circle

apothem (A-puh-them) a line segment that is drawn from the center of a regular polygon to a side and is perpendicular to that side

arc on a circle, an unbroken part that is formed by two points on the circle and the continuous part of the circle between the two points

arc length part of the circumference of a circle

area the number of square units contained in the interior of a figure

argument a set of statements, called premises, that are used to reach a conclusion

axis of a cylinder the line connecting the centers of the bases of a cylinder

axis of revolution a line about which a plane figure is revolved to create a solid (*See* solid of revolution)

axis of symmetry a line drawn through a figure so that one side is a reflection of the image on the opposite side; also called line of symmetry

base the bottom side or face of a geometric figure

base angle in an isosceles triangle, either of the two angles opposite the legs

base area of a prism, *B* the area of one of the two bases (triangular, rectangular, etc.) of a prism (*See* the Formulary for how to find the area of various figures.)

base of a parallelogram the designated side of a parallelogram that is considered the bottom side or face; any side of a parallelogram can be its base

base of a triangle the designated side of a triangle that is considered the bottom side or face

base edge one of the edges of a base of a prism or pyramid

bases of a prism the parallel, congruent faces of a prism

bases of a trapezoid the pair of parallel sides of a trapezoid

between the position of a point that has collinear points on either side; if point B is between points A and C, then the length of $\overline{AB}$ plus the length of $\overline{BC}$ equals the length of $\overline{AC}$

biconditional statement a true statement that uses the phrase *if and only if* and whose converse is also true

binary number system a system that uses only two digits—0 and 1—to represent all numbers; also called base 2 number system

block in taxicab geometry, a square that is part of the grid that is used to measure distance along paths

bridge in graph theory, an edge whose removal would disconnect the graph

Cantor Dust a fractal created by dividing a square into nine congruent smaller squares, removing all but the four corner squares, then repeating the process indefinitely

Cantor Set a fractal created by dividing a segment into three congruent smaller segments, removing the middle third, then repeating the process indefinitely; each segment represents a set of points, the coordinates of which are the numbers that make up the set

center of a circle a point in a circle that is the same distance *r* from the set of all points that make up the circle

center of a regular polygon the point inside a regular polygon that is equidistant from each vertex

center of dilation in a dilation transformation, the point of intersection of the lines connecting each point on a pre-image with its corresponding point on an image

center of projection in central projection, the point where the lines of transformation of a figure intersect

central angle an angle that has as its vertex the center of a figure

central projection a transformation of the points of a figure along lines, or projective rays, that meet at a single point

centroid the point of intersection of the three medians of a triangle

chord a line segment that connects any two points on a circle

circle the set of all points in a plane that are the same distance, *r*, from a fixed point called the center

circuit in graph theory, a path that begins and ends at the same vertex

circumcenter (SUHR-kuhm-sen-tur) the point at which the perpendicular bisectors of each side of a triangle meet

circumference (suhr-KUHM-fruhnts) the perimeter of a circle

circumscribed encircling and touching each vertex of another figure; a circle is circumscribed about a triangle if each vertex of the triangle lies on the circle

collinear (kuh-LIH-nee-uhr) lying on the same line

complementary angles a pair of angles for which the sum of their measures is 90°

compound statement a statement that connects two statements with either the word *and* or the word *or*

concave polygon a polygon in which at least one line segment that connects any two points inside the polygon does not lie completely inside the polygon

concentric having the same center

conclusion in an argument, the answer that is reached at the end of the statement of premises; in a conditional statement, the words following the word *then*

conditional statement a statement in the form "if *p* then *q*" in which the hypothesis (the "if" part) implies the conclusion (the "then" part)

cone a solid with a circular base, a vertex, and a curved surface

congruent angles angles that have equal measure

congruent arcs arcs with equal arc length

congruent circles circles with congruent radii

congruent figures figures that have the same size and shape

congruent line segments line segments that have equal length

congruent polygon polygons that have the same size and shape

conjunction a compound statement that has two statements connected by the word *and*; a conjunction is true if and only if both statements are true

contraction a dilation for which the absolute value of the scale factor, as related to the pre-image, is between 0 and 1

contradiction a statement that disagrees with another statement and can be used to prove that an assumption is false

contrapositive a conditional statement that both switches and negates the hypothesis and the conclusion of the original conditional statement

converse a conditional statement that switches the hypothesis and the conclusion of the original conditional statement

convex polygon a polygon in which every line segment connecting any two points inside the polygon lies completely inside the polygon

coordinate a number on a number line or axis, giving the location of a point

coordinate axis a reference line in a coordinate system; for example, the *x*-axis and *y*-axis in the coordinate plane

coordinate plane a plane in which the coordinates of a point are its distances from two intersecting perpendicular lines called axes

coplanar (koh-PLAY-nuhr) lying in the same plane

corollary a proposition that follows directly from a postulate or theorem and can be proven easily

corresponding angles the angles that lie in the same position or "match up" when a transversal crosses two parallel lines

corresponding angles of polygons the angles of two or more polygons that lie in the same position

corresponding sides of polygons the sides of two or more polygons that lie in the same position

cosine ratio in a right triangle, the ratio of the length of the adjacent leg of an acute angle to the length of the hypotenuse

counterexample an example that shows that a conjecture, statement, or theory is not a valid generalization

CPCTC abbreviation for "corresponding parts of congruent triangles are congruent"

cross section the intersection of a plane and a solid

cube a right rectangular prism on which every face is a square

cylinder a solid with two parallel, congruent, circular bases joined by a curved surface

deductive reasoning a type of reasoning that uses previously proven or accepted properties to reach conclusions

degree of a vertex in graph theory, the number of edges connected to a vertex

depth the length of a three-dimensional figure from the front to the back

diagonal of a polyhedron a line segment that joins two vertices that are in different faces

diagonals segments that connect two vertices of a polygon and do not lie along any side of the polygon

diameter a line segment that connects two points on a circle and contains the center of the circle

dihedral angle an angle formed by two noncoplanar half-planes and their line of intersection

dilation a transformation that changes the size, but not the shape, of a figure

direct proof a method of proving theorems, in which the conclusion is drawn directly from previous conclusions, starting with the first statement

disjunction a compound statement that has two statements connected by the word *or*; a disjunction is false only when both statements are false

edge of a graph in graph theory, a line segment or curve that connects two vertices

edge of a polyhedron an intersection of two of the faces

equiangular polygon a polygon with all angles congruent

equilateral polygon a polygon with all sides congruent

equilateral triangle a triangle with three congruent sides

Euler (OY-lur) characteristic in topology, for a polyhedron, the value of the expression $V - E + F$

Euler circuit in graph theory, an Euler path that begins and ends at the same vertex

Euler path in graph theory, a path that uses every edge once and only once

even vertex in graph theory, a vertex that connects an even number of edges

exclusive *or* a disjunction that excludes the case where both p and q are true

expansion a dilation for which the absolute value of the scale factor, as related to the pre-image, is greater than 1

exterior angle of a polygon an angle formed by two sides of a polygon, one of which extends outside the polygon; each interior angle of a polygon forms a linear pair with an exterior angle

exterior of an angle the region outside the sides that make up an angle

external secant segment a secant segment that lies in the exterior of the circle with one of its endpoints on the circle

extremes in a proportion, the first and last numbers or variables; in $a : b = c : d$ or $\frac{a}{b} = \frac{c}{d}$, a and d are the extremes

face a flat surface of a polyhedron

first octant in a three-dimensional coordinate system, the plane in which the values of x, y, and z are all positive

fractal a geometric figure having the property of self-similarity

geodesic (jee-uh-DEE-zik) the path of the shortest distance between two points on a given surface; for example, on a plane, the geodesics are lines; on a sphere, the geodesics are great circles

golden ratio a ratio of about 8 to 5, or 1.618; the exact ratio is $\frac{1 + \sqrt{5}}{2}$

golden rectangle a rectangle with a length-to-width ratio equal to the golden ratio

graph in graph theory, a set of points (vertices) connected by line segments or curves (edges)

great circle a circle on the surface of a sphere that has a diameter that is a diameter of the sphere

half-plane a figure that consists of all the points on either side of a line that divides a plane

Hamiltonian circuit in graph theory, a circuit that uses every vertex once and only once

height the length of an altitude of a figure

hypotenuse (hiy-PAH-tn-oos) the side opposite the right angle in a right triangle

hypothesis (hiy-PAH-thuh-sis) in a conditional statement, the words that follow *if* and precede *then*; the plural of hypothesis is hypotheses (hiy-PAH-thuh-seez)

identity in trigonometry, an equation containing a trigonometric ratio that is true for all values of the variable

iff abbreviation for *if and only if*

image in a transformation, the figure that is the result of the transformation

incenter the center of the circle that can be inscribed within a figure

included angle the angle between two sides of a triangle

included side the side between two angles of a triangle

inclusive *or* a disjunction that includes the case where both *p* and *q* are true

indirect measurement a way of measuring a quantity that is difficult to measure by comparing it to a standard ruler or scale

indirect proof a type of proof in which the first step is to assume the opposite of what is to be proven; also called proof by contradiction

inductive reasoning a type of reasoning that is based on observations of patterns and past events

input-output table in computer logic, a table that records the outputs for all possible inputs for a set of logic gates

inscribed angle an angle that has its vertex on a circle and its sides as chords of the circle

inscribed circle a circle inside a figure and touching exactly one point on each side of the figure

intercept in space, a point where a figure such as a plane crosses an axis

intercepted arc in an inscribed angle, the arc whose endpoints mark where the sides meet the circle

interior angle any of the angles inside a polygon; an interior angle forms a linear pair with an exterior angle

interior of an angle the region between the two sides of an angle

invariant in topology, the characteristic of a figure of remaining unchanged when bent, twisted, or stretched

inverse a conditional statement that negates both the hypothesis and the conclusion of the original conditional statement

inverse cosine the angle that has a given value as its cosine ratio; ususally denoted $\cos^{-1}$

inverse sine the angle that has a given value as its sine ratio; usually denoted $\sin^{-1}$

inverse tangent the angle that has a given value as its tangent ratio; usually denoted $\tan^{-1}$

isometric drawing a drawing that shows three sides of a solid figure from a corner view; segments that are parallel or congruent in the solid figure are drawn as parallel or congruent in an isometric drawing of the figure

isometry (iy-SAH-muh-tree) a transformation that preserves the size and shape of an object's original image

isosceles (iy-SAHS-leez) triangle a triangle with at least two congruent sides

kite a special quadrilateral with exactly two pairs of congruent, consecutive sides

Koch (kawk) Snowflake a fractal created by starting with an equilateral triangle, dividing each side into thirds, building an equilateral triangle with the middle third as its base, removing the original middle third, and then repeating for each remaining segment

lateral area the sum of the areas of the lateral faces of a polyhedron

lateral edge an edge of a polyhedron that is not a base edge

lateral face one of the parallelograms that form a prism and is not a base

lateral surface the curved surface of a cylinder

legs of a right triangle the two sides of a right triangle that form the right angle

legs of a trapezoid the nonparallel sides of a trapezoid

legs of an isosceles triangle the two congruent sides of an isosceles triangle

length of a line segment the distance between the segment's endpoints

line a collection of points arranged in a straight path

linear pair two angles with the same vertex and one common side and whose other sides point in opposite directions

line segment a part of a line; it includes any two points on the line and all the points in between those two points

logic gate in computer logic, circuitry that determines whether a compound condition is true or false

logical chain a chain of premises that leads to a logical conclusion; logical chains are represented by several circles within Euler diagrams

logically equivalent the characteristic of two sets of logic gates such that each set has the same input-output table

major arc an arc that is larger than a semicircle

means in a proportion, the second and third numbers or variables; in $a : b = c : d$ or $\frac{a}{b} = \frac{c}{d}$, b and c are the means

median of a triangle a segment drawn from the vertex of a triangle to the midpoint of its opposite side

Menger Sponge a three-dimensional fractal that begins by dividing a cube into congruent smaller cubes, removing all but the corner cubes, then repeating the process indefinitely

midpoint a point that divides a line segment into two congruent parts

midsegment of a trapezoid the line segment that connects the midpoints of the legs

midsegment of a triangle the line segment that connects the midpoints of two of the sides

minor arc an arc that is smaller than a semicircle

Möbius (MOH-bee-us) strip a three-dimensional surface with only one side (or face)

net the appearance of a solid if it is unfolded; it can be thought of as a pattern for making a solid

noncollinear (nahn-kuh-LIH-nee-uhr) not lying on the same line

non-Euclidean geometry a geometry that has at least one different assumption from the geometry in Euclid's *Elements*

nonoverlapping regions regions that have no points in common

number line a line that has equally spaced intervals labeled with coordinates

oblique (oh-BLEEK) cone a cone whose axis is not an altitude

oblique cylinder a cylinder whose axis is not an altitude

oblique prism a prism whose lateral faces are not perpendicular to the bases

oblique pyramid a pyramid whose altitude does not intersect the center of the base

obtuse angle an angle that measures greater than 90° and less than 180°

obtuse triangle a triangle with an obtuse angle

octant one of the eight parts of a three-dimensional coordinate system

odd vertex in graph theory, a vertex that connects an odd number of edges

opposite side in a right triangle, the side that is opposite the angle being discussed

ordered pair a pair of numbers in which the first number is the x-coordinate and the second number is the y-coordinate of a point's location

ordered triple the coordinates of a point in a three-dimensional coordinate system; the form is (x, y, z)

orthographic views a set of two-dimensional figures that describe a three-dimensional figure from different points of view

paragraph proof a proof in the form of a paragraph

parallel lines coplanar lines that never intersect

parallel planes planes that do not intersect

parallelogram a quadrilateral with two pairs of parallel sides

parametric equation an equation that expresses variables in terms of another variable, called the parameter; the variable t is often the variable used to represent the parameter

perimeter the distance around a figure

perpendicular bisector a line, line segment, or ray that passes through the midpoint of and is perpendicular to a line segment

perpendicular lines lines that meet at right angles

perspective drawing a drawing that gives the illusion of depth and relative size as would be seen by the human eye looking at an actual three-dimensional object

pi for any circle, the circumference divided by the diameter; pi is a constant and is denoted with the Greek letter π; it is an irrational number that is approximately 3.14

plane a flat surface with infinite length and width but no thickness

plane of symmetry a plane that divides a three-dimensional figure into two congruent parts

point a location in space with no length, width, or depth

point of tangency the point where a circle and a tangent intersect

polygon a closed figure formed by three or more line segments in a plane, such that each line segment intersects exactly two other line segments at their endpoints only

polyhedron a solid enclosed by polygons

postulate a mathematical statement assumed to be true

pre-image an original figure before transformation

premise a statement that is presumed to be true in the course of a logical argument

prism a polyhedron with two parallel, congruent faces called bases

projective rays in projective geometry, a transformation that transforms points of a figure along lines, or projective rays, that meet at a single point

proof a clear, logical structure of reasoning that begins from accepted ideas and proceeds through logic to reach a conclusion

proof by contradiction an argument in which the first step is to assume the initial proposition is false, and then the assumption is shown to lead to a logical contradiction; the contradiction can contradict either the given, a definition, a postulate, a theorem, or any known fact

proportion an equation that states that two ratios are equal; often written as $a : b = c : d$ or $\frac{a}{b} = \frac{c}{d}$

proportional the characteristic of corresponding sets of values if every pair of values has the same ratio

pyramid a polyhedron with a polygonal base and lateral faces that are triangles and meet at a common vertex

Pythagorean (puh-tha-guh-REE-uhn) triple any set of three integers that can be the lengths of the sides of a right triangle

quadrilateral a four-sided polygon

radius a line segment that connects the center of a circle to a point on the circle; the plural of radius is radii (RAY-dee-iy)

ray part of a line that begins from an endpoint and extends infinitely in one direction

rectangle a parallelogram with four right angles

recursion a repetitive process in which the same sequence of steps is performed over and over, creating a fractal

reflection a transformation of a figure by flipping it across a line or line segment, creating a mirror image of the figure

reflection symmetry the characteristic that a figure has if it has at least one axis of symmetry; when the figure is reflected, it can be folded along an axis of symmetry and both halves will match up

regular hexagon a six-sided polygon that is equilateral and equiangular

regular polygon a polygon that is equilateral and equiangular

regular pyramid a pyramid with a base that is a regular polygon and lateral faces that are congruent isosceles triangles

remote interior angle an angle inside a triangle that is not adjacent to a given exterior angle

rhombus a parallelogram with four congruent sides

right angle an angle that measures 90°

right cone a cone whose axis is an altitude

right cylinder a cylinder whose axis is an altitude

right prism a prism whose lateral edges are perpendicular to the bases

right pyramid a pyramid whose altitude intersects the center of the base

right triangle a triangle with a right angle

right-handed system a three-dimensional coordinate system in which the positive z-direction points upward if the x- and y-axes lie on a plane in their standard orientation

rise the vertical distance between two points

rotation the turning of a figure a certain number of degrees around a central point

rotation symmetry the characteristic a figure has if it can be rotated around its center less than one full turn and retain the appearance of the original figure

run the horizontal distance between two points

same-side interior angles in angles created by a transversal crossing two lines, the angles that are on the same side of the transversal and in between the two lines that are not the transversal

scale factor in a dilation, the ratio of the length of a side on the image to the length of its corresponding side on the pre-image

scalene (SKAY-leen) triangle a triangle with no congruent sides

secant (SEE-kuhnt) a line that intersects a circle in two points

secant segment a segment of a secant with at least one of its endpoints on the circle

sector in a circle, a region with boundaries of two radii and a part of the circle

segment bisector a line, line segment, or ray that passes through the midpoint of a line segment

self-similarity in fractal geometry, a characteristic of a figure such that it is similar to a part or parts of itself

semicircle an arc that has endpoints that are also the endpoints of a diameter

side in a polygon, one of the line segments that form the polygon

Sierpinski Gasket a fractal that begins by dividing an equilateral triangle into four congruent smaller equilateral triangles, removing the center triangle, then repeating the process indefinitely on the remaining triangles

similar the characteristic of figures such that they have the same shape but not necessarily the same size

similar solids solids that have the same shape and proportional corresponding dimensions

simple closed curve in topology, a curve that does not intersect itself and can be traced by starting at one point and ending at the same point without passing over any part twice

sine ratio in a right triangle, the ratio of the length of the leg that is opposite an acute angle to the length of the hypotenuse

skew lines lines that are neither parallel nor intersecting

slant height the length of the altitude of a lateral face of a pyramid

slant height of a cone the distance from the vertex of a cone to a point on the edge of the base

slope a number that describes the steepness of a line

solid a three-dimensional figure; a figure that has the dimension of depth in addition to width and length

solid of revolution a three-dimensional solid that can be generated by rotating a plane figure about a line that lies in the same plane as the figure; sometimes called a solid of rotation

solve a triangle to find all the missing side and angle measures of a triangle

sphere the set of all points in space a given distance from a point called the center

spherical geometry a non-Euclidean geometry that can be modeled in terms of points and circles on the surface of a sphere

square a parallelogram with four congruent sides and four right angles

statement a sentence that is either true or false; examples in mathematics include compound statements and conditional statements

straight angle an angle that measures exactly 180°; a straight angle is a line

supplementary angles a pair of angles for which the sum of their measures is 180°

surface area the sum of the areas of the outer surfaces of a solid

surface area to volume ratio the ratio found by dividing the surface area of a solid by its volume

syllogism (SIH-luh-jih-zuhm) a logical argument that always contains two premises and a conclusion; syllogisms have the following form: If a, then b. If b, then c. Therefore, if a, then c.

tangent ratio in a right triangle, the ratio of the length of the leg opposite an acute angle to the length of the leg adjacent to that angle

tangent segment a segment of a tangent line with one of its endpoints at the point of tangency

tangent to a circle a line in the plane of the circle that intersects the circle in exactly one point

taxicab circle in taxicab geometry, the set of all the points, or intersections, that are a given taxidistance from a given intersection

taxicab geometry a non-Euclidean geometry in which distance is measured along paths made of horizontal and vertical segments

taxicab perpendicular bisector in taxicab geometry, the set of all points that are the same taxidistance from two given points

taxicab radius in taxicab geometry, any path from the center point to a point on a taxicab circle

taxidistance in taxicab geometry, the length of the shortest path between two points

theorem (THIR-uhm) a mathematical statement that has been or is to be proven on the basis of established definitions and properties

three-dimensional coordinate system a coordinate system with three axes—an x-axis, a y-axis, and a z-axis

three-dimensional drawing a drawing that represents a three-dimensional figure on a two-dimensional plane

topologically equivalent the characteristic of two figures such that one can be transformed into the same shape as the other without tearing or breaking it

topology the study of a figure's properties that remain unchanged, or invariant, when the size and shape of the figure are deformed through continuous bending, twisting, or stretching

torus a nonconvex figure formed when a circle is rotated about a line that does not intersect the circle

trace the intersection of a plane with one of the three coordinate planes, the *xy*-, *yz*-, and *xz*-planes; a trace is always a line

transformation a one-to-one mapping between two sets of points

translation the sliding of a figure in a straight path without rotation or reflection

transversal a line that intersects two or more lines in a plane

trapezoid (TRA-puh-zoyd) a quadrilateral with exactly one pair of parallel sides

trigonometric ratio the ratio of the lengths of two sides of a right triangle

truth-functionally equivalent a characteristic describing a pair of statements that have identical truth tables

two-column proof a proof shown in two columns, the first column of which shows the steps and the second column of which shows the basis for each step

valid argument an argument in which, if the premises are all true, then the conclusion must also be true

vertex angle in a triangle, the angle opposite the base

vertex of a cone the point at which the curved surface of a cone comes together

vertex of a graph in graph theory, an endpoint in a graph

vertex of a polygon a point where the sides of the polygon intersect; the plural of vertex is vertices (VUR-tuh-seez)

vertex of a polyhedron a point at which the vertices of three or more faces meet

vertex of a pyramid the common vertex at which the triangular faces meet

vertex of an angle the common endpoint of the angle

vertical angles the pair of nonadjacent angles formed by two intersecting lines

volume of a solid the amount of space inside a solid, measured in cubic units

x-axis the horizontal number line in a coordinate plane

x-coordinate the first number in an ordered pair of numbers that designates the location of a point on the coordinate plane

y-axis the vertical number line in a coordinate plane

y-coordinate the second number in an ordered pair of numbers that designates the location of a point on the coordinate plane

Symbols

$\wedge$	and	$\perp$	is perpendicular to
$\vee$	or	$\approx$	is approximately equal to
$\rightarrow$	implication	$\therefore$	therefore
$\leftrightarrow$	2-way implication	$\angle$	angle
$\rightarrow\leftarrow$	contradiction	$\triangle$	triangle
π	pi	$\overleftrightarrow{AB}$	line AB
ϕ	phi, the golden ratio	$\overline{AB}$	line segment AB
$'$	prime	$\overrightarrow{AB}$	ray AB
$^{\circ}$	degree	$m\angle CAB$	measure of angle CAB
$\ldots$	continues infinitely	$\overset{\frown}{AB}$	arc AB
$\sim$	is similar to (in similarity statement) *or* not (in logic)	$m\overset{\frown}{AB}$	measure of arc AB
		$\sqrt{x}$	square root of x
$\cong$	is congruent to	$\sqrt[3]{x}$	cube root of x
$\parallel$	is parallel to	$|x|$	absolute value of x

Formulary

Circle

Circumference $C = \pi d = 2\pi r$

Area $A = \pi r^2$

Length of an arc with degree measure m $L = \left(\dfrac{m}{360°}\right) 2\pi r$

Equation with center (h, k) on a coordinate plane
$(x - h)^2 + (y - k)^2 = r^2$

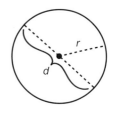

Cone

Volume $V = \dfrac{1}{3} Bh$

$= \dfrac{1}{3}\pi r^2 h$

Surface area $S = L + B$

$= \pi r l + \pi r^2$

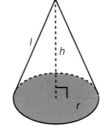

Cylinder

Volume $V = Bh$

$= \pi r^2 h$

Surface area $S = L + 2B$

$= 2\pi r h + 2\pi r^2$

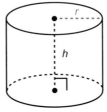

Line and Segment

Slope $m = \dfrac{\text{rise}}{\text{run}} = \dfrac{y_2 - y_1}{x_2 - x_1}$

Coordinates of midpoint $\left(\dfrac{x_1 + x_2}{2}, \dfrac{y_1 + y_2}{2}\right)$

Distance $d = \sqrt{(x_2 - x_1)^2 + (y_2 - y_1)^2}$

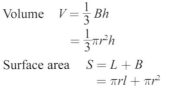

Parallelogram

Area $A = bh$

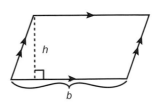

Polygon with *n* sides

Sum of interior angles $\quad I = (n-2)180°$

Interior angle of regular polygon $\quad i = \dfrac{(n-2)180°}{n}$

Perimeter of regular polygon $\quad P = ns$

Area of regular polygon $\quad A = \dfrac{1}{2}aP$

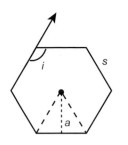

Prism: Cube

Volume $\quad V = s^3$

Surface area $\quad S = 6s^2$

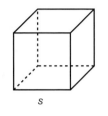

Prism: General

Volume $\quad V = Bh$

Surface area $\quad S = 2B + L$

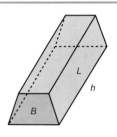

Prism: Right Rectangular

Volume $\quad V = lwh$

Surface area $\quad S = 2lw + 2lh + 2wh$

Length of diagonal $\quad d = \sqrt{l^2 + w^2 + h^2}$

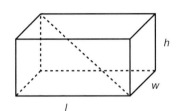

Pyramid

Volume $V = \dfrac{1}{3}Bh$

Surface area $\quad S = \dfrac{1}{2}lP + B$

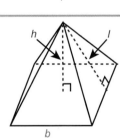

Rectangle

Area $\quad A = bh$

Perimeter $\quad P = 2b + 2h$

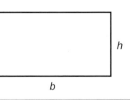

Sphere

Volume $\quad V = \dfrac{4}{3}\pi r^3$

Surface area $\quad S = 4\pi r^2$

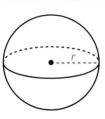

Trapezoid

Length of midsegment $\quad length = \dfrac{b_1 + b_2}{2}$

Area $\quad A = \dfrac{1}{2}(b_1 + b_2)h$

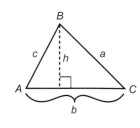

Triangle: General

Sum of interior angles $\quad m\angle A + m\angle B + m\angle C = 180°$

Area $\quad A = \dfrac{1}{2}bh$

Length of midsegment $\quad length = \dfrac{1}{2}$ length of parallel side

Law of Sines $\quad \dfrac{\sin A}{a} = \dfrac{\sin B}{b} = \dfrac{\sin C}{c}$

Law of Cosines $\quad a^2 = b^2 + c^2 - 2bc \cos A$
$$b^2 = a^2 + c^2 - 2ac \cos B$$
$$c^2 = a^2 + b^2 - 2ab \cos C$$

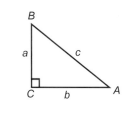

Triangle: Right

Pythagorean Theorem $\quad c^2 = a^2 + b^2$

Tangent $\quad \tan A = \dfrac{\text{opposite}}{\text{adjacent}} = \dfrac{a}{b}$

Sine $\quad \sin A = \dfrac{\text{opposite}}{\text{hypotenuse}} = \dfrac{a}{c}$

Cosine $\quad \cos A = \dfrac{\text{adjacent}}{\text{hypotenuse}} = \dfrac{b}{c}$

Special right triangles

Angle Measure	sine	cosine	tangent
30°	$\dfrac{1}{2}$	$\dfrac{\sqrt{3}}{2}$	$\dfrac{\sqrt{3}}{3}$
45°	$\dfrac{\sqrt{2}}{2}$	$\dfrac{\sqrt{2}}{2}$	1
60°	$\dfrac{\sqrt{3}}{2}$	$\dfrac{1}{2}$	$\sqrt{3}$

Three-Dimensional Space

Distance between points $\quad d = \sqrt{(x_2 - x_1)^2 + (y_2 - y_1)^2 + (z_2 - z_1)^2}$

Coordinates of midpoint $\quad \left(\dfrac{x_1 + x_2}{2}, \dfrac{y_1 + y_2}{2}, \dfrac{z_1 + z_2}{2}\right)$

General equation of a line $\quad Ax + By + Cz = D$

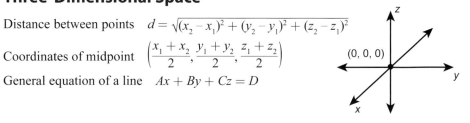

Other Formulas

Euler characteristic $\quad V - E + F$

Taxidistance $\quad taxidistance = |y_2 - y_1| + |x_2 - x_1|$

Illustrations Credits

Key: t=top; b=bottom; c=center; l=left; r=right

All artwork: © K12 Inc.

Front cover: © Philip Wallick/Corbis.

Back cover: (t) © Royalty-Free/Corbis; (c) © Yann Arthus-Bertrand/Corbis; (b) © Pat Doyle/Corbis.

The Geometer's Sketchpad®, Key Curriculum Press, 1150 65th Street, Emeryville, CA 94608, 1-800-995-MATH, www.keypress.com/sketchpad.

Unit 1: 3 (tl) © Fridmar Damm/zefa/Corbis; (tr) © Royalty-Free/Corbis; (bl) © Jupiterimages; (br) © Pat Doyle/Corbis. **7** © Getty Images. **11** © AbleStock/Index Stock. **15** © Royalty-Free/Corbis. **23** © David Muench/Corbis.

Unit 2: 43 © Royalty-Free/Corbis. **47** © PhotoDisc/Getty Images. **55** © Hulton Archives/Getty Images.

Unit 3: 65 © Yann Arthus-Bertrand/Corbis. **69** © Royalty-Free/Corbis. **75** © Fridmar Damm/zefa/Corbis. **93** © Richard Hamilton Smith/Corbis.

Unit 4: 101 © Ron Watts/Corbis. **101** © Kim Sayer/Corbis. **105** © Pat Doyle/Corbis. **111,121,131** © Jupiterimages. **115** © Nik Wheeler/Corbis. **124** © Getty Images. **127** © Yann Arthus-Bertrand/Corbis. **135** © Royalty-Free/Corbis.

Unit 5: 143 © MapResources.com. **147** © WorldAtlas.com. **151,152, 155,159** © Jupiterimages. **165** © Ruediger Knobloch/A.B./zefa/Corbis.

Unit 6: 175 (tl) Alinari/SEAT/Art Resource, NY; (tr) Vatican Museums and Galleries, Vatican City, Italy, Giraudon/The Bridgeman Art Library International. **183** © Don Farrall/Photodisc. **191** © Royalty-Free/Corbis.

Unit 7: 205 © Alan Schein Photography/Corbis. **209** © Barry Iverson/Woodfin Camp. **213** © Andre Jenny/Alamy. **217** © Image Source/Alamy. **221** © Photodisc/Punchstock.

Unit 8: 237 © Niall Benvie/Oxford Scientific/Jupiterimages. **243** © Dorling Kindersley. **251** © Stan Osolinski/Index Stock Imagery/Jupiterimages. **255** The World Factbook.

Unit 9: 261 © Royalty-Free/Corbis. **265** © Dinodia Images/Alamy. **269** © Paul Heartfield/Alamy. **277** © Lauree Feldman/Index Stock.

Unit 10: 289 © Keith Levit Photography/Index Stock. **293** © DesignPics Inc./Index Stock. **303** © AbleStock/Index Stock.

Unit 11: 309, 313, 327 © Photodisc/Punchstock. **333** © Ian Evans/Alamy. **336** (t) Menger Sponge. This image has been released into the public domain by the artist, Solkoll. This applies worldwide. http://commons.wikimedia.org/wiki/Image:Menger_sponge_(Level_1-4).jpg; (bl, br) © Art Matrix/Visuals Unlimited. **337** © Image State/PunchStock. **343** © Royalty-Free/Corbis.

S

same-side interior angles, 70
scale factor, 234
scalene triangle, 62
secant, 265
secant segment, 279
sector, 151, 218
segment bisector, 16
self-similarity, 333
semicircle, 261
side, 61
Sierpinski Gasket, 334
similar polygons, 239, 255
similar solids, 256
simple closed curve, 324
sine ratio, 293
skew lines, 179
slant height, 210
slope, 93
solid of revolution, 227
solids, 175
solve a triangle, 306
sphere, 221
spherical geometry, 330
spherical triangle, 331
square, 67
statement, 37
straight angle, 13
Substitution Property of Equality, 51
Subtraction Property of Equality, 51
supplementary angles, 13
surface area, 178, 199
surface area to volume ratio, 203
syllogism, 34
Symmetric Property of Congruence, 51
Symmetric Property of Equality, 51

T

tangent ratio, 290
tangent segment, 277
tangent to a circle, 265
taxicab circle, 315
taxicab geometry, 313
taxicab perpendicular bisector, 316
taxicab radius, 315
taxidistance, 314
theorem, 5, 52
three-dimensional coordinate system, 188
three-dimensional drawing, 176
topologically equivalent, 323
topology, 323
torus, 225, 327
trace, 194
transformation, 23
Transitive Property of Congruence, 51
Transitive Property of Equality, 51
translation, 24
transversal, 69
trapezoid, 67
30°-60°-90° triangle, 160
45°-45°-90° triangle, 159
trigonometric ratio, 289
truth-functionally equivalent, 39
truth table, 38
two-column paragraph proof, 51

V

valid argument, 34
vertex angle, 111
vertex of a cone, 217
vertex of a graph, 317
vertex of an angle, 11
vertex of a polygon, 61
vertex of a polyhedron, 180
vertex of a pyramid, 209
vertical angles, 56
volume, 178, 200

X

x-axis, 27
x-coordinate, 27

Y

y-axis, 27
y-coordinate, 27